The Mortdecai ABC

The Mortdecai ABC

A BONFIGLIOLI READER

Margaret Bonfiglioli

VIKING
an imprint of
PENGUIN BOOKS

VIKING

Published by the Penguin Group
Penguin Books Ltd, 80 Strand, London WC2R ORL, England
Penguin Putnam Inc., 375 Hudson Street, New York, New York 10014, USA
Penguin Books Australia Ltd, Ringwood, Victoria, Australia
Penguin Books Canada Ltd, 10 Alcorn Avenue, Toronto, Ontario, Canada M4V 3B2
Penguin Books India (P) Ltd, 11 Community Centre, Panchsheel Park, New Delhi – 110 017, India
Penguin Books (NZ) Ltd, Cnr Rosedale and Airborne Roads, Albany, Auckland, New Zealand
Penguin Books (South Africa) (Pty) Ltd, 24 Sturdee Avenue, Rosebank 2196, South Africa

Penguin Books Ltd, Registered Offices: 80 Strand, London WC2R ORL, England

www.penguin.com

First published 2001
I

Set in 12/14.75pt Monotype Bembo
Typeset by Rowland Phototypesetting Ltd,
Bury St Edmunds, Suffolk
Printed in Great Britain by Clays Ltd, St Ives plc

A CIP catalogue record for this book is available from the British Library

ISBN 0-670-91084-8

*Frontispiece: the many faces of Bon: Young Man; Balliol Man; Businessman Bon
Whisky Man; Jersey Writer; Irish Writer
Cowboy Bon; Shercock; Charlie*

In Memoriam Zara Bruzzi 1935–2000
Best of friends and encouragers in the making of this book

Contents

Introduction

How did I happen to put together this book? Laughter began it. The Mortdecai effect hit the publisher Simon Pettifar when, alone in an almost empty house hunting for a read, he stumbled on an old Penguin *Don't Point that Thing at Me*. His quest for Bonfiglioli then began with his publishing the three Mortdecai novels as a trilogy in paperback in 1991. On learning that, as Bon's ex-wife and literary executor, I had boxes and folders of his correspondence, stories, reviews, bank statements and unfinished work, he asked me to put together a Mortdecai reader and write about life with Bon. Neither he nor I had any idea of what an undertaking this would be or how long it would take.

Researching the life of a dead husband, however ex, is an odd experience. Taking old pain off the shelf to share some of that pain with his children and with some of his friends and lovers. Discovering how much closer the realities of his finances were to the impression of poverty he projected towards me than they were to that air of affluence he sported to others.

Bon loved conviviality, telling jokes, setting the table in a roar — often with the laughter that says 'it doesn't really hurt'. A voracious reader and rereader, he was always exchanging learned information and discussing the meaning and use of words. People are still telling his jokes and anecdotes, and also jokes about him — not always true or publishable ones.

He was also a man who challenged friends and spouses to love and forgive him, whatever he did. Close encounters with him were always memorable. Living with him was a commando training in emotional resilience and dealing with the unexpected. Staunch friends rose to this challenge, and continue to love his memory and regret his death. He recognized his own destructive character: often compassionate to others and remembered for acts of tenderness and goodness, he found it hard to love or forgive himself.

Like so many men of his generation Bon was a victim of the macho culture that he both endorses and satirizes in the character of Charlie Mortdecai. While both sexes enjoy his books for their wit, they read differently for men and for women; any woman who knew him intimately would not describe him in the same way as his men friends. At the time of our marriage I was a kind of naively liberated woman who believed the world more equal and less prejudiced than it proved to be. Sometimes I was staggered by Bon's male chauvinist piggery (as it was then called), yet I never quite believed it, even when I should have. He treated me to love and to hate. Sometimes his ill-treatment seemed to cover something darker and beyond me; other times we were in a world of confusing jokes, provocations and lies.

Why an ABC? It is the name for a beginner's guide to an area of knowledge. For me, as a novice editor and partial biographer, it provides an organized yet appropriately arbitrary method of approaching the enigma of the life and writings of Kyril Bonfiglioli. It is a way to order an incomplete narrative where chance as much as choice governs what is known and what is unknown. We were married for ten years, parents to five children – yet how little we knew of each other. It is a strange experience to know now so much more about his childhood and family than he ever told me directly and to be still receiving new information that shifts the precarious balance of how I think and feel about him. Bon himself was particularly fond of little ABCs.

The ABC section of this book has no pretensions to be a full-scale, warts-and-all biography. It is designed as much for seren-dipitous browsing as it is for reading in sequence. The ultimate mystery of the whole man cannot be conveyed by me; it is partly to be found in his delightful fiction and letters.

It is not possible for me to unlove or forget the man I married in 1959 and – at his request – divorced in 1969. My life with his five children became hugely more manageable and more lighthearted when his protracted departure for Lancashire, with many comings and goings, was completed. But how could I not miss the excite-ment and adrenalin-flow of living in perpetual crisis? Reading his letters saved by other people and hearing their anecdotes revives my loss.

My purpose in this book is to celebrate an extraordinary man and writer, and to contemplate the farce and tragedy of a life.

Margaret Bonfiglioli
July 2001

Note on the text: I have called Kyril Bonfiglioli 'Bon' throughout, as this is the name he was most generally known by, except when 'Cyril', the name of his childhood, schooling and army days, is appropriate.

Page numbers in references to the novels are from the following Blackspring Press editions: *The Mortdecai Trilogy* (1991, comprising *Don't Point that Thing at Me, After You with the Pistol* and *Something Nasty in the Woodshed*), *All the Tea in China* (1991) and *The Great Mortdecai Moustache Mystery* (1999).

The Mortdecai ABC

𝔄

AA The acronym for Alcoholics Anonymous, an organization occasionally recommended to Bon by friends writing to him in the 1980s.

ABC The acronym formed from the initial letters of the Aerial Board of Control, a post-millennial science-fiction invention of Rudyard Kipling.

The ABC, that semi-elected, semi-nominated body of a few score persons, controls the planet. Transportation is Civilization, our motto runs. Theoretically we do what we please, so long as we do not interfere with the traffic *and all it implies*. Practically, the ABC confirms or annuls all international arrangements, and to judge from its last report, finds our tolerant, humorous, lazy little planet only too ready to shift the whole burden of public administration on to its shoulders.

This is a passage from Kipling's short story 'With the Night Mail' that he used to introduce its sequel, 'As Easy as ABC', published in 1912. In 1964 Bon included 'As Easy as ABC' in the magazine *Science Fantasy*, which he was editing at the time. Kipling was a significant influence on many aspects of his writing and was felt to be a kindred spirit.

Kipling's anticipation of the current British quango, but in his story swollen into a multinational organization controlling a world where democracy is a bit of quaint folklore (an election could be staged by the Serviles as a public amusement), reflects that common uncertainty about who's really in charge shared by Kipling and Bon and many others. It was a prescient warning about globalization.

Aliases

'Pseudonymists tend to repeat offenders' – Kevin Jackson, *Invisible Forms*

Adam Chipplewhite, Jasper Doulton and Jeremy Fraser were all pen-names used by Bon in 1958 when writing for the *Oxford Times*, about furniture, collecting china and motoring in Scotland. In the sixties he used the name P. R. A. Lingam, Ph.D, when editing an unexpurgated version of John Cleland's *Memoirs of a Coxcomb* (first published in 1751). Cleland's earlier and notoriously sexy novel, *Fanny Hill*, was also included on the front cover, but in larger letters to make the book attractive to connoisseurs hoping for antique semi-pornography. The name was a joke disguise – if you don't know what a lingam is, then read John Masters's Indian novels, where Bon first found this word.

From the sixties onwards, as he became an established art dealer, Bon contributed reviews and wrote letters to the newspapers and began editing a science-fiction bimonthly using his own name, Kyril Bonfiglioli, having changed its initial letter from C to K – an adjustment that he later reverses for Karli, his fictional ancestor, in *All the Tea*, who in changing K to C provides Charlie Mortdecai with a name that both reflects and anglicizes his foolishness.

Bon was always alias someone or other, briefly recognizing affinities with other people, invented or real, and he has fun with this tendency in giving it to Charlie Mortdecai, his fictional hero.

As Karl Bellamy, MA, tricycle-riding reporter, Bon wrote reviews of local church services for the *Pilot*, an Anglican monthly published in Jersey. Although this last of his recorded pseudonyms amounts almost to a heteronym, it was in many ways essential for him to distance himself from this carefully cultivated persona as revealed under SUNDAYS.

Alka-Seltzer Part of a battery of late-morning helpers for Bon and Charlie alike:

I have little time for foreigners but I must say that Drs Alka and Seltzer should have won the Nobel prize years ago; my only quarrel with their brain child is its *noise*.   – *Something Nasty in the Woodshed*, p. 478

Alphabets Collecting alphabetical lists of almost anything that interested him for amusement and possible future use in writing or talking was habitual to Bon. Fragments of some of these remain among his papers. They include an obscene acrostic poem on so thin a tissue of folded paper that I have found it easy to lose, but see under ZEBRA.

Cyril (later Kyril) Bonfiglioli was one of the few people who can claim to have been named after the inventor of an alphabet. Cyrillic is the name given to the Slavonic alphabet because it is reputed to have been invented by St Cyril when he translated the scriptures into the vernacular for his mission to the Slavs in the ninth century. In naming his first-born son after this saint, Bon's father was making an informed choice.

Analphabet An illiterate ignoramus, a term of derision used by Bon's father to goad his children, implying idleness rather than misfortune as the cause of this benighted state. See DUMMKOPF.

Ancestors Writing to his literary agent Hilary Rubinstein, Bon described himself as 'a scion of a decayed house'. From time to time, he returned to researching the various lines of Bonfigliolis in Italy, particularly the branch that had had a palazzo in Bologna and been patrons of artists and collectors of pictures. He was not able to finish sorting out the lines of his family tree. I know there was a Rodolfo Bonfiglioli, a financial adviser to a sixteenth-century pope 'who soon became unpopular in financial circles' – is this genetic? We were once contacted by an Italian–Swiss Dr Bonfiglioli whose name was Rudolph and had a convivial evening with him and his wife, assuming he was some sort of cousin. Bon had identified a Tyrolean branch of the family. He was far more interested in his ancestors than in his more recent family.

Because he liked it and could not sell it for the price its artistic quality deserved, Bon kept a fine portrait of a distinguished-looking elderly lady for an unusually long time and through many house moves. Without provenance, a named sitter or a convincing attribution, it could never become a 'good trade picture', but by the time he died in Jersey – as I was solemnly informed – it was a portrait of his paternal grandmother.

In his historical novel *All the Tea in China*, he gives the hero Dutch–Jewish ancestry. He was aware of Jewish Bonfigliolis in Ferrara. See also JEWISHNESS.

Angel A word often used to describe Bon's younger brother, Christopher (who died, aged nine, in 1943) – in uncomfortable contrast with the many times Cyril, as a child, was called a little devil or Bon, as an adult, was described as Mephistophelean.

Anonymous Without name or renown was what Bon sometimes wanted, sometimes feared to be. In a word and a pun, we have the ever-present metaphysical question for him: are you a man or a mouse? But see how he plays with this idea to introduce himself as a wooer:

BLOB.
(unintentional)

Dear Judith

Here is a small present from an anonymous admirer. And here is a picture of a nonnymouse, trying to look important.

In a story called 'The Aquatint', the writer Keith Roberts, who joined Bon as associate editor of *Science Fantasy* in 1966, portrays him with little fictional adaptation in the character Toby Warrilow: 'I have to jump up and down and make a noise,' he said once, sadly. 'Or people don't notice me. All *you* need to do is walk in and look round . . .' In fact Bon was unable to slip into a room unnoticed and took pains to ensure people were aware of his presence. His full name was sometimes a problem, sometimes an advantage. See NAMES.

Armigerous Bonfiglioli

[Y]ou may remember that I do not love to be addressed as though I were a tradesman or common author (God save the mark!). Pray explain to her [the new PA] that I have an absurd, antique Wop title which I wouldn't dream of using in GB but I do claim the lowest gentle rank of 'Esq.', which is due to anyone (I know I've said this before but we all have our little quiddities don't we?), to anyone who is armigerous, whose father was armigerous, who has held HM's commission, who is a member of one of the learned professions (you may recall that authors have been put into the order of precedence – only two or three places below the commissioners in lunacy) or who is a Master of one of the three universities. I qualify . . . I suppose all scions of decayed houses . . . cling on to such shreds of silly dignity.

Hilary Rubinstein indulged this request of Bon's by ensuring that the literary agency A. P. Watt put 'Esq.' on cheques for him, although this was no longer their practice. Bon was well aware of an anachronistic absurdity in this search for due rank. Yet in Jersey he was known to some as Count Bonfiglioli. He told me that it helped him get extended credit with the local newsagent. His family researches contain sketches of various Bonfiglioli coats of arms. See COWBOYS and HERALDRY.

Arms and the art dealer

> Never never let your gun
> Pointed be at anyone.
> Though it may not loaded be,
> Matters not a whit to me.

This instruction for children of gun-owners was always recited by Bon when instructing his own and other people's sons in the handling of guns. I include it for the benefit of American parents.

Knowing about, purchasing and owning guns was an inescapable aspect of Bon's character and runs through all his fiction. Shots were often fired at home, and he had occasional opportunities to go shooting. Once a considerable explosion shook the house. I rushed upstairs from the kitchen and opened the drawing-room door on shafts of sunlight illuminating a haze of brick dust and soot from the chimney. Covered in soot and dust, Bon and a stockbroker friend peered at me with sheepish and apologetic faces and explained they had been testing an ancient fowling piece by firing it up the chimney.

This extract from the *Oxford Times* of 30 January 1968 reports a little trouble with the law:

Oxford art dealer Kyril Bonfiglioli admitted to a court yesterday that he had several revolvers, part of a Winchester rifle and some ammunition for which he had no firearms certificate. He was fined £75.

Bonfiglioli, of 18 Norham Gardens, asked through his solicitor, Mr Edgerton Ferguson, that the weapons should not be destroyed but instead should be given to the Pitt Rivers Museum because of their historical value . . .

Mr David Wright prosecuting had said that the revolvers, the rifle and the ammunition had been found at Bonfiglioli's home by Det.-Sgt Graham Mapson, who had been visiting the house on another matter . . .

'It was a foolish thing to have these weapons without a certificate. But it was a negative action, not a positive one. It is also a very humiliating thing for a man in his position to plead guilty to.'

Mr Ferguson said that some of the older antique guns 'which are lawfully owned by my client could be more dangerous than the weapons the subject of the charge'. Mr Ferguson said that at one time Bonfiglioli had been an expert target shot. He said that Bonfiglioli came from a well-known Oxford family who had been in business in the area for three generations. There had been no previous trouble.

So what really happened on the day in question? Three police-men arrived at the house at about midday with a search warrant – Bon was a known associate of a villain suspected of a recent country-house robbery of a large collection of antique and valuable snuffboxes. It so happened that Bon had recently purchased the contents of a Welsh natural-history museum. Thus several tea chests full of small treasures happened to be standing in the hall ready to distract the two constables. While they, poor fellows, were laboriously unwrapping more and more shells, each shrouded indi-vidually in the newspaper, and the Detective Sergeant was question-ing me with the utmost courtesy, Bon – still in his rather Noël Coward dressing gown – had rapidly conveyed his more up-to-date small arms into the jacket of a visiting gun-licensed friend who, after some polite goodbyes, drove off with them in his Land Rover. Bon then confessed to the presence of the rest, which could, up to a point, be defended on grounds of historical interest and antiquity. Dear Fergie's touch about the well-known Oxford family in business in the area for three generations was almost nonsense. It's true that for a few months in 1960 and 1961 Bon's father had kept shop for him in Little Clarendon Street, Oxford, and then been installed in a tiny cottage shop in the nearby village of Eynsham. But see GUNS, SMITH & WESSON and WEAPONRY.

Army

I was taught, long ago, always to choose the smallest piece of cover which will hold you; if you are behind the most barely adequate of the hummocks or bushes you will be the last to be rushed and may well be able to rake the other chaps with flank-fire while they are rushing the bigger ones. I don't know what they teach soldiers in these days of neutron-bombs. Prayer, perhaps. *– After You with the Pistol*, p. 267

This comment from Charlie as he seeks to hide from she-soldiers in a complicated scene of combat training sounds as if it comes directly from Bon's experience.

The flavour of the following suggests that it is an authentic reminiscence, but could it belong to Bon's father rather than to himself?

I felt just like an infantry subaltern who has thrown away a platoon against a machine-gun emplacement he forgot to mark on his map. (Listening to the Colonel's remarks afterwards is not nearly so unpleasant as sitting down to write twenty letters to next-of-kin while the people in the orderly room pretend you're not there. The worst bit is when your batman brings you your dinner to the foxhole or bivvy tent, saying, 'Thought you might be too tired to dine in mess tonight, sir.' But I reminisce.) *– After You with the Pistol*, p. 306

Here the painfulness of the subaltern's task and the batman's tactful way of showing that he understands remind readers of moments when manservant/thug Jock's warm understanding of his master's needs is expressed in comforting action rather than words.

Bon was in the army between 1947 and 1952, first as a conscript, then as a regular soldier in the Royal West African Frontier Force. His first five and a half months after training were spent in the Royal Army Medical Corps. According to Dr George Turnbull, this was 'a soft number to be in which excused one a great deal of square-bashing and marching up and down which Bon would have loathed'. Bon, not being on the way to a medical career as Turnbull was, would have soon become fed up and found the record-keeping and store-keeping boring. Transferred to the Royal Army Educational Corps and promoted to acting sergeant in February 1947, he became a substantive sergeant three months later and in October was posted to West Africa.

At the time of his application to Balliol College, he was a sergeant instructor with the Royal Army Educational Corps in barracks in Brighton. He was well supported in the references his senior officers wrote for him, and they show how much he had been able to seize the educational opportunities presented by the army.

He told me how his name inspired many variants from mocking sergeants: 'Ho yes, Mr Bonfickle-me-slowly' being one of these. In turn, he ridiculed and enjoyed other sergeants' introductions to his brief talks on literature: 'Today we 'ave a lecture on Keats and I expect there's some 'ere that 'ave never seen a Keat.' This was a sample of an RAEC joke, probably not unique to Bon. He admired the army's succinct formula for a lecture and developed there the skill, confidence and power to entertain and inform as a lecturer.

He married and became a widower during his time in the army. See WEST AFRICA.

Army prose

Your average general, when fighting his country's foes, writes a crisp and nutty prose but when he turns to Literature he comes out in a rash of epithets: 'bushy-topped tree bearing 235 degrees' becomes 'shady verdure' and 'square-topped church at 3,000 yards' becomes 'hallowed precinct'. We are not blessed in the change. But make no mistake,

General Sir Geoffrey Evans knows his Kensington from butt-plate to fore-sight and tells his story well.

> – from a review of *Kensington* by General Sir Geoffrey Evans,
> in the *Guardian*, 1975

This opening paragraph from a book review may be hard on the author's style, but it does show Bon's fascination with different speech registers, which he would have experienced as a Royal Army Educational Corps instructor. He was also familiar with Henry Reed's sequence of poems *Lessons of the War*, and he once turned a potentially dull and constrained party into a convivial and delightful one by his reading of these poems aloud, doing the voices that alternate the jargon of an army instructor with the poet's private thoughts, both packed with latent sexual imagery.

Artists' letters A substantial collection of letters written by well-known artists was perhaps the only collection Bon made with the hope of keeping and augmenting as the opportunity arose. Almost everything else in his life was potential 'stock' and ultimately for sale: 'easy come, easy go', as he would say.

The different styles of writing and writing paper were occasionally more interesting than the contents. I remember Landseer's letterhead included a fine stag at bay with the day of the week already printed.

Bon took his collection seriously enough to arrange for Margaret Parsons, a friend going through a marital crisis, to come regularly to our house to catalogue it. Finding such a task to distract someone in a stressed state from their problems was also one of his oblique acts of kindness. For this friend's view of him, see SANDWICHES.

Years later, when this collection had travelled to Lancashire with him and he was somewhat desperate for money, Judith Todd, with whom he was living, saved it from public sale and possible dispersal by buying it herself.

Art dealer The newspaper article that follows is an accurate description of the career Bon took up in Oxford in 1958. Anthony Harris, who wrote this for a series headed 'Other People's Jobs' in the *Oxford Times*, was a close friend and a director and shareholder of the company Bonfiglioli Limited (set up around 1960).

'What, make your living out of selling *pictures*. It can't be done – after all who wants them?' Disregarding all this discouraging advice, Mr Kyril Bonfiglioli set up shop in Oxford just over six months ago, and they have been six successful months.

A dealer needs a curious compound of skills and talents and some of them take a lifetime to acquire. Some must probably be inherited – Mr Bonfiglioli is the son of an antique dealer. Inheritance may help to account for his astonishing visual memory, which enables him to attribute on sight an obscure picture by an obscure painter – a memory sharpened by some months spent in the University Department of Fine Art cataloguing files of which the titles had been lost. It may also have fostered a passion for the darker corners of antiquarian learning. Through many years of other pursuits – as a regular soldier, at Balliol reading English – he remained part-antiquarian.

His persuasiveness is almost alarming. A customer with no more than a fleeting liking for a picture will soon find that he has acquired a great enthusiasm for the artist, his period and for this picture in particular, he will not only be on the edge of buying it, but halfway to becoming a collector. A few have actually started collections.

'I like to encourage young collectors,' Mr Bonfiglioli explains. 'A customer who is going to come regularly and get to know what he is buying is far more valuable in the long run, and far pleasanter to deal with, than the chance caller who will pay a fancy price for a picture and then vanish.'

But only a minority of pictures are worth collecting. Where do they all come from? Some come into the shop under the arms of sellers who may or may not know the value of what they have to offer. 'Sometimes I can pay five times what they ask, to their great delight – though I have to be careful about this. Some people, as soon as they conclude their picture is a bit better than they thought, conclude it must be worth thousands and walk out again.

'And sometimes, of course, one has to disappoint them – some people have an astonishing idea of the value of a Bible – "it's nearly a hundred years old" – or a framed colour reproduction, or a really bad watercolour – "it's hand painted you know".'

Many of the pictures are bought at auctions, where they come in lots, and thus a dealer acquires the host of run-of-the-mill 'furnishing pictures' and 'good trade pictures' and sheer rubbish which must be sorted, thrown away or cleaned, and shown to the right customer. 'Good trade pictures' are ones which will always sell in the end, and are steadily exchanged among dealers themselves – pleasant landscapes (but there must be human figures in them), seascapes (but not shipwrecks), the right kinds of prints and etchings. These rules are part of the mythology of art dealing whether they make sense or not.

Many others just as pleasant but not quite 'trade pictures' will qualify as 'furnishing pictures' – to be sold to undergraduates, farmers' wives, landladies and others, according to taste, to decorate a blank wall. There is also a steady trade in 'ancestors' – unidentified portraits of moderate merit, which must be fairly old.

What about the 'finds', the great legend of the art world – the master-pieces rotting in old lofts? They do happen in a less spectacular way. Mr Bonfiglioli has already been in the news with a landscape which turned out on cleaning to be a Richard Wilson; he will soon be in the news again with an exciting literary haul. He has found old master drawings hidden behind worthless prints when he took them out of the frames; he has found customers – and customers can also be 'finds' – for such curiosities as a mantrap, some architect's details of the eighteenth century, a craftsman's design for a sword hilt.

But these finds, you will notice, do not happen by chance. They happen because Mr Bonfiglioli buys a lot of pictures in the first place; because he knows which ones to clean, how to clean them, and, most important, he knows what they are when he has cleaned them. He finds them because he is ready to look through the great heaps of junk he acquires with the one or two things he knew he wanted. This is the real slogging work of a dealer, and it has a fascination for him that will keep him up all night on occasions. And this is why a dealer can earn a living – for his living is really the measure of the value he adds to what he buys, by sorting and cleaning it, by explaining and extolling it, and, on rare and exciting occasions, by identifying it. It is far from easy money, but it is never dull.

In a letter to his literary agent Hilary Rubinstein about a plan for a book (about cookery), Bon writes: 'I am confident that you'll see through the scruff as a picture-dealer sees through the oxidized varnish. When I was an art dealer I made a great deal of money out of dirty pictures – and I don't mean porn; I mean pictures which curators could not visualize through the accumulated layers of varnish and dirt.'

By the time he wrote this he was a writer; his career as an art dealer was substantially over, though dealing of one kind or another came too naturally to him to leave it behind completely. From his student days, he had often paid for his dinner and that of his children by spotting quality in an oil in a junk shop, cleaning it and selling it on. His first exhibition was in the Gloucester Arms, a pub frequented by actors. It consisted of colourful watercolours of theatrical subjects. See DEALING, PICTURES, TINTORETTO and WATERCOLOURS.

Ashmolean Museum Bon revered and frequented the Ashmolean Museum, counting it one of Oxford's key resources and essential to the art-historical education that he pursued alongside his reading of English at Balliol. After graduating, he worked there as research assistant to Professor Wind, Professor of Art History, cataloguing and checking the identity of unlabelled slides – an invaluable exercise of visual memory for someone about to become a serious picture dealer.

He was always delighted if the Museum bought something from his gallery. Between 1964 and 1967 they made eleven purchases, including watercolours by Landseer and John Linnell. Between 1965 and 1967 he gave the Museum nine works of art, including a Renaissance bronze plaque of St Jerome in penitence and a watercolour and a self-portrait by Nathaniel Bliss Stocker. See WATERCOLOURS and ZEUS.

Auctions Like all dealers in antique furniture and art, Bon was well versed in the rituals of the auction room. In the sixties the *Oxford Mail* ran the following article by him under the title 'Picking up Things at Auctions':

You never buy things at auctions – you only 'pick them up'. One of the most cherished superstitions in this penny-wise kingdom is that if it is sold under the hammer it's a bargain. Like the (slightly defective) Anglepoise lamp which was picked up at a local auction this month for just a few shillings more than a brand-new one costs with a year's guarantee.

Years and years ago (when you were all very small, dears) the auction rooms were haunted only by furtive, seedy dealers, and the private person who was not too proud to venture in – his nosegay firmly clamped under his quivering nostrils – could make a killing.

The wicked dealer, suitably cowed by the delicately raised bidding-finger of the carriage-folk, would realize that he was out-classed and slink away to gibber in a corner while the Private Person would send his footman round to collect the Ming vases he had secured for half a sovereign.

Those were the brave days when you could really 'pick things up'. They were a very long time ago.

Why can't you do it now? Well one of the things you are up against is a lot of people who know much less than you but are much richer.

Glance round any auction room (if you can stop bidding for a moment) and observe the rich, silly women in their auction-slumming disguise (just a sheepskin coat, an old cashmere sweater and a simple row of pearls). Every bid they make relieves boredom and satisfies a whim and if their husband's bank balance takes more than a body-blow, why, that makes it more of a giggle.

Travel miles to a remote country sale these days and you will find the lane choked with glittering Bentleys and Jaguars. Perhaps you will be able to buy a galvanized pail (slightly defective) in one of the outhouses for a few pounds but if you hoped to buy any of the nice pieces you might as well go home. Another thing you're up against is that you don't know too much about this sort of thing yourself – after all you don't do it all day long for a living as the dealers do.

The piece you buy for £5 may seem cheap until you get it home and see that much of it is restored, the rest is riddled with worm and anyway it doesn't fit in the alcove you intended it for.

A similar piece may cost twice as much from a reputable dealer, but you have ample leisure to examine it, measure it, try it at home if necessary and meanwhile the dealer has cleaned and restored it and knew what he was doing when he bought it in the first place and will, if asked, give you an invoice stating the age and nature of the article categorically.

He will deliver it and those words should be inscribed in gold.

A man standing next to me in an auction made a purchase once. He turned excitedly to me and the following dialogue took place:

Him: Did you see that? I bought a beautiful rosewood grand piano for a mere song!

Me: Wow!

Him: Right under the dealers' noses, for a fraction of its real value.

Me: Er, yes.

Him: How do I set about getting it home?

Me: Ah.

Him: I daresay you know lots of carriers who will run it out to Kidlington for me?

Me: No.

Him: You mean they won't?

Me: That's right.

Him: Who will, then?

Me: Any good piano dealer will move it for you, given plenty of notice.

Him: But it says all goods must be cleared within *xxx* hours.

Me: So it does.

Him: Will they charge very much?

Me: Well it takes a team of specially trained men with trolleys, ramps and a *sxxx* truck, you know.

Him: Oh dear. What do you advise, then?

Me: Emigrate.

The third factor against successful 'picking up' these days is the dealer himself. Fine things are growing ever scarcer and every dealer has a queue of customers looking for really good things.

If you are willing to pay £50 for a piece the chances are that someone else would give £60 and probably there is a specialist high-powered dealer in London or abroad who can afford to give £70.

The spiralling prices in the antique shops are due to your upraised finger in the auction rooms: you cannot bid the dealer up at auctions and then complain that his goods are dear.

The last obstacle is the auctioneer (not, I need hardly say, in Oxford). There are those who indulge in terrible practices like 'trotting'. This is also known as 'picking bids off the wall' and simply means that an obviously zealous and innocent bidder is kept in play by the acceptance of imaginary bids.

Many a purchaser, flushed with his victory, has whirled round to confront his late antagonist with a sneer of triumph, only to find that the bids which have cost him so dear seem to have emanated from a usually taciturn object such as a hatstand or a three-piece suite in uncut moquette.

'Trotting', I grieve to say, is also sometimes practised by the owner of the goods being auctioned, in his anxiety to ensure that his goods fetch as much as may be. When you see a man in the auction biting pieces out of his hat or striking his wife with a fireside-companion set (slightly defective) you may depend upon it that it is someone who has been bidding-up his own goods – and has got landed with them.

Here are some things not to buy, or try to buy, at auction: anything obviously very fine (unless you are so rich it doesn't matter); anything you haven't been able to examine properly, like bundles of sheets firmly tied up, rolled-up carpets, heavy furniture against a wall, etc.; old silver (you can't compete with the London dealers); good pictures (ditto, ditto); anything amazingly cheap (there's sure to be a good reason); lawn-mowers in the spring – you'll find the new ones are cheaper; anything above all which has the casual words 'and sundries' after it in the catalogue – unless you are prepared to dispose of three baths full of bed-pans, barbed wire, antique mincing-machines and a flock mattress. (Have you ever tried to get rid of a large and smelly flock mattress? Believe me it is a grim and costly business.)

What you can profitably buy at auction are things dealers don't much want and other people are frightened of: beds; sewing machines (except very nice new ones); television sets (often very good but everyone supposes they are useless, naturally); mowing-machines in winter; domestic china and glassware; three-piece suites; large ugly useful furniture (but remember that the carriage is extra); refrigerators and things like that (tip the porter liberally and he will tell you the truth about whether it works). Oh yes, and grand pianos.

Audubon John James Audubon (1785–1851) was a self-taught naturalist and engraver who raised zoological illustration to its highest art. Born in Haiti, half French, half creole, and illegitimate (*hors du Bon? Eau du Bon?*), he was sometimes thought to be a lost son of Louis XVI. He was famous for his *Birds of America*, and a rare copy of the original edition was an object of admiration, almost veneration, among the Bonfigliolis in Eastbourne during Bon's childhood. The family's treasure in the 1930s, it remained for Bon a memorable standard for everything beautiful, informative and interesting. A chance to review a biography of Audubon for the *Irish Press* in 1978 was a poignant event for him, stimulating this rare recollection of his childhood pre-1943:

Bastard, bankrupt, liar and cheat, vain and vulgar poseur, a spendthrift vagabond, barely literate and wholly immoral, John James Audubon would scarcely seem a candidate for canonization. Nevertheless, millions of people all over the world revere him, rightly, as a sort of patron saint of ornithology, a founding-father of wild-life conservation and the greatest bird artist of all time.

The man himself is a weird and gaudy shadow, posturing behind the rich solidity of his achievement: a book. Well, perhaps 'a book' is an understatement. Audubon's *Birds of America* is more of a monument; magnificently conceived, dazzlingly executed and majestically produced, it comprises 435 enormous (Double Elephant Folio – 30" × 40" – far too big for a coffee-table to carry!) hand-coloured engravings, depicting each species – even the largest – life size. Such a work had never been projected before and could certainly never be contemplated again: the price to the 161 subscribers (many of whom dropped out) at $1,000 a set and from first to last (1827–38) the production cost Audubon $115,000.

One of my earliest recollections is standing tip-toe and saucer-eyed at a sort of table which my father would open to reveal a huge magical book full of pictures of unbelievably colourful birds. I knew it was called 'Audubon' because my little brother had been christened with the same name. Later I learned that my father had sold it in the hungry 1930s for the then unheard-of sum of £120 – a year's wages for a working man. Had I that book to sell today – and if I could bear to sell it – I could confidently expect it to make something very close to a quarter of a million pounds.

John Chancellor is unusually well equipped to write this life of Audubon, for he is a distinguished antiquarian bookseller, a scholarly collector of natural-history books, an experienced biographer and the founder of the part-work 'Knowledge'. (Audubon's 'Birds' was a part-work – 87 parts, each comprising five plates, delivered in specially made wooden boxes.) Mr Chancellor knows where to find and how to handle his source material and he has the gift of knowing what is boring – and leaving it out. The Audubon who emerges from his book irresistibly invites comparison with another genius of that age: Robert Burns. Both these men set standards in their own fields of endeavour which have never been surpassed, both had the morals of a parish bull, both possessed extraordinary physical beauty and magnetic personalities. (Yes, there really is such a thing as personal magnetism: ask anyone who has been in the same room as Douglas Bader, the legless air-ace.) Both, too, were venally content to pose as the stereotypes which their public expected. Plato once said, 'Be what you would wish to seem' – both Burns and Audubon cynically did their best to seem what society and the journals wished them to be. Burns, well educated, well read, cheerfully adopted the character of 'the heaven-taught ploughman', while ex-naval cadet and entrepreneur Audubon – who used to shoot in silk stockings and dancing-pumps – slipped into the role of the lonesome, buckskin-clad frontiersman.

These images persist; who wants facts when 'codology' is so much more appetizing?

> – 'Birds in the Hand', a review of *Audubon: A Biography*
> by John Chancellor, from the *Irish Press*, 5 October 1978

Audubon had earned his living as a trapper, taxidermist, a dance and fencing master and a farmer before dedicating himself to natural-history illustration.

Charlie Mortdecai has Audubon binoculars, which a bird-watching friend of mine tells me are the best, and are made by Swift, a Japanese firm.

Autobiography Bon did not exactly write one. First-person accounts of his experiences that do not come filtered through some pose, accent or fiction are rare. The self-descriptions for his book jackets are playfully inaccurate or exaggerate some of his characteristics at the expense of others. His novels are not autobiographical in any simple sense, although they are redolent of his personality and some of his preoccupations. He omits his serious and constant money problems, and, unlike Fielding, he does not make them part of the human comedy. See MONEY.

Names and addresses, mannerisms and possessions of friends are used to tease, occasionally to compliment, and suggest more than they give away. The name Karli Van Cleef in *All the Tea in China* suggests that it might be a *roman-à-clef* – I think this is another tease. The main sense in which his writing is strongly autobiographical is in the states of mind of the heroes: Charlie, always ready to dodge the next danger from whichever side it might come, always trying to fathom who are his enemies and who his friends, often misinterpreting situations, a fall guy always getting to his feet again after crushing blows; and Karli, younger, more sexually confident, fearful of many things yet resilient; both *picaros* going from one adventure to another and, like Bon, constantly precipitated into new situations.

In this book I shall pluck out some visible threads from the infinitely problematic relationship between the writer and the works, and decode a few references. The more bizarre events of our lives do not appear in the fiction. For Bon's own slightly disingenuous statement of the matter, see FICTION AND FRIENDS or the following blurb written to express a mood rather than for a real book jacket, one of several examples of the genre among his papers.

Kyril Bonfiglioli says that his life is an open book but he does not like people reading it over his shoulder. He much dislikes cats, noise, feminism, Cambridge and decimal coinage; in fact he doesn't like anything much. He was born a few decades ago but doesn't look it and has no intention of dying for ages yet. He lives in Ireland and doesn't really do anything else. His friends say he is all heart but his doctor says it's liver. He is a keen observer of work. Having given up eating, drinking, gambling, swearing, wenching, stamp-collecting and religion, he is now reduced to giving up giving up things, which is why he eschews Yoga, jogging and the manufacture of soft toys. He has had three vaccinations and a vasectomy but none of them took. His ambition is to keep a pig.

Audodidact   One who is self-taught, used with admiration or scorn by Bon and his father according to whether fellow feeling or a sense of speaking from the position of a highly educated man was dominant. Audubon, Bewick and Kipling are exemplars of rich significance to Bon.

As Bon left school at sixteen, most of his education came from his own varied reading and the opportunities provided by his father's stock-in-trade. His leap from sergeant in the regular army to undergraduate at Balliol eleven years later was not an easy one and could not have been achieved without his habitual pursuit of knowledge from a wide range of sources.

This is his account of his studies written for university entrance:

Detailed particulars of studies pursued since school:

The only organized courses I have attended were in advanced French and Spanish at Eastbourne Evening Institute during the winter of 1950/ 51, when I gained the Royal Society of Arts' Diploma in Advanced French with Distinction. During these years I also studied some Latin intermittently under Mr John Brewer, MA, and Revd E. Ridley Lewis, BA, BD, both of Eastbourne.

From time to time during my army service I have been able to attend various lectures from WEA courses of interest to me, but no other tutorial classes. My closest studies have been in English, French and Scottish literature. I have no Anglo-Saxon, but from Middle English onwards I can claim to be moderately well read in all but certain C17 dramatists and homilists and C18 novelists.

French. I have read (with some difficulty) the *Chanson de Roland*, Béroul's *Roman de Tristan*, *Aucassin & Nicolette* and some Marie de France. I am tolerably familiar with representative works of the following: Rabelais, Ronsard, Villon, Molière, Montaigne, Voltaire, Balzac, Flaubert, Prévost, Gautier, Verlaine, Baudelaire, Stendahl, Daudet, Mérimée, Maurois, France. The main lacunae are, perhaps, Corneille and Racine (although I have read the *Phèdre*). I am particularly interested in Scottish literature and can claim fairly close acquaintance with all but two or three of the important texts.

I can read most English court hands and book hands.

Was he overestimating the level of knowledge Oxford would expect of him?

He was a perpetual user and collector of reference books; the idea of anyone not owning and constantly using a good dictionary was a scandal to him. He liked to know the proper and improper words for things and to use them with precision. If he lacked information about anything, he always knew a man – and occasionally a woman – who could tell him. He had an excellent verbal and visual memory and loved puzzles and codes of all sorts.

See also BEWICK and KIPLING.

Balliol College, Oxford Getting into Balliol from the army was a considerable achievement and an ambition realized. Initially he was proud to be photographed with tie and scarf, not realizing that in the snobbery of the times this was to risk being 'a little grey man' or a 'trog'. The men's colleges were more riddled by considerations of class and clique than the women's. There were seven men to every woman student, as the university had put a limit on the numbers the women's colleges could accept. Men coming in from army service had a certain glamour for other less experienced men and for women. Like Bon, they could find themselves in the mutually disconcerting situation of being older than the tutor in their subject, as Bon did with his tutor Ted Gang, whom he later came to like and respect enormously. The varied and intelligent company of friends was a huge pleasure to Bon, but he had to deal with being the only widower and father among them. This he did by cooking delicious and copious meals from cheap ingredients and luring company home rather than paying a babysitter. See CRANHAM STREET.

Dryden, the chief Oxford don of his fiction, is closely modelled on John Bryson, who was his tutor for the language side of the English degree. Bon liked and admired Bryson but also feared him – I have seen him break out in a sweat trying to impress him. Bryson it was who discovered the Lothian portrait and identified it as a painting of John Donne, the metaphysical poet, in his dandified youth. Bryson and Bon discussed pictures, and Bryson later bought from Bon's gallery in the Turl.

The passage below is a brilliant evocation of a tutorial.

'You see,' he went on, wiping his spectacles in a disappointed sort of way, 'there is just a little more to it than I have so far related.'

I screamed inside my head, for I knew those tones of old: they were the tones of a Fellow and Tutor who has something ripe and squashy up his sleeve. (I had last heard them a couple of decades before, when, as a second-year undergraduate, I was reading my weekly essay to Dryden. The subject was 16th Century English prosody and, having passed the week amongst bad companions, I found myself with but half the morning in which to lay a learned egg. I sped to the Bodleian Library, as better men have sped before: found a relevant article in some obscure American Review of Renaissance studies forty years old and copied it out entire. As I read it to Dryden that afternoon he appeared to be dozing at first, then roamed the room, taking out a volume here and there and saying 'Pray continue, dear boy' in precisely those flat silken tones to which I have just referred. I read on, he continued to fidget at his bookshelves, then – *joined in*. I faltered, breaking the duet. 'Yes,' he said returning the book to its shelf, 'I remember considering that to be a rather sound analysis at the time. I wonder whether I might ask you to delight me with two essays next week. How kind. Good day.' You see the kind of contender I was matched against – a master of ring-craft.

– *The Great Mortdecai Moustache Mystery*, p. 31

An envelope of letters held in Balliol Library concerned with Bon in his student days reveals his severe financial stress and the concerted efforts from Balliol authorities to argue for an increase in the pathetically small allowance he received for having his two small sons with him. He could not of course live in college.

Three Balliol undergraduates committed suicide while he was there. I remember being aware how disturbing this was to the group of friends who drank at the buttery and lay on the grass laughing and joking.

Bon wasn't much of a one for political demonstrations, but Oxford students post-Suez and after the occupation of Hungary had been newly awakened to transnational issues. In a photo that appeared on 2 June 1968 in the local paper, we see him marching from Balliol with the prettiest in a spoof protest march to Ban the Pong. This march against marches was accompanied with flags and music and succeeded in covering the distance between the Lamb and Flag in St Giles and the White Horse in Broad Street. A spokesman for the march, who gave his name as Smith, said, 'We are not disappointed with the number who have decided to march. It is remarkable that so many Balliol men have been persuaded to get out of bed on a wet Sunday morning. The purpose of our march is to prove that marches do not prove anything, and we regard the outcome as highly satisfactory.' Opponents of the demonstration were pelted with chocolate éclairs – the kind of civilized warfare, the organizers explained, that they wished to encourage.

Bon had a lot of fun at Balliol, was involved in a Balliol debating society and contributed to many a Balliol rhyme. He strongly resented the idea of Balliol opening its doors to women students and, as far as I can gather from an opaquely diplomatic reply, must have written to the Master deploring the idea.

Bank managers

. . . the sun shone as mercilessly as a bank manager's smile.

– After You with the Pistol, p. 234

By the time I had grown out of train-spotting, stamp-collecting and bird-watching, in the order stated, I was old enough to take up the study of bank managers. It is not a rewarding branch of Natural History because in England there is only one species: the English bank manager (known to naturalists as Palgrave's Golden Treasurer). Age and diligence may cause variants in weight, waistline and value of motorcar but the species remains *sui generis*, so to speak, and impossible to mistake. Irish bank managers, now, may look like bishops or burglars, Beatles or bookies, but the English bank manager looks like an English b.m. Stand him in an identity parade, clothed in prison garb (which he will probably be wearing sooner or later anyway) and the veriest housewife – nay, even another bank manager – will instantly pick him out as a Lord of the Overdraft.

Fortunately, they never read anything lighter than Snurge's classic *Short-Term Loans*, so my own particular bank manager is unlikely to give me a hard time for writing the above.

Armed with this early training, no sooner had I been shunted through the door inscribed MANAGER than I had the chap behind the desk identified as the manager of that bank – Bronwen's Bank. Since I was neither a borrower nor a lender he did not rise, nor did he offer me a cigar, and the brief twitch of his pursed lips was a smile from the very bottom of the discards. I took the chair at which he waved a pallid flipper and spread out before him my credentials. He looked at them with unfeigned disinterest; his conscience must have been clear that week.

He said that no, he didn't mind if I smoked. He went to a window and opened it; perhaps he thought that he'd scored. He moved well and lithely, I guessed that he had once been runner-up for the Junior Cashiers' Welter-weight Cup. He was wearing stays and one of those moustaches that bank managers are born with. (Clean-shaven chaps who claim to be bank managers are always impostors, mark my words.)

– *The Great Mortdecai Moustache Mystery*, pp. 66–7

Autres temps, autres mœurs? Actual bank managers were necessarily important to Bon, and they crop up in his fiction. Here are two real bank managers of his acquaintance who had their own eccentricities.

An English Bank Manager. In the sixties, we are invited to a cocktail party at the country house of the manager of Bon's business account in Oxford. A little way into the party when talk has got noisy, though not much livelier, someone is seen to drop a crisp. From then on, the manager in his nice pinstripes crawls around on the new fitted carpet among the feet of his guests with a dustpan and brush ready for further crisps.

An Irish Bank Manager. In the seventies, a young friend arrives in Shercock unshaven and grubby after several days' driving round Ireland. On being introduced, and knowing that there is no means of having a bath in Bon's cottage, the hospitable manager of the local bank gives the young man a huge bunch of keys and says that this one opens the door on the left which goes into the bank itself, but that he should use this other key to open the door on the right to reach the bathroom. This is, I think, the manager who wrote to Bon severely but kindly and granted him 'a sanctioned overdraft'. They drank in the same pub in County Cavan.

Bargains Bargains and sometimes barter were critical for the family's financial survival.

Bon's most extravagant bargain was the contents of a Welsh natural-history museum – all but the two stuffed ostriches and the emu. Even he recognized these as too large in their great mahogany cases for our huge Norham Gardens house.

He is out. He has forgotten to tell me of this buy or when the Smith brothers will be delivering. Tired and hugely pregnant, I am already in bed when the doorbell jangles on its wires and pulleys. In my dressing gown, I go down and open the door.

'We've brought the birds. Where would you like 'em, missus?' There is no good answer to this question. I get back into our bed and watch with mounting depression as forty cases of stuffed birds are stacked around me to ceiling height. I feel as if I am being walled in with dead creatures. In deference to my state, the Smiths kindly turn the two-headed lamb and the King Charles spaniel to face the wall.

Four tea chests of exotic shells are put in the hall. I fall asleep staring at mute swans, great northern divers, pochards, etc., etc., trophies of Victorian sporting colonels – triumphs of taxidermy. Bon himself, when he finally arrived home, was pretty startled by the effect of his proud purchase on our bedroom, but assured me they would make our fortune and soon be off to Sotheby's or Christie's.

Episode two – months later. At 2 a.m., sleepless in bed I lie, hating all the birds facing me, but most of all hating the mute swans now moved into the inner porch and showing miserable traces of parasitic collapse about the tail. I visualize beside them a fine porcelain umbrella-stand full of walking sticks. In a trance of built-up rage, I go into the hall, seize a stout staff from the stand and bash glass case and failing birds to bits. Bon leaps out of the study, pistol cocked, expecting to confront burglars, and is astonished to see me standing there in my nightie, stick in hand, amid the alien shards and feathers. Oddly then, calm and harmony descended on us. Together, we cleared up the mess before lodgers, au pair and children woke up. Bon went out and fetched a Chinese takeaway – chicken corn soup for me. This was our meal of reconciliation and a recognition of the strength of my feelings. He promised me that Christie's and Sotheby's longed to have the remaining birds in their next suitable sales. Friends remember the birds as clogging up hall, stairs and landings for years.

Bon loved a bargain in wine or food, although with wine he never fell into the trap of believing you could taste in the glass – in any positive sense – the money you had saved. His food bargains were less successful and had no bearing on the daily bread of a family of seven, although it amused and delighted him to come back from Mrs Palm's – a celebrated Oxford delicatessen – with the tinned ants in chocolate, lumpfish roe and snails in garlic that had stood too long on her shelves and to rearrange the larder to accommodate these little tins and jars among the baked beans and more boring staples of everyday life.

But for the great bargain, see TINTORETTO.

Betjeman

The buildings range from the gloomy to the absurd via the pretentious. St Helier is a positive barrel of architectural fun: even Sir John Betjeman himself would be unable to keep a straight face.

– Something Nasty in the Woodshed, p. 376

Bon loved John Betjeman for the kind of person he was and for his championing of then unfashionable Victorian architecture, his interests in the quirky and his poetry, which was undervalued and considered insufficiently modern in the sixties. For Bon, he remained a person with whom, for instance, he could imagine sharing a laugh at, and a taste for, the architecture of Jersey.

How well they knew each other, I do not know: the photograph below was certainly taken by Bon when they went for a walk in the university parks. Some years later Bon must have sent him his first novel and was tickled to pass on (in a letter to the writer Christopher Priest) the literary advice Betjeman offered: 'Steady on the adverbs.'

Bewick Thomas Bewick (1753–1828), father of modern wood engraving, wrote and illustrated one of Bon's most treasured books, *History of British Birds*. He was one of the first to draw birds from life and show them with appropriate landscape and foliage. End pieces to sections of the book contain charming vignettes of the seasons of country life, some humorous, some melancholy, some emblematic. In a few, tiny devils seem to be threatening or harassing the countryman. Bon's copy of this dearly loved and relatively rare book cost him one guinea – only twice as much as its published price in 1797. In a printing press he acquired from the Vicar of Deddington, there was (along with many a scene of the Vicar's

Airedales seen against the church tower) a set of reproductions of Bewick's blocks. Finding them was a real thrill. The '*robin*' was our hand-printed Christmas card one year.

CHRISTMAS GREETINGS
from

April and Margaret Bonfiglioli
Eighteen, Norham Gardens, Oxford

Bible

Having exhausted the tepid pleasures of 'Jane Austen' and vainly attempted to woo sleep with the incomprehensible logic of Norie's *Seamanship*, I was at last forced to borrow a tattered copy of the Bible from the fo'c'sle.

I learned to love this book. There is no finer compendium of factual and fictional lore to be had, with the possible exception of Captain Burton's translation of the *Arabian Nights*, which is unexpurgated. I took care to avoid the more inflammatory passages such as the Song of Solomon and certain parts of Ezekiel, but my state was such that even when trying to drug myself with the lists of the ancestors of Abraham, I found myself not so much marvelling that Nahor begat Terah but wishing that I could be relishing the begetting-act myself. Such is the magic of the written word.   – *All the Tea in China*, p. 143

Like Karli, like Damon Runyon, Bon was a constant reader of, and quoter from, the Bible. He owned several, including a handsome leather-bound folio. One day as I went to hang out the washing, I met him coming guiltily up the garden from the bonfire heap where he had just put this Bible to burn, having first blasted it with airgun pellets. For someone who cherished books and taught others to turn pages carefully from their outer edges, this was extraordinary. Were they shots fired in anger? Was evidence being destroyed? He was visibly embarrassed to be seen and did his best to laugh it off.

'The heart is deceitful about all things and desperately corrupt; who can understand it?' cried Jeremiah XVII:9 and, as you know, Jeremiah was a chap with great insight into these matters, as well as being a little barmy himself.   – *Don't Point that Thing at Me*, p. 9

Back in my cell I asked for something to read; he was back in ten minutes with a tattered Bible.

'I think I've read this,' I said.

'It's all we've got,' he retorted, 'Enid Blyton is only for trusties.'

The Good Book was printed on fine India paper and the first few pages had been used by sacrilegious chaps for rolling fags with (that's *cigarettes*), so that Genesis began at the bit where Cain says 'My punishment is more than I can bear. Behold, thou hast driven me out this day from the face of the earth; . . . and I shall be a fugitive and a vagabond in the earth; and it shall come to pass that everyone that findeth me shall slay me.' I never did find out what happened to Cain except that he went to the land of Nod which is to the East of Eden; I joined him there.

–After You with the Pistol, p. 341

There are shades here of Brendan Behan's experience of the reading matter on offer in prison as recounted in *Borstal Boy* – a book both Bon and I had read. Behan found himself unexpectedly savouring Jane Austen and only allowed himself a chapter at a time to spin out the pleasure. Here the implication is that by Charlie's time the stock of the prison library would have deteriorated. The reference to Cain has real emotional resonance for Bon – no wonder he grants Charlie forgetfulness and sleep at this point.

Birds Birds indoors and out interested Bon in more ways than you can imagine. The following passage, with its curious little autobiographical asides, comes from a single sheet of his notes under the heading 'Wordbag'.

The Barbary Partridge has 'a necklace, red-brown, with white spots'. (The Red-Legged Partridge, on the other hand, has 'necklace black, breaking into short streaks' – one fears for its health . . .) The Common Partridge, of course, has a 'dark horse-shoe mark' on his belly. Pride forbids me to comment on this★ . . . Both are related to a bird I cannot claim acquaintance with – the ANDALUSIAN HEMIPODE.

The Great Spotted Cuckoo, as well as having a 'bright orange orbital ring' – goodness! – and 'rich chestnut primaries', enjoys one of those superbly daft German names: HAHERKUCKUCK. (You think I'm making this up, don't you? Wanna bet?)

The Pallid Swift (story of my life).

The Spotless Starling (This, we are scarcely shocked to be told, has no spots.)

Tits. Well, we all know that you can create 40 Blue Tits by forcing 20 WRNS into an Arctic Sea but it needs a certain dedication to produce a Crested Tit, a Coal Tit or, God forbid, a Bearded Tit. Tits, as every *coureur* knows, vary in the most engaging way, from the Long Tailed Tit to the aunt-like Penduline Tit, but what really breaks my heart is the Sombre Tit. Need I say that its Latin name is *Parus lugubris*?

This part of Lancashire contains some of the best bird-watching terrain in England: sea and shore birds in their millions haunt the vast salt-marshes and tidal flats of Morecombe bay, and the reeds of Leighton Moss – an RSPB sanctuary – are alive with duck, swans, gulls and even the bittern . . .

I let my now grizzled hair grow long and fluffy, bought a good pair of field-glasses and mingled with the bird-watchers. It's astonishing how many there are nowadays: ornithology used to be an arcane hobby for embittered schoolmasters, dotty spinsters and lonely little boys but now it is as normal a weekend occupation as rug-making or wife-swapping. I was terribly keen on it when I was at school, so I knew the right cries, and, as a matter of fact, I became rather keen again and thoroughly enjoyed my outings.   – *Don't Point that Thing at Me*, pp. 154–5

. . . the dominant species are the magpie and the sparrow. There is no shooting land and therefore no gamekeepers, so the ubiquitous magpie

---

★ A curious allusion to a birthmark on his belly.

munches up all the nestlings; only the sparrow, that bird of Venus, can outbreed the magpies by diddling his mate all the year round, sturdy little chap. In the late autumn small rare birds may sometimes be seen on passage, resting in the fields of unborn daffodils.

— *Something Nasty in the Woodshed*, p. 375

The husband who has taken to drink and hitting his wife in the short story 'How to Frighten Your Wife to Death' might have been able 'to adjust his addictive personality by watching warblers, tending terns' if only he had been sent off with a packet of sandwiches by his wife.

Each of the Mortdecai novels has its passage for 'twitchers'. As long as it wasn't at 'sparrow fart' (an army expression for dawn used by Bon), bird-watching was an unfaltering pleasure for him all his life and also a source of calmer moods. Each time he moved to a different landscape, his responses were renewed.

He was sometimes a rather unsuccessful keeper of actual birds and felt guilty when they died. See CANARIES and PARROT.

His last bird reference was to the 'great blackbacked bugger', a self-description that is featured in his letters to his editor at Secker, John Blackwell.

'Blast Off' An anonymously published story, purporting to have been translated from the Finnish, written to fill a precisely defined gap in the June/July 1964 issue of *Science Fantasy* – the first number that Bon edited for Roberts & Vintner Ltd. This is probably Bon's first published short story, written when he thought of himself as an editor rather than a writer. Judith Merril later included it in her anthology of science-fiction writing.

Bookseller Son of an antiquarian bookseller, buying and selling books was habitual to Bon. At twenty-three, he was antiquarian books manager of Messrs Cox in the King's Road for a year. In the sixties, he was a director of Sanders of Oxford which had a large antiquarian book section managed by Philip Jaggard, a name Bon later gave to a vile policeman. It probably did need policing – the writer Brian Aldiss says old Mr Sanders, the original owner, was found to be smuggling out books under his mackintosh *after* he had sold the shop.

Bon was a knowledgeable bibliophile and printed the card for an Oxford bibliophiles' meeting. Once in a country gentleman's library, he won a *coup d'estime*; when, trying to explain what a fore-edge painting was, he reached for a book on the shelves, saying it was just the kind of book that might have one, and found to his surprise and delight, as he slightly splayed the gilt edges of the pages, that there was indeed a delicate landscape hidden there. Although he would have been quite capable of staging such a find, this occasion was a beautiful example of dealer's hunch.

Borborygmus

... chill 'n' trepidation were playing the devil with my small intestines and my borborygmus was often louder than the engine of the Rolls, which loped on, quietly guzzling its pint of petrol per statute mile.

– Don't Point that Thing at Me, p. 102

This favourite Latinate word of Bon's, also used by his father, describes onomatopoeically a condition he frequently suffered.

Brothers   In the poem quoted in full on p. 163, the line 'Have my spirits no brother?' is a cry for a kindred spirit, always seen as male, for the ideal brother and companion, for the missing brother. Bon's papers suggest that in a projected novel, *Lord Mortdecai* (q.v.), he planned to explore the theme of brothers further.

Characteristically, he thought of brothers as opposites, often in a strongly polarized way. An imaginary Russian novel of his was called *The Brothers War and Peace*. His father and uncle had chosen contrasting life styles: the active life for Emmanuel, Amazonian adventurer, soldier, antiquarian bookseller and father of three; and for Giuseppe, the contemplative life, celibacy and a career in the Catholic Church. Bon's own younger brother, Christopher, by taking shelter like every good boy during an air-raid and dying at nine in the same bomb blast that killed his mother, left the indelible message that goodness is destroyed and naughtiness survives. From this time on, survival became of prime value, often

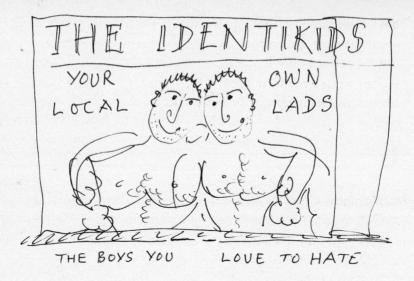

Bon's sketch for a poster for an imaginary wrestling event, perhaps involving the Kray twins

referred to and carrying with it survivor's guilt. Cain too was a survivor.

He gave the two sons of his first marriage names that differentiated the brothers strongly. Aeneas Methodius Alexander he expected to fill the role of *pius Aeneas*. He had given Roderick George Gordon the family name of his Scottish mother and the name of the hero of Robert Southey's poem *Roderick, The Last of the Goths*, plus his own last name of George. He tended to expect one brother to be good and the other bad. See NAMES.

Saints Kyril and Methodius were actual brothers and also brothers in arms in the great campaign to evangelize the Slavs; their names alternated between generations in the Bonfiglioli family.

Jock and Charlie are also brothers in arms. The correspondence with the writer Christopher Priest is one between brother writers polishing their weapons.

The nature of the brother bond was part of the appeal for him of the story of the Kray twins; he was particularly intrigued by the fact that one twin was homosexual, the other not. See FILM.

Through all his travels, Bon kept a small oil painting of a charming boy, a reminder of his lost brother. I do not know if Charlie's resentment of his brother, Robin, in the novels is based on his feeling towards any living person or whether Bon transferred to Robin a resentment he felt towards Christopher for acquiring an advantageous reputation by dying young.

Calligraphy Good handwriting was an art and legibility a courtesy, in Bon's view. He admired fine calligraphy and with the right sort of pen could do splendid flourishes himself. His own hand seems to have been developed after the age of thirteen. Here he is in a letter advising his daughter Catriona to cultivate a good hand:

I'm very pleased at your handwriting; it's an inexpensive hobby and a valuable skill. So many people write so foully that when one receives a handsome letter it is with a pleasant shock. Two points: take a little more care over capital letters (e.g., the middle of the M should go right down to the line) and leave larger margins all round.

Canaries 'There must be more of the canary, *passim.*' So wrote John Blackwell of Secker & Warburg in a letter of detailed criticism of the manuscript of *After You with the Pistol*. Bon underlined 'must' in ink and wrote 'Yes!' above it.

Bert was, I think, Bon's first canary, which he had in Lancashire, a much sweeter pet than the abominable parrot that he had left behind in Oxford (see PARROT). The Javanese finches he'd had in Oxford died in a locked conservatory in a heat wave. Bert was followed in Jersey by Spink – a name neatly combining art dealing and onomatopoeia. When Spink was out of sorts, Bon used to cheer him up with the sound of running water. The bird keeps his name in the Mortdecai novels and is used, as a pit canary was used by miners testing for dangerous gases, to register the emotional climate with particular reference to endings.

Towards the end of *After You with the Pistol* in an absurd display of jealous rage, Mortdecai gets his foot 'trapped in the ruptured plastic and three-ply of a kitchen fitment' and has to be cut free from his shoe by Jock with the kitchen scissors. The following dialogue takes place:

'Reckon that old kick done you a power of good, Mr Charlie, better than a week at the seaside, anything else you fancy?'
    'How is the canary?' I countered. 'Still sulking?'
    'Nah, he's back in lovely voice, a fair treat to listen to him, I had to put a clorth over his cage to shut the little bugger up. What I done was to give him some hard-boiled egg, a pinch of cayenne in his hemp seed and a sup of rum in his drinking water and now, bing-bong, he's ready to take on all comers. Booking for smoking concerts now.

Charlie asks for the same cure – leaving out everything except the rum. Then Jock reassures him that his jealous suspicions about his wife's relationship with another man are misplaced. There is a mood change and when Mortdecai says to Jock 'unswathe the said canary; I long to hear a few of its dulcet notes', we know that we have reached the end of the novel and for the moment a happy ending.
    The dark and death-laden endings full of unspoken pain in *Something Nasty in the Woodshed* are reinforced by the implication that the canary too is dead.
    In *All the Tea in China* (p. 118) Charlie's ancestor Karli also has trouble keeping his canary alive:

I remember Las Palmas, the port of Gran Canaria, only because there I caught from a young person a tiresome little infestation which is of no interest and also because I bought a canary-bird which sang so indefatigably that I felt obliged, on my way back to the ship to cool its ardour in sea-water. I did not mean it to die; I have felt unhappy about it ever since. It must have been frail, frail.

It is as if when the singer dies happiness goes. In his last novel, the canary has the final gesture: it shrugs its shoulders.

Car crashes Despite failing his first test for speeding, Bon was a reasonable driver when sober and an hilarious or horrendous one

– depending on road conditions and the mood of his passengers – when not.

On 14 July 1964 we were driving in evening dress to Mark Lennox-Boyd's twenty-first birthday dance at Hurlingham. As we came down a slope to a major crossroads on the A40, the brakes failed. The lights turned to red and cars streamed across in front of us. Bon did the only thing possible to avoid plunging forwards into dense fast-moving traffic and causing a multiple crash: he brought the car to a standstill by steering it into the bollards just to the right of us. Those were pre-safety-belt days, and the windscreen shattered all over my face and the steering wheel impacted on Bon, severely bruising his chest. My eyelids were cut and my face covered in blood so I could not see. However, I was conscious and can remember thinking this is not so bad, we are not dead. It is bad enough so that I can lie here and wait for help, I haven't got to get out of the car or do anything. Endorphins must have cut in powerfully, because I felt no pain, only an extraordinary euphoria and gladness about being alive and a powerful sense of all the human resources for rescue as stretchers and ambulance took us to Hillingdon Hospital. I cannot describe the deep sense of love and healing that radiated to me from each encounter in that hospital: the stretcher bearers; the man with the warm vibrant voice who x-rayed my head; the neat-fingered Asian doctor who stitched my face so meticulously with fifty-four stitches; the nurses; and the consultant, Mr Scorer. I was put in a side ward with french windows opening into the garden. Each time the long curtains billowed, bird song and heavenly scents wafted in; and, on the second day, I was aware of the lights and colours of sunshine and flowers beyond the red curtains just visible through my barely raised lids. I saw that the world was good. When my damaged face returned to being recognizably my own, I saw it as an assurance that I was meant to be me: I should not try to be anyone else or to be that unimaginable woman who could have pleased Bon in every way.

The impact of this event was enormous for both of us, but it affected each of us completely differently. For Bon, it compounded his sense of guilt and destructiveness. It did not help that I was scooped up by my parents for further convalescence. Their thought was to make it easier for Bon to return to his many preoccupations; Bon's comment later was that this had prevented him from looking after me as he would have liked. My face healed up well, and most of the time the scars had no effect on my sense of myself. However, whenever Bon and I met in later years, he would scrutinize me carefully and make some comment about how the scars hardly showed at all. On his agenda, though not on mine, was the hope that I would find a rich man to marry me. To me this was an absurdity, yet perhaps Bon would have felt better if I had. The sense of gladness at being alive lasted in full strength for at least the next eighteen months and often returns to me still.

Bon had a knack of being associated with car crashes as a passenger – two in the summer of 1981 alone. In August of that year, in a 'bread and butter and soft drinks letter' to Ilfra and David Goldberg, he recalls the recent head-on collision between their Volvo and a speeding motor-bike and, after inquiring whether the insurance company did after all 'cough up for my gents' natty small clothes, the blood-boltered unmentionables', he recounts another scrape:

Would you believe it, as we left Dublin airport I was in another accident: the first the driver had had in thirty years. It was minor damage only, but the driver of the other car (who had forgotten we drive on the wrong side here) was a Dutchman with no English and he seemed sure that we all ought to make depositions in front of a *juge d'instruction* before moving a wheel. We were now blocking ingress and egress to the airport; the Dutchman and I could speak a little German, his wife could speak a little French, Ned Haughy could only run up and down the queues of cars asking whether anyone could speak foreign. I got the giggles and the Frau burst into tears.

In the fiction, car chases are common; in life, car crashes were the more usual occurrence.

Catchphrases For a man so inventive with language, Bon's everyday talk was surprisingly full of catchphrases. The following favourites of his indicate some of his attitudes to life:

you're better without it – I can be hurt – well, fuck an old rat! – you/he must be tenacious of life – to coin a phrase – to name but a few – don't bother your pretty head about it – I've changed more nappies than you've had hot dinners – you win some, you lose some – so it goes – 'twas ever thus – easy come, easy go – an enemy hath done this – a glutton for punishment – nothing queer about the Bonfigs! – philoprogenitive Bonfig – Hell's teeth!

Then there are the Latin words and phrases, still just about usable in the sixties.

autodidact – borborygmus – *caveat emptor* – *crambe repetita* – *locus classicus* – pococurantist – *tu quoque*, etc.

Catholicism Cyril/Kyril Emmanuel George could hardly have been given more Christian or more saintly names. Despite a rejection of religious belief at the rational level, his conscience, his consciousness and his learning were irreversibly permeated with it. He continued a family tradition of Christian names for his children and sent his two older sons to St Aloysius School, a local Catholic primary school, saying they would be better taught and acquire better handwriting there, but also quoting the Jesuit saying 'give me a boy until he is seven and I'll give you the man'. He admired the authority and thought systems, the learning and the art treasures of the Roman Catholic Church. He knew the types of Christ, the signs and symbols of saints, the litanies of the Virgin, the names of the four cardinal virtues and the three theological virtues and explored the names, numbers and definitions of deadly sins as part of his preparation to do research on medieval iconography for a second degree, a subject he returned to in Ireland in the 1970s.

Giuseppe, the younger brother of Bon's father, was ordained as a Catholic priest in 1934 and rose in the Church to be Archbishop of Cagliari in Sardinia – a war-front in the battle between the Church and the Mafia. Once I heard that after the war he sent his brother Emmanuel a message in Latin to say that he had survived. He was still alive in the 1970s, but it seems Bon lost touch with him completely.

Bon was absolutely against all forms of religious bigotry and occasionally used his wit as a stalking-horse to spring a discomforting surprise on a bigot. He greatly relished the moment when, after a newcomer to his gallery had casually uttered a number of anti-Semitic and then anti-Catholic remarks, he glanced at the other visitor standing quietly by and said to the bigot: 'By the way, I'm sorry I don't think I've introduced you to my friend Father Peter Levi, SJ'. He uses this conflation of Catholic and Jew playfully again in *After You with the Pistol* (p. 289), when Johanna gives the name Tom Rosenthal, his publisher at Secker, to the Jesuit priest. See also JEWISHNESS, PRIESTS and SUNDAYS.

Charlie

Charlie: a credulous person; an inefficient ineffectual person, a fool (often in the phrase a proper Charlie) . . . a night-watchman (obs.); the small triangular beard familiar in the portraits of Charles I; a small moustache resembling that worn by Charlie Chaplin; a name for a fox.

These definitions from *Chambers Dictionary* are obviously relevant to Bon's hero, Charlie Mortdecai, and may have contributed to his collection of terms for face-fungus in his research for *The Great Mortdecai Moustache Mystery*.

Childhood

'I am going back to bed,' I said firmly. 'I want no part of any of this. Nobody ordered bombs.'   – *Don't Point that Thing at Me*, p. 68

Cyril Emmanuel George Bonfiglioli was born on 29 May 1928 in Eastbourne to Emmanuel Bonfiglioli, an Italo-Slovene, who was forty-two, and Dorothy née Pallett, his English wife, who was twenty-eight. His sister, Inez, had been born two years earlier. Pre-war beach photographs suggest family life might have been ordinarily happy, although it is impossible to know for certain: Inez is picking up shells, Cyril sits with a little dish in his hands and looks forward with a slightly puzzled sizing-up expression.

His younger brother, Christopher John Audubon, was born in June 1934. War broke out in 1939. 'Next year a land mine was dropped in the back garden,' his older sister Inez writes. 'We *immediately* were hauled out by the air-raid wardens – the whole family. We children went to stay in a Sussex village with a friend of our mother. Later we were all [the children] sent to Hitchin in Hertfordshire. That year was effectually the end of the family as a unit.'

The following reminiscence seems to belong to 1940:

During the war, when I was a little boy, my father settled me on a farm. One day the War Agricultural Committee or Milk Marketing Board sent us a stern letter saying that our cows' milk was deficient in 34% of non-fatty solids (or some such %). We, or rather the farmeress, wrote back saying what the **** was she supposed to do about it. Within a few days a great sack arrived, full of cow-chocolate. Great fist-sized nuggets of rock-hard black chocolate, studded with coarse sugar crystals like pyrites. The cows got some of it. I was not a very happy child at the time but I vividly remember happy afternoons in the hay-loft, devouring a great bound volume of the *Boy's Own* paper (*c.* 1890) and gnawing at the rock-hard cow-chocolate. You had to spit out the bits of sacking-thread embedded in it. Sweetmeats were rare in those days.

– from a letter by Bon to the cookery writer Helge Rubinstein,
quoted by her in The Chocolate Book

After some time at 'a public elementary school', he went on at eleven to Eastbourne Grammar School with an LEA grant giving total fee remission. The school was later evacuated and then shared premises with Hitchin Grammar School in Hertfordshire.

'We didn't integrate, but met for air-raids.' Cyril and Inez were billeted separately and were at different schools in Hitchin. Gerald Denley, a school friend, says Cyril had been placed with a family in conflict, where he was not happy or well fed.

Returning home to Eastbourne for the weekend in April 1943, while he was being a 'bad' boy skipping about the streets during an air-raid, his mother and brother died in a direct hit on the air-raid shelter where they had virtuously taken refuge. Fifteen-year-old Cyril was standing outside a tobacconist's at that moment and had his clothes torn by the blast. His Oxford friend Anthony Harris says that Cyril then had the burden of going round to the shop to tell his father what had happened. According to Harris, Emmanuel's anguished cry was: 'If only it hadn't been Chris.' Or 'If only it had been you!', which was how Bon recounted it to me. However, it is clear that day scarred the fifteen-year-old for life. This deep trauma damaged Cyril and his father and their relationship for the rest of their lives. To survive was to be guilty and to be the 'wrong son'. See GUILTY.

Gerald Denley, who was slightly older, describes him as a fellow loner and remembers riding about with Cyril on the bar of his bike. He says Cyril was astonishingly knowledgeable about classical music and that they used to listen to records together. They shared an interest in languages. In Gerald's autograph book is a pair of before-and-after drawings signed 'Cyril Bonfiglioli' and showing the unhappy *bouleversement* of 'two in a hammock attempting to kiss'. The handwriting is without its later practised elegance and the drawing is crude. The subject matter, although standard autograph stuff of the era, seems to anticipate the way the course of his true loves never did run smooth.

Another friend, Peter Bowyer, who was at Hitchin Grammar School, knew Cyril as George – his middle and most acceptably English name. He relates:

We were a gang of two – he was older than me – two years. We struck up a friendship by chance – I didn't know where he lived – we always arranged to meet out of school. We used to go to Oughton Head – a spring in a lovely piece of countryside. We sat by the river watching for kingfishers. We used to go to a pond on a farmer's land and fish for great crested newts with string and a worm. We swung through trees on ropes at the Meads. George used to keep his background more or less to himself. The people who found out he was Italian didn't want to know him. Other children found cruel nicknames to call him – George just walked away from aggression.

Bowyer, suffering himself in the war-time confusion of being an evacuee and being absent from school during his own mother's illness, returned to school and, finding Cyril was now absent, believed he had also died in that direct hit. In December 1997

Kevin Jackson wrote a feature on Bon for the *Mail on Sunday*. For Bowyer, this article was a discovery that his friend Bonfiglioli had lived very much longer than he had supposed.

In a rare tribute to a real person in his fiction, Bon honours this friend from Hitchin with the title of Peter, Lord Stevenage, and this loving vignette:

Peter Stevenage was a strange and valuable man and I often blame myself for not having prized him more at that time, when my character was being formed. He had the rarest and truest sort of charm: that is he did not exude a charm of his own but gave you the certainty, simply with a special sort of silence, that you were charming him. This is not an art that can be learnt by taking thought or by studying books; it is not an art at all, it is a gift from God, if you will pardon the expression. (There was a boy at my school who had this gift. He was neither tall, nor strong nor handsome; at lessons he was always just halfway up, or down, the form.

Cyril salutes in the OTC

At games he was reliable but did not shine. He spoke little and never harmfully, even of us few Jews at the school, but he would listen intently to anyone who spoke to him, even the masters; this was his gift. When you had finished he would say 'yes' or perhaps 'no' and you would go away purged and happy, like a Papist from the confessional-box. All of us in my year would cheerfully have died for him, except that he would have thought this a bizarre thing to do. He is now, without a doubt, the teller in a bank, trusted by one and all, and goes home each evening to a fat wife in a house smelling of cabbage and children's urine.)

The parenthesis is Bon speaking directly to the reader, the only time in *All the Tea in China* that he departs from the main narrative voice of his hero Karli. Though tempted to omit the last sentence – which so painfully undercuts the rest – from the quotation, I have retained it because it is so typical of Bon's frequent attempts to cover pain with cynicism. Curiously, Bowyer, here remembered so vividly from school, did work as an accountant, although Bon had no means of knowing this.

See CHIPS, FATHER and MOTHER.

Children

Fuimus et sub Deo erimus – We have been and by God we shall be.

– a Bonfiglioli motto

Bon had five children: Aeneas and Roderick, by his first wife, Elizabeth; Christopher, Catriona and Amanda, with Margaret, his second wife.

Aeneas, Roderick and Catriona are all married and live and work in Australia, Christopher in Spain and Amanda in Oxford. There are three grandchildren, Elizabeth, Vincent and Frank.

Chips Handwritten on Bon's yellow draft paper, I have found the following stylishly Bonnish passage, a foodie recollection of childhood that was to be part of that great unwritten book on the eating habits of the English:

Waiter, There's a Chip on My Shoulder

This chapter is about vegetables and it is only just that it should start with that great leveller, the common or garden-path chip. I refer, of course, to the sort shaped like this:

– not the sort you have with game if you are rich or out of a packet if you are a pub-user. I am prepared to go on record as stating fearlessly that The Chip is a good thing. Crisply golden outside, fluffy and tender within, it is the prince of starchy foods. Limp and reeking of whale oil, drenched with malt vinegar and stuck to a scurrilous newspaper, it is still fine filling sustenance. I have eaten many a chip in each of these conditions and intend to eat many another.

As a little boy I was taken to Sadler's Wells or Covent Garden or somewhere like that and all I remember of the evening is that on the way home we saw tiny, ungenteel, lucky ragamuffins each munching on one enormous chip. My researches have not produced a single London chipmonger still frying these prodigies – they all repeat the phrase so hated by the shopper: 'There's no call for them nowadays/hereabouts' – but I had the privilege of interviewing an ancient chip craftsman who told me they were sold at one farthing a piece in the '30s. As I recall them (and how I recall my envy) they were the size of a well-developed banana, but memory is often a flatterer. Last year I ate muffins for the first time since childhood and was indignant at their smallness: I remember them as being at least eight inches in diameter. Memo: make giant chips one day. One huge chip per guest, with a plate of tiny whitebait?

This passage is followed by detailed instructions under the headings: 'Elementary Chip-making' and 'Advanced Chip-making'.

Clothes

The secret-agent cloak was now falling across my shoulders so snugly I felt like an ivy-mantled tower.   – *After You with the Pistol*, p. 227

The following anecdote about England's arbiter of dress was told to me by Bon, who liked a good put-down, an equalizer between social unequals. 'Beau Brummell to the Prince of Wales, whom he met at Windsor wearing a rather loud check suit: "Goin' rattin'?"' Bon could identify with both parties in the interchange. In *Don't Point that Thing at Me* (p. 64) he sets this put-down into the mouth of Charlie's brother, Robin, as he looks disdainfully at Charlie's clothes.

In matters of dress a Jock is a less secure arbiter of taste than a Jeeves – Bon had neither. Always ready for mockery from a superior person and nervous about not, or not quite, being dressed for the part, Bon still enjoyed the possibilities of dressing-up and of wearing different clothes for different situations.

As soon as he could afford to as an art dealer, Bon had two suits made for himself by Hall Brothers of Oxford. Unfortunately he did not enjoy them long, as they were burned in a bedroom fire, and by the time the insurance money came through it was needed to buy stock for the gallery. He liked gentlemanly sportsman clothes in good-quality fabrics but tended to overdo the effect when he had the money. Clothes were important to him and closely linked with his identities, but in the novels their importance is wildly exaggerated for comic effect.

Clothes are one of many running themes in the fiction and are about recognition and position in society. Mortdecai is shown over and over again as getting it wrong, although in contexts where getting it right would be hard to gauge. Here he is being received by Britain's ambassador to Washington during the Wilson era:

'I won't beat about the bush, Mortdecai,' he honked, 'you are clearly an awful man. Here we are, trying to establish an image of a white-hot technological Britain, ready to compete on modern terms with any jet-age country in the world and here you are walking about Washington in a sort of Bertie Wooster outfit as though you were something dreamed up by the Tourist Board to advertise Ye Olde Brytysshe Raylewayes.'

'I say,' I said, 'you pronounce that last bit marvellously.'

'Moreover,' he ground on, 'your ridiculous bowler is dented, your absurd umbrella bent, your shirt covered with blood and you have a black eye.'

Posterity will want to know that I was wearing my Complete American

Disguise: a cream tussore suit, sunglasses and a cocoa-coloured straw hat with a burnt-orange ribbon. The effect was pretty sexy, I don't mind telling you. Mr Abercrombie would have bitten Mr Fitch if he'd seen it and the *Tailor and Cutter* would have been moved to tears.

                                                    – *Don't Point that Thing at Me*, p. 89

My tie, if I recall correctly, was a foulard, predominantly *merde d'oie* in colour, though why you should be interested I cannot imagine.

                                                    – *Don't Point that Thing at Me*, p. 28

Here *merde d'oie* – goose-shit green, the name of a colour used by interior decorators in the thirties – is the colour for Mortdecai's situation. As usual he is aware of being in deep shit and sauntering towards further dangers, but on the way he will cheer himself up by inspecting and blessing pelicans and other feathered friends in the park.

At his funeral in Jersey, I was touched when his dentist, introducing himself, said he was wearing a golden-yellow silk tie because he thought Bon would have liked it. He assured me that he also had a black tie in his pocket and pulled it out to prove it.

What is the correct dress for conferring about a hunt by night for a rapist on the island of Jersey?

At noon, clad in thick Irish thornproof tweeds and brandishing an ashplant, I clumped in my great boots into the drawing room at Les Cherche-fuites. George was wearing flannels and a white shirt, Sam was wearing Bermuda shorts and a silk Palm Beach shirt. They gazed at me wonderingly.

'This is only a conference,' George explained gently.

'Oh. I see.'

'Have you brought many beaters?' Sam asked.

'No.'

'But a *loader*, perhaps?'

My riposte was swift as light.

'I usually drink a glass of bottled beer at about this time,' I said, and went out to the kitchen to fetch it.

                                                    – *Something Nasty in the Woodshed*, p. 394

'Compliments you on your tog, Mr Dutch,' he said, wiping the froth from his upper lip, 'looks quite the thing, werry gentleman-like.' (My coat, you may recall, was modelled upon his.) 'But I feels the kickseys – for trowsers I shall not call them – is somewhat below your station in life – have a kind of groomish look. Pantaloons is the harticle; pantaloons and boots. Marks you out as a sportsman of quality.'

– All the Tea in China, p. 63

Chemise de femme,
Armure ad hoc
Pour la gaie prise
Et la belle choque.

– Something Nasty in the Woodshed, p. 387

'He said he loved me because I only read *Vogue*,' says Judith Todd.

He liked women's clothes to be stylish and sexy and worn with aplomb, but in the sixties he was stuck in a forties time warp and would have preferred me to appear at parties in a little black dress with diamanté clips such as his and my mother wore. Maybe I was in a Laura Ashley phase. His fictional women are adventurously dressed: Mrs Spon inclines towards the bizarrely smart, Johanna and Blanche towards the sexy. Johanna's clothes are expensively and delightfully exiguous. They bring to mind a shortie nightie made of transparent layers of nylon he brought home to me from Paris. He had been much amused by the buying of it – he couldn't remember my measurements in inches let alone do a quick translation into centimetres. To help him, the massive *vendeuse* put her hands on her hips and revolved majestically before him, displaying her magnificent bosom and saying: '*Votre femme est de ma taille peut-être?*' This little scene he enacted before me at bedtime.

The last letter I have concerning his final days in hospital is about the loss of his nightshirts.

Contradictions Trying to write about Bon frequently results in a crisis of interpretation, just as trying to live with him did. Anything anyone says about him seems to call immediately for some directly contrary statement. He was so stimulating, threatening and endearing because all the human characteristics found in lesser form in most people could be found in him *in extremis*. Living with him was an education in dealing with the unexpected, and one learned to acquire a complex system of inner defences. Such skills may have had their uses in everyday life, but they were less helpful when it came to loving relationships.

Trying to work out what Bon wanted and how to please him in a wifely way was an absurdity I often laboured under; yesterday's want was often anathema today and swift changes of appetite and mood were the norm. On one occasion a psychiatrist who became concerned about our family problems grew almost apoplectic and, to my astonishment, could offer no more helpful diagnosis of Bon than that he was 'a cad'.

Bon was not only aware of his contradictory nature, he embodied it in a contradiction in terms, frequently denying his good name ('Bon') by referring to himself as bad or wicked. He took pride in being a baddy; he never gave himself stars or ticks for good actions, which, when they came, were usually accompanied by an apology of some sort. He sent his first wife this picture of himself in the army with the caption 'With love from your wicked husband'.

'You can't win' was Bon's thought as much as it was Charlie Mortdecai's, yet sometimes he thought himself absolutely a winner. A minor leitmotif in *The Great Mortdecai Moustache Mystery* is Charlie's placing of bets on the horses via the college porter; he always wins, in contradiction to the general theory – which makes him uneasy. In his career, Bon showed a strange need to move on from his successes and make them look like failures.

Conversations

I'd lost that rally, anyway . . .   – *Don't Point that Thing at Me*, p. 58

Conversation with Bon was almost always combative. This is done in the novels with great art and implication – the reader is certainly supposed to notice all the finer points of verbal combat and may ironically find it difficult to determine the real winner. There is often a misunderstanding at the heart of the conversation that leaves each person able to claim victory. In daily life, this could be tedious as well as funny and sometimes made other modes of

'With love from your wicked husband'

communication impossible. Failures in communication form some of the most poignant moments in the books.

Cookery at Home

. . . for it was not in his nature to refrain from cooking.

When Bon thus describes the ship's cook in *All the Tea in China* (p. 111), he could certainly be describing himself. Depending on whom you talk to, Bon was a brilliant cook or he was a nightmare in the kitchen.

Curry and cassoulet were the two fetishes of Bon's cookery, and tales both sad and happy abound from those who were ever excluded from their own kitchen (except for the clearing up) while he cooked. Taking the lid off a saucepan to release marvellous smells was often followed by reeling back in pain from the chilli-power of the merest spoonful. Bon's curries got hotter and hotter till they were inedible. He once spent forty-eight hours in a scholarly re-creation of the Boston Baked Bean only to find to his amused disappointment that he had perfectly matched Mr Heinz's famous product (see FOOD).

He certainly improved the quality and range of my cooking. This was partly because his sons, who according to Bon had lived happily on beans and black pudding, had anticipated something more from me when we all began to live together. At one stage, he asked me to show him how to make pastry; he then devoted himself to perfecting the Cornish pasty. They were delicious. In Cranham Street days, Custance, the local butcher, was a heavy drinking and betting man, a first-rate butcher and witty with a philosophical turn. When he won on the horses, meat was free for the day. He was a genuine help to a family living on very small and unreliable supplies of housekeeping money. He supplied the ingredients for some desperately long-winded and ghastly recipes tried in the name of economy and experiment. Never again do I want to demonstrate how to make good use of every single part of a pig's head. Curiously, this *cuisine pauvre* was briefly fashionable in the nineties, or so I'm told.

People from the pub who knew that Bon would cook all sorts of things and had a family to feed sometimes brought unexpected gifts. One dark night at pub-closing, I heard someone fall cursing against the front door, which opened directly on to the pavement. Custance stood there and presented me with incoherent explanations and a bowl of blood. A hare was to be jugged and Bon had specially asked, as Custance had belatedly remembered, for the blood to go into the gravy. On another occasion the doorbell rang at seven o'clock on a Sunday morning, and I opened the door in my dressing gown to a hooded and cloaked figure streaming with rain water who silently handed me a large and very slippery pike. By this time I was the main cook.

Despite the elaborate references to food in the books, Bon liked quite humble dishes and had developed a repertoire of hearty, tasty food to encourage his Balliol friends round to his place when he was a widower–student supporting his two boys on a minute allowance for dependants.

Cookery books

If ever I should fall upon evil times, the one possession I would hide from
the bum-bailiff and smuggle under my ragged shirt as the beadle marched
me to the workhouse would be my LAROUSSE GASTRO-
NOMIQUE. It is an Eldorado of information and a feast of fun. Printed
in 1938, when I was a mewling child, its leather spine bears a crossed
spoon and fork and the front cover is stamped with three fat birds spitted
over quite unsuitably raging flames. But . . .

This fragment of a text left uncompleted conveys some of the
interest and glamour cookery books held for Bon. He saved from
our first house fire a book known as *Lady Clarke of Tilliepronie* and
despite its charred corners continued to use it for reading aloud –
especially the passage describing how to catch and kill a turtle for a
grand soup – and for instruction. The cloth cover was chosen to
match the autumn colour of the beech trees at Tilliepronie. (Helge
Rubinstein, perhaps a little fed up with Bon's constant reference to
it, calls her 'Lady Clarke of Tiddlypush'.) Much delighted in were
Common Sense Cookery and *Culinary Jottings from Madras* by Colonel
Kenney-Herbert, alias 'Wyvern'. The Colonel's advice on the
cooking of rice and omelettes was wholly practical, but the main
charm of the book was the picture of life under the British Raj.
Bon loved to read aloud the Colonel's comments on 'kitchen
butter' and his advice against presenting elaborately decorated dishes
on the grounds that 'people will think black fingers have been at
work'.

   After leaving Oxford, Bon continued to increase his library of
cookery books, giving, receiving and exchanging them with friends
and forming the research base for a projected history of British
eating habits. He had lectured on this subject successfully in Abingdon and used some of the historical material for the gargantuan
meals in *All the Tea in China*. His annotations of Boswell's *Life
of Samuel Johnson* show him collecting further material for this
never-to-be-written great culinary work. I have quoted an autobiographical passage from a surviving handwritten fragment of it in
CHIPS. Elsewhere he writes of the projected book:

There are not so many recipes in it as there are prejudices but then you can buy a hundred books of recipes – indeed you can make them up yourself, as I shall presently show – whereas real brass-bound, polished mahogany, baize-lined prejudices are hard to come by. To acquire such prejudices about food you must undergo a rigorous course of schools, college, barrack, Colonial messes, public dinners, AA recommended hotels and other hotbeds of food spoiling.

Much of his extant cookery writing wavers uncomfortably between the patronizing and the sexist and is so congested with learning or prejudice as to be unpublishable. But the following from a review of a cookbook by Barbara Cartland is more fun:

An English earl once got into serious money-trouble through his spend-thrift ways and summoned his 'Man of Business' to help him to get the creditors off his back. The lawyer urged large economies in his private spending, such as cutting down his establishment. 'For instance, my Lord, you could get rid of your *chef pâtissier* – that Italian confectionery chap is being paid more than the Prime Minister.' 'Rot me and damn me eyes!' roared Lord Sheffield (for it was he). 'Things have come to a pretty pass when a gentleman can't have a biscuit with his sherry in the afternoon!'

Miss Cartland certainly takes the biscuit – and deserves it. In her case, having studied this book, I'd say it should be a heart-shaped biscuit and topped with a cheeky cherry. She truly deserves the finest biscuit that money can buy, for she is no member of the idle rich. Rich, yes – idle, not at all. Apart from her well-known daily task of swallowing enough vitamin-pills to pave every walk in Phoenix Park, she catches her own salmon, shoots her own game, works hard at her chosen charities and, in between times, keeps ladies who like such things swooning in a happy, roseate mist of daring (but never fully-frontal) romance. How many marriages has she saved by giving these ladies a happy, harmless dream-world? I couldn't begin to guess – but she has written more than 350 books, with an average sale of over 1,000,000 copies per book. In other words, she has made a great many people happy: is that such a bad thing? Plato, surely, would better improve their minds, but there is a certain lack of story-line in Plato – and Platonic love isn't really what the disillusioned housewife wants to read about as she dozes off. Moreover, his output was small and one cannot, in 1984, put one's head round the newsagent's door and ask for 'the latest Plato'. Miss Cartland is faithful to those who need her: from 1976 she has hammered out an average of one book a fortnight. I mean, *every* fortnight. Would you believe twenty-five books in 1981 alone?

Yet there she is on the back of the dust-jacket, at an age which I happen to know but am too well bred to divulge, smiling ravishingly out of a cloud of mauve tulle, white roses, scarlet osprey-plumes and all the other romantic apparat which one would have expected to find in La Pompadour's boudoir. 'Her eye is not dimmed, nor her natural force abated.' A living testimony to hard work and vitamin-pills, she certainly shames me. If there is a hint of Danny La Rue on his Diamond Wedding Day (slightly used, one careful owner, body-work needs a little attention) – well, blame my jealous admiration. (For Miss Cartland, I mean. Not Danny.)

This book is the first of Miss Cartland's that I have read. (Had I been a lifelong devourer of her works – a Barbarophage? – I do not think the Literary Editor of your paper would have entrusted it to me.) I find it shattering – if I were ten years younger I would have said 'mind-blowing'. It is superbly produced – trust Hamlyn's for that – modestly priced (at £7.95 UK it is cheaper than most novels, although rich in colour-plates). The recipes are given by Miss Cartland's chef; the comments to each recipe are her own: medicinal, aphrodisiac, legendary, commendatory and sometimes superbly daft.

Will you sample with me? Hold on to your hats. Chicken Supreme: BC's comment (I hope she doesn't take 'BC' personally . . .) 'This looks so pretty and I am continually surprised at how few people bother to decorate their dishes with flowers . . . rosebuds, fruit blossoms, and of course, carnations can make every dish a dream of delight.' (Come back, Lord Sheffield!) Coq au Vin: BC's comment 'One of the first dishes a French girl learns to cook, so that she will attract a handsome husband.' Peking Drumsticks (with honey): 'Children enjoy eating them with their fingers . . . I thought how imaginative the Japanese were with their food and like the Chinese use many things we throw away.' Chicken with Peaches: 'Sincere, romantic with the softness and the fragrance of love.' I swear I took these quotes at random: had I picked out the juiciest you would have thought that I was making them up.

For my part, if I asked a young woman to supper in my rooms and confronted her with one of the amorous table-settings displayed in the illustrations to this splendid book, I would expect her to get a fit of giggles. If she invited me to her flat and after a glass of pink champagne, led me into a supper-room full of eroticized oysters and Crinoline-Lady Cake surrounded by porcelain Cupids, I would grab my hat and run for my life – or my virtue. This is not to say that this book will not do lots of people a whole power of good. I only mean that it's not really my cup of tea; I prefer cookery books without the cupids and rosebuds.

– 'Dishing It Up', a review of *The Romance of Food* by Barbara Cartland, from the *Irish Press*, 4 February 1984

Cowboy Bon in Dublin

Cowboys

At noon I crossed the State line into the panhandle of Texas, a solemn moment for any man who rode with the Lone Ranger each Saturday morning as a child. — *Don't Point that Thing at Me*, p. 98

The cowboy interest goes back a long way. Bon's father, Emmanuel, recalled for his family the excitement of seeing Buffalo Bill's Wild West Circus on its last European tour and especially the amazing tricks done with lassos. Cowboys stayed with Bon as one of his imagined identifications, reinforced perhaps by the image of a poor knight on a cow that he claimed was part of the Bonfiglioli arms in the Tyrol. He owned a genuine cowboy hat, cowboy-style boots and a genuine holster, bought in 1967 at the same time as a Smith & Wesson.

His daughter Catriona recounts going on her own at fifteen to meet him outside a pub in Dublin and being very anxious that she might not recognize him:

My fears were put to rest when I saw a middle-aged man sporting a goatee and a cowboy hat swaggering down the middle of the street, only to be revived when he swaggered right past me to greet some friends, saying something like: 'What are you doing in Dublin looking so pleased with yourselves?' Rather put out, I said, 'What are you doing in Dublin looking like a cowboy?'

After recovering from the shock of having failed to recognize his own daughter, he told me not to call him a cowboy in public because of the rude implication he was walking bow-legged from having had too much sex.

Being a trusting soul, I had no idea whether this was a joke or a serious lesson in etiquette, of which there were plenty.

Here is Mortdecai facing new dangers and armed, but only with a rather shaky old gold-plated riverboat gambler's revolver:

But this wasn't for killing anyone, it was for making me feel young and tough and capable. People who have pistols for killing people keep them in boxes or drawers; wearing them is only for making you ride tall in the saddle. I used some mouthwash, renewed the Vaseline on my blisters and cantered back into the drawing room, tall as can be in my high canted saddle.   – *Don't Point that Thing at Me*, p. 36

Like Charlie, Bon could be brave and absurd. In Jersey he was found late at night creeping round a friend's house, trousers tucked into cowboy boots, pistol in waistband. When she asked him what he was doing, he said, 'Well you never know what you might need protecting from.'

Cranham Street No. 66 Cranham Street, Jericho, Oxford, no longer exists. His friend Anthony took the house to improve his own and Bon's living conditions soon after Bon's second son was brought by the NSPCC to live with his father. Bon was still at Balliol, but with two children could not have lived in college. The house was always full of people. Bon was ever hospitable.

It was a small detached Victorian house with four bedrooms, no electricity upstairs and an outside lavatory in a small but charming garden. An *Oxford Mail* reporter and expert on Japanese prints lived in the front parlour on the deep litter system, surrounded by milk bottles with an inch or so of sour milk in each. He was much mocked by Anthony and Bon for his knack of walking through to the kitchen or loo whenever they opened a bottle of Scotch. The kitchen and larder beyond it were icy cold. The washing machine was kept in the garden until it started to give me electric shocks. Balliol men came for meals and poker and stayed the night on the tiny sofa if shut out of college. Anthony and his new wife, Alison, and Alison's whippets stayed while the house they were to move to was being renovated. The Radcliffe Arms near by was a useful annexe where chaps retired to play shove-ha'penny (q.v.) while children were put to bed and supper cooked. Bon continued this tradition of hospitality, although I was now the cook. Without Wiggy's, the corner shop opposite, with easy credit and cardboard boxes full of almost anything you asked for, this would all have been very difficult to manage. Jericho was still a non-gentrified traditional working-class area and, despite many disadvantages, a wonderful place to live.

Crossword puzzles

They draw me a pint of the very best bitter and lay beside it a ball-point pen because they know I have come there to solve a crossword-puzzle.

                – from letter of Bon's while living in Ireland

When he first proposed to Maggie Noach, the literary agent, Bon asked how long she took to do *The Times* crossword. He certainly used this as a measure of his own fitness for verbal combat. Ann Turnbull relates passing the pub in Silverdale, Lancashire, and finding Bon within, looking exceptionally glum. The trouble was he'd finished all but one clue. He raised the eyebrow of scepticism when she offered to help. She provided the correct answer, 'aurora': 'He looked at me as if I'd been shot and treated me differently ever after.'

For Maggie Noach's description of what happened when Bon took the crossword to the theatre, see MAYHEM.

Dates

The feast of St Hilary of Poitiers. A happy 1983 to you and let no one say I don't date my letters.

Though generally notorious for not dating letters, Bon always preferred a saint's day or a reference to a season of the Church to anything with numbers in it that might give the appearance of a business letter written by a secretary. This heading from one of Bon's letters to the literary agent Hilary Rubinstein is both a friendly provocation and a complimentary reference to Hilary's saintly patience in his dealings with Bon. A glance at Bon's copy of *Martyrs and Saints of the First Twelve Centuries* by Mrs Rundle Charles tells us 13 January is the date in question.

Dealing

I walked all the way to Sotheby's, holding my tummy in nearly the whole time, terribly good for one. There was a picture belonging to me in the sale, a tiny canvas of a Venetian nobleman's barge with liveried gondoliers and a wonderfully blue sky. I had bought it months before hoping to persuade myself that it was by Longhi, but my efforts had been in vain so I had put it into Sotheby's, who had austerely called it 'Venetian School, XVIII Century'. I ran it up to the figure I had paid for it, then left it to its own devices. To my delight it ran for another three hundred and fifty before being knocked down to a man I detest. It is probably in the Duke Street window this moment, labelled Marieschi or some such nonsense. I stayed another ten minutes and spent my profits on a doubtful but splendidly naughty Bartolomaeus Spränger showing Mars diddling Venus with his helmet on – such *manners*! On my way out of the rooms I telephoned a rich turkey farmer in Suffolk and sold him the Spränger, sight unseen, for what is known as an undisclosed sum, and toddled righteously away towards Piccadilly. There's nothing like a little dealing to buck one up.

Bon's sheer zest for dealing comes out beautifully in this passage from *Don't Point that Thing at Me* (p. 47) and recalls for me the time when penicillin restored him to his dealing self. He had been rushed into hospital looking alarmingly green-faced with acute pneumonia and a heart murmur, which our Douglas Hurd look-alike doctor had been slow to diagnose. After a few days on penicillin, Bon persuaded the nurses that of course he could not cease from business activity just because he was mortally ill and in a general ward. So, at visiting time, the famous Smith brothers of Thame came into the ward carrying huge canvases trailing cobwebs, flaking gilt and gesso from the frames as they processed to Bon's bedside at the far end of the ward. (Other patients were being brought grapes and flowers by their visitors.)

All the rituals of dealing, where both parties understand the game and know they will eventually do a deal (or will they?), were gone through at length: with Bon claiming not to be interested in the pitiful rubbish they had brought him, and with them claiming that they couldn't go down below what they had paid. At last the Smiths packed the pictures back up and began to carry them out. When he judged they had reached Reception, Bon sent me running along with a final offer for several of the pictures, provided they threw in the one for which he'd been expressing the most contempt. Everyone was happy and I knew he would live. Even the nurses, whose ward hygiene had been compromised, seemed to consider the entertainment worth the mess.

See also ART DEALING and YARNS.

Death

... there's a great deal to be said in favour of a cup of hemlock, you know; at least you drink it in confidence that you won't have to drink the same on the following night.

> – *The Great Mortdecai Moustache Mystery*, p. 90

'I do not fear you Deathie, old boy,' I said, 'but you are a knock to me among my neighbors. Your visit is sure to get noised about and cause gossip. You know you are not considered a desirable character by many persons, although mind you, I am not saying anything against you.

> – Damon Runyon, *Death Pays a Social Call*

Runyon's last story, written in mortal sickness, and among the last things Bon read.

In choosing Mortdecai for his hero's surname, Bon ensures that there is a *memento mori* before us all the time. Ordinary life had presented him with the idea of death often enough: bearing in mind that, by the time he had left school, his mother and younger brother were dead; by the time Roderick, his second son, was three months old, his wife Elizabeth was dead; the birth of our first child was long and difficult, either mother or baby would have died without medical intervention. I had suddenly realized as he said goodbye, leaving me in labour in hospital, that he feared my death. Our first-born was named Christopher, after his dead brother. When Bon was rushed to hospital with pneumonia, I found a love note in his pyjama pocket, saying farewell to me and the children in case of his death. In 1962 Chris was in danger of death from a serious fire, but was rescued by his father. We both came near to death in a car in 1964 (see CAR CRASHES). In those days Bon would occasionally lie back on his bed with the whisky bottle, saying he would drink himself to death and it would be my fault – a relatively frivolous statement, it seemed then.

Death sometimes seemed attractive to Bon as a means of escape from pressing immediate problems; keeping the idea of it in play without letting it breathe too closely down his neck was one of his mental habits. Writing to his friend Tom Braun and enclosing a short story in which the main character came to a grotesque and violent end, Bon wrote: 'I had a love affair with him [death] a few years ago but now he's just an amiable ex-mistress with whom I can have a giggle. Pain terrifies me but death is just the pay-off line to a long boring dirty joke.'

When Bon was dying in hospital in Jersey, he wished at first that no one in England should know of it. One of his visitors at that time says Bon believed till the last that he could control whether he died or not. He was certainly sometimes tempted to die, and at others to assert a vehement intention of living.

He died of cirrhosis of the liver and was cremated on 12 March 1985. Barbara Cox, whose house he had been sharing, Aeneas, Catriona, Amanda and I scattered his ashes into the sea at Bonne Nuit Bay on the north coast of Jersey.

Didacticism

And gladly wolde he lerne, and gladly teche.
  – Chaucer's Clerk of Oxenford, 'The Prologue', *The Canterbury Tales*

I waxed informative, a vice of mine which I can by no means cure.
  – *Something Nasty in the Woodshed*, p. 414

Mortdecai sometimes excuses himself for his didactic passages, and Bon as a father excuses himself in letters to Chris and to his daughters for a sermonizing or didactic passage. Part of his love for his children came in the form of a wish to contribute to their cultural education. In general, he could not bear not to inform the uninformed. For some readers, this is an essential and enjoyable ingredient in the novels.

Some of his letters to younger writers are astonishingly didactic in tone, and in the case of Grahame Hall drew a strong protest, but a literary correspondence with the then aspiring writer Christopher Priest was a source of great interest and pleasure to them both.

How amused he would have been to learn that the latest CD-ROM version of the *Oxford English Dictionary* contains seventy-seven citations from his works (seventy-five with his name spelled correctly and two with it misspelled).

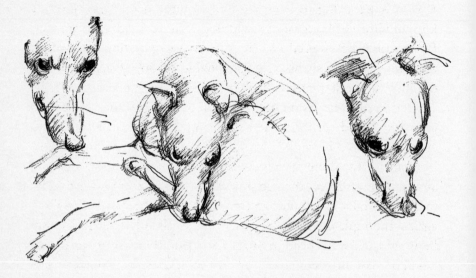

Sketch for Aeneas of Hervey the Whippet by John Newberry

Dogs

He was a vicious man, but very kind to me. If you call a dog *Hervey*, I shall love him. (Dr Johnson)   – Boswell's *Life of Samuel Johnson*

He was tacking about like a spaniel in a turnip field.

– *All the Tea in China*, p. 139

If possible, Bon was never without a dog. If he didn't have one of his own, he loved other people's and fed them illicitly with left-over curry.

Our first dog was a white whippet called Hervey, bought as a tiny pup shortly after the birth of our son Christopher. He developed into a dog of great character and resourcefulness, with his own routines and routes round town. If you met him coming out of the University Press with a piece of cake in his mouth, he would greet you with the utmost friendliness but make clear that he was busy and would see you later. He usually contrived to be around as the children came home from school and was a friendly and witty dog with a vast circle of acquaintance. It amused him to get several larger dogs into a speed chase: keeping just ahead, he would turn very sharply and shoot off while the other dogs collided with one another.

Bon liked a dog to have a good pedigree – this was the only known virtue of Fred, our second dog, a thick-headed bull terrier. By the time he entered our lives, Bon was spending most of his mornings in bed, so his vast knowledge of dog psychology and training methods never came out to play. At the same time, he wanted Fred to be *his* dog, not the family dog; no one else was to train him. Fred – named after the song 'Right Said Fred' – was easily bored and incredibly stupid. He did discover two games for himself: racing along the washing line, pulling all the clothes off and trailing them on the ground; and seizing a rubber dustbin lid in his mouth by its handle and careering about the garden, crashing against the apple trees, unable to see past his shield. After each crash, he would shake his head in puzzlement and then set off again. He never tired of this – which caused me to fear for his intelligence. The first time Bon saw this act, Anthony Harris found him practically extinguished with laughter. As Fred's strength and size increased, Hervey lost his status as senior dog. He became a victim of Fred's power to catch him by the neck and shake him like a dish rag and he lost his nerve. This was a nightmare phase, as all toing and froing in the house was hampered by hasty door-shutting to keep the dogs apart. One day, a visitor opened the kitchen door and let Fred in to seize Hervey. Roderick knew pouring water over dogs was the way to separate them and emptied a bucket full of water and peeled potatoes over them. This had no effect on Fred, and Bon had to be called to the rescue. Fortunately, Fred became an escaper. After a few calls to collect him from farms the other side of the river and to pay damages for slaughtered chickens (always taken home and cooked), he made his final escape and got *stolen* – never was I more grateful to a thief. Luckily I was away that weekend, otherwise I would have been a suspect.

Trying to separate the dogs became a nightmare. I was amazed to discover Fred again accurately recalled in Keith Roberts's novel *Kaeti on Tour*.

The pet he insisted on keeping . . . Fred the bull terrier, was her private bane; though the dog had never offered her any harm. Just taken her arm once in his powerful jaws, squeezed slowly from wrist to elbow, moving his teeth in steady delicate stages. Kaeti froze with shock; but Toby had roared with laughter. 'He's only being friendly,' he said, 'make a fuss of him; say hello . . .' But the animal was on borrowed time. Lately he'd taken up chicken killing as a hobby; leave the side door open an inch or the front, and he'd be through and gone, heading for the edge of town and the nearest undefended coop.

Bon tried to take Hervey with him and Aeneas to Lancashire when he finally moved out, and packed bed and bowl into his removal van. Throughout the day Hervey tried frantically to herd all his Bonfigliolis into one place: by departure time he had disappeared and Bon had to leave without him. Hours later, he crept out of the cellar to join the remainder of the family. Some months afterwards, I sat up all night with him as he died. Although I tried to persuade him to lie down comfortably, he fought death standing up.

Bon had Labradors called Caesar and Pompey in Lancashire and other relationships with friends' dogs there and in Jersey.

In the following letter to Judith after he had left for Ireland, he takes on the identity of his Irish terrier:

Dog Days in Ireland
from idiots cottage some where in ireland
> dear mr s o'crates

> (and jazus there cant be much wrong with you if you have a decent irish name like that) i hear you need a penpal to improve your mind so i'm taking the liberty & to hell with what the old biddies says

> i am a rough coated tipperary fox terrier aged three months and tracin me family back to the high kings of the dog-bogs no less

> last week i bought myself an idiot called bonfig to keep me in idle luxury for the rest of me days he is kind but not quite right in the head

the food is good but bones from admirers always welcome although i wouldnt think of suggesting

i was christened jezabel but he started to call me jess and had now got enough sense in his head to call me gersha which is irish for gossoon but female

when he is in a good mood he calls me gersha alanna but he isnt often in such a mood because i have destroyed most of his clothes footwear and books it is very funny to watch him trying to keep his temper because i am only an innocent little puppy har har i think i will have him trained in a few weeks

my best trick at the moment is to howl at the door and he takes me out in the frost and the rain and stands shivering for ten minutes while i explore the landscape then we go in and i pee on his favourite rug you should hear his language he has a wonderful gift of it

i hear your own idiot is always burning her house down well my tip to you is to have a good alibi for when the gardai come round those divils will blame anyone they're in league with the insurance company itself

well must close now because i have a few shoes to destroy and then must get my rest so i can terrify the postman eddie cassidy in the morning hoping this finds you as it leaves me i e covered in cowpats har har

> – letter from Bon's dog in Ireland to Judith's dog in Lancashire

Duels Not surprisingly for a sabre champion and keen marksman, Bon had a lively interest in duelling. The following extract from a review of a book marries this interest with romantic notions of cowboys and the Wild West.

It might seem strange that the great hordes of starving, evicted Irish who sailed to the Americas in the last century's coffin-ships did not eagerly take up the millions of free acres that were to be had for the settling, but chose rather to huddle together in the rookeries of Quebec, Boston and New York, where the more successful took up the characteristic trades of saloon-keeping, politics, soldiering and, perhaps ironically, the police force. The reasons, however, are not hard to seek: few of them had any knowledge of trade, most of them had no capital wherewith to buy a covered wagon and 'grub-stake', none had any knowledge of clearing forest and building log-cabins (indeed, few had ever used other tools than the potato-shovel and slane-spade) and, perhaps above all, they dared not venture into a wilderness where there was no priest to say Mass and where they might die without Extreme Unction.

However, an earlier wave of Irish, the Catholic aristocracy dispossessed by the Penal Laws, had made their way (disdaining the Puritan Eastern sea-board) to the far South-West, where they joined their Spanish co-religionists in Baja California and what are now Texas and New Mexico. It was this meeting of the two most duel-happy races which gave rise, arguably, to the last and greatest manifestation of the *duello*: the gun-fight of the Wild West.

In its purest form the duel was not, to my mind, the absurd and barbarous proceeding which now we think it. If gentlemen of breeding quarrelled on a point of honour they could hardly punch each other's noses in a tavern-brawl nor, if a lady were involved, could they drag her name through a court of law, so the affair was settled with a gentleman's weapons, in private. The theory was that God would see that the righteous party won. This stems from the earliest Saxon laws, whereby the culprit could elect to be tried by Ordeal (if you were innocent you survived), by Combat (the innocent would win) or by your Country (i.e. by a jury of your neighbours).

Of course, like so many institutions of well-meant devising, the duel became corrupt. Professional duellists came into being, some men developed a morbid taste for the danger and death and notoriety, others used the duel as a means of eliminating husbands or professional rivals; the highly skilled swordsman or the natural crack-shot would win how-ever unjust his cause and some duellists became so famous that every man who fancied himself with sword or pistol would force duels upon them, in the hopes of making a 'reputation'. (Do you notice how exactly this all parallels the careers of the Western gunfighters?)

The few duels fought today are almost always between Frenchmen – characteristically a politician and a newspaper editor, two professions not wholly respected in that country. (Indeed, it is said that when a Frenchman has exhausted his store of filthiest abuse he will call his enemy the unpardonable and vilest name of all: *Député!*) Let us pray that we shall never hear 'TD!* used in such a context . . . Such duels usually culminate

---

* This reference to the Taoiseach, the Irish Prime Minister, is typical of Bon's carefulness as a writer and of his awareness of the fact that he was writing for an Irish readership.

in a slight scratch from an *épée*, or by both parties firing into the air. To count this altogether ridiculous is to miss the point: each of the two men has felt strongly enough to keep their dawn appointment and to risk the (admittedly small) chance of dying or committing murder and, quite certainly, to break the very stringent law against duelling. I think we laugh because 'honour' has become an empty word used only by scoundrels. You might say that we have forgotten Honour; it's as simple as that.

> – 'Firing into the Air', a review of *An Affair of Honour:*
> *Irish Duels and Duellists* by Michael Barry, from the *Irish Press*,
> 7 January 1982

Dummkopf, or Dunce One of Bon's father's most discouraging sayings to his son was *'Der dümmster Bauer hat die grösste Kartoffel.'* The implication is that you must never pride yourself on any achievement – even if you have got the biggest potato, you are still only the dumbest peasant. For Bon this seems to have functioned all his life as a whisper at his ear saying that, for all his cleverness and education, he was just a *dummkopf*, a dunce or idiot, which is what he called himself sometimes too.

Englishness To be or not to be English was a perpetual question in Bon's life and would sometimes give him pronoun trouble, as in the following letter to the *Oxford Times*:

I had the pleasure, not long ago, of watching three sturdy though languid council employees clearing away a piece of snow measuring about 14ft by 4ft by 1in thick. They accomplished this in the brisk time of 43 minutes. Other ratepayers, not sharing my childlike faith in the City Engineer, had done their own spadework.

This experience, diverting though it was in itself, led me on to graver reflections. During at least one third of the year these islands are subject to sudden heavy falls of snow and the formation of ice. Each year this contingency occurs and each year the people responsible for the roads

Dear Sir

   Mr Kyril Bonfigilioli wants to lern a thing or two about "English Winters" before he start writing to a Paper. From his name he must be more foreign than he pretends. As a builder with 50 yrs. Experience in the Trade (and all english too). I can tell him there is a good reason for putting the drain pipes on the North-east walls of a house. On the south-west wall they might get too hot in the summer when plumbers are not about, and on holiday.

   Oh yes Herr Bonfiglioli (some of us fought the germans twice in two wars you know) plumbers need holidays just like the men that you stood idelly watching by while they cleared your dirty snow away.

   The Englishman respects the weather what GOD gives him and it appeals to his sense of fair play. These Complaints are going to get a brick threw a shop window if he is not careful.

   I am an old reader and always enjoy chipper
       Yours very faithfully
          Bert Gusset.

24A Marston Street
Oxford.

*Brian Aldiss, as a stout Englishman, replies to Bon's letter of
1 January 1963*

and railways raise their hands in shocked surprise, proclaim that chaos reigns and sit back to wait for a thaw.

When the thaw arrives, half a million homes whose pipes have frozen are inundated and the welkin rings with the cry of the plumber to his mate. But the builder, unruffled by these annual flaps, goes on running the main water inlet pipes up the north-east walls of his villas and placing the header tank against the uninsulated slates – for want of a colder spot.

Each year since Christmas cards were invented by some thoughtless humorist, about a zillion cards and parcels storm the gates of the Post Office. At other times it is the best Post Office in the world – even Americans admit it – but halfway through December it bursts into tears and admits defeat.

Christmas cards have been sent since early Victorian times, but the GPO has not yet devised a secret weapon against them. (I telephoned about an urgent registered letter on 11 December and was told I couldn't speak to anyone because of the Christmas rush.)

I am only one half English, and therefore never know whether to speak of 'we English' or 'you English', but this semi-detached state enables me, after a lifetime (so far) spent in this country, to retain my sense of wonder at its strangeness. What a curiously long-suffering people we – or you – are!

It is no doubt the Englishman's resilience that enables him to show such fortitude in war – perhaps even we may think of it as a generalized expression of the rigours of a public-school training, once considered so essential to the development of a useful subaltern. But why is the resentment, if it exists, so passive and silent?

Is a revolution perhaps silently brewing and shall we one day see the blood of waiters, retailers' assistants, shop stewards, bus conductors and minor civil servants flowing down Park Lane? That certainly is my devout wish.

– 'Reflections on an English Winter', letter to the *Oxford Times*,
1 January 1963

This letter generated some correspondence relished by Oxford citizens experiencing an appalling winter. In the following weeks, Bon claimed to have pushed nine motorists out of the icy quagmires of the Turl. At Norham Gardens, we had indeed been inundated. Treasured among Bon's papers is the reply that pleased him most – a spoof from Brian Aldiss addressed to Herr Bonfiglioli using the name Bert Gussett. Months later he was amused, if also a little disappointed, to be pursued at an airport by a lady who seemed to consider him famous – not as an art dealer but as the writer of 'the snow-clearing letters'.

For Bon's father, Englishness was something to be admired unequivocally; for Bon it was not so simple. Englishness in his fiction is a running theme for satire and misunderstandings. Mortdecai settles into his hotel room in America:

Like a true-born Englishman I turned the ridiculous air conditioning off and threw open the windows.

Fifteen minutes later I turned the air conditioning back on and had to telephone the desk to send someone up to close the windows for me, oh the shame of it.   – *Don't Point that Thing at Me*, p. 82

All the Tea in China is, among other things, the story of the making of an Englishman. For Karli, a runaway Dutch Jew, learning how to be English is a process of constant puzzlement and comic misunderstanding, an attempt to reach a world that remains incomprehensible. Success, Englishness, a safe haven are all suddenly withdrawn from Karli in the last pages of the book. Being English carries no guarantees.

By the time Orace entered to put me into my nightshirt I was in the mood to throw pieces of Italian sausage at him and he stalked out looking very English although but a bastard and small of stature. Peter and I finished the bottle and fell asleep in our clothes. He probably washed his face first, for he was English, English.   – *All the Tea in China*, p. 142

Being English is about using oblique ways of expressing fellow feeling and hiding kindness under the useful 'hrrmph'.

Epigraphs Epigraphs are a feature of all the Mortdecai books and used with some subtlety and aptness.

. . . Bearing aloft another Ganymede
On pinions imped, as 'twere, but not past bearing,
Nor unfit yet for the fowler's purposes;
Feathered, in short, as a price o' th'air – no moorgame.
If Paracelsus weighs that jot, this tittle,
God knows your atomy were ponderable –
(Love weighing t'other pan down!) . . .
. . . in a word,
In half a word's space, – let's say, ere you flinched,
Or Paracelsus wove one of those thoughts,
Lighter than lad's-love, delicate as death,
I'd draft you thither.

– Paracelsus

Epigraphs in *Don't Point that Thing at Me*, Bon's first novel, are all from Browning, except this one, which is a 'palpable forgery', that is to say, acrostically signed 'Bonfiglioli'. *Paracelsus* is such a long poem, and Browning's celebrated obscurity is such, that even the most dedicated Browning reader might accept this as being by him. It is open to interpretation as a kind of description of what Bon is up to in his writing. Bon/Ganymede (cupbearer to the gods) hopes to fly on borrowed plumes of inspiration, on flight feathers from other writers imped – i.e. grafted – on to his own less experienced wings.

Browning's *Pippa Passes* is heavily drawn on; though the references are frequently jokey, the poem has a deeper relevance in that Pippa functions as a moral touchstone: she is natural, spontaneous goodness itself passing unseen by dramatized scenes of wickedness.

One such scene from *Pippa* inspired the episode in which Johanna and Charlie fall upon one another lustfully while in the next room lies the scarcely cooled corpse of Johanna's late husband, Mr Krampf. Partial quotes from Browning's poem abound: Mortdecai's mornings are broken in a different sense from Pippa's and all's not right with his world. For Bon, morning almost always felt broken.

Swinburne, a Balliol man too, provides atmospheric epigraphs for *Something Nasty in the Woodshed*.

By the One who may don the black raiment
Of the goat that was never a goat
Now come I to exact the dread payment
For the lie that was born in the throat.

In a High Place, to decent men nameless,
Guarding ever the Branchless Rod,
Lies a thing which is pallid and shameless,
Ill with lust for a frightful god.

O, Ashtaroth, darling of Sidon,
Loathly Chemosh, who raves in the night,
I bring the red kiss which shall widen,
For thy servant, a way to thy sight.

– Asmodeus

The Swinburnian rhythm and the sinister power of its occult references could easily enough distract one from noticing that this too is signed.

Victorian poets, not then on Oxford's English syllabus, which stopped at 1842, had an unstudied freshness for Bon. Tennyson supplies the epigraphs for *After You with the Pistol*. The entirely female combat training college for young ladies to which Johanna sends Charlie for an update of his army training contrasts amusingly with Tennyson's college for ladies with its 'sweet girl graduates' as described in *The Princess* – Tennyson's contribution to the debate about higher education for women in 1847. Charlie is forced to accept a rapid updating of his lengthily expressed views on male versus female combat. Bon's imagination is stirred to scenes of action that come more from Emma Peel and Steed in *The Avengers* than from Tennyson.

For his last published novel, *The Great Mortdecai Moustache Mystery*, Bon turned for his epigraphs to an earlier writer, Sir Thomas Wyatt (1503–42). That moustache-wearing lover of Anne Boleyn laments, as Bon might have done, 'They flee from me that sometime did me seek'. By the time he died Bon had chosen epigraphs for only four of the chapters; the rest were supplied by his daughter Catriona and me.

Evening-class tutor Anticipating the *Antiques Road Show* by many years, in 1964/5 Bon ran an unprecedentedly successful 22-week series of lectures on collecting antiques for the Workers' Education Association in Abingdon. The first evening eighty-three people arrived and had to be moved to a larger room. The class register had to be closed at a hundred. An *Oxford Times* article about the class quotes Bon as saying: 'I insisted on being allowed to talk money. You can't collect without money, any more than you can play poker for matchsticks.' The well-permed audience pictured in the local paper gazing up at an ingratiatingly smiling Bon look as though they had never played poker for anything.

Each session included a discussion of objects brought by class members and by Bon from his collections. One evening as usual he had hardly had time to prepare his lecture during a busy day in the gallery and had not had time to look at a box of fans someone had brought in for him to consider buying. He took the box along with him unseen and produced a dazzling display of knowledge as he took out fan after fan. He is also still remembered for the classes he taught in Jersey.

Exorcism Strange dealings with the occult are a powerfully unnerving element in *Something Nasty in the Woodshed*, which is set in Jersey, and make Bon's own efforts at practical exorcism seem rather simple and tame. While staying in a huge old granite house in St Aubin, Jersey, where several members of the Johnston family had experienced a ghostly presence like a harlequin in diamond-patterned clothes, Bon was found one afternoon muttering incantations and strewing herbs and salt to exorcize the ghost. I am sure he meant to be of practical help to a family he was fond of. I have no idea what he actually believed. What happens in his Jersey novel is well grounded in Jersey's folklore, ancient sites such as La Houge Bie, a prehistoric burial mound with a chapel on top of it, and his reading about Paisnel, the Jersey rapist.

Expertise

Fortunately for me . . . from my very childhood, she had played games with me and her treasures until I could tell pottery from porcelain with one flip of the back of my fingernail, soft-paste from hard-paste with one nibble of the tooth, lead-glaze from tin-glaze with one caress of a wetted finger. Blindfold.   – *All the Tea in China*, p. 12

See also BOOKSELLER, FINDS and WATERCOLOURS.

Family

If they *should* ask you about your home life, be sparing with info. For instance an ideally bad answer: 'Daddy deserted Mummy and she has to take in lodgers . . .' You could *quite truthfully* say: 'Mummy is in great demand as an English coach in Oxford, Aeneas is in some kind of transport business in London, Roderick is a highly qualified psychiatric nurse, Chris is in the USA considering TV work, Amanda is doing brilliantly at school, Daddy's an eccentric, always dashing around, he writes these up-market black-comedy thrillers. (4 hardback in UK, 2 ditto USA, 3 Penguins, 2 Spanish translations, 1 Japanese – that makes 12 books, right?) We're a kind of *dispersed* family but we get on well.'

What I'm trying to say, I suppose, is 'don't tell lies but don't actually offer unpalatable truths'. Liars are fools and, in the end, losers.

This advice to his elder daughter on how to respond in an interview for university entrance, written in August 1980, shows Bon's acute embarrassment at thinking about his family and an attempt to offer constructive advice. Seen through the eyes of guilt and his own habit of reticence about his family's past and present, there's an uncomfortable falsity about this account of the family.

At one time, he had wished to celebrate the family by commissioning a family portrait, and some preliminary sketches were done. Towards the end of his life, he was arranging his photographs in a huge album with a date scheme for a kind of pictorial autobiography. He had made some progress in collecting together photographs he had taken of former girlfriends but was having trouble working out how to include his second wife (me) and five children. But by then I had most of the photographs.

FAMILY is written on his folder of research notes on past Bonfigliolis.

See CHILDREN.

Emmanuel Bonfiglioli as a young man

Father 'Study, children, *study*,' says Charlie Mortdecai's grandfather, hero and narrator of *All the Tea in China*, and I have no doubt that the words were often spoken by Bon's own father.

Bon rarely spoke of his father; when he did, it was as if he were speaking of a legendary figure from the past. Before his marriage, Emmanuel Bonfiglioli had been an explorer in Brazil, collecting tropical fish and birds for zoos. A certain parrot in the London Zoo kept a range of vocabulary for his visits only. Inez, Bon's sister, remembers 'that there was literally no room to move at home because of books everywhere. Not to mention aquaria, vivaria, terraria & plants. Our father used to take us for nature-study walks. He was a fierce task-master *vis-à-vis* study and exam results . . . My father spoke many languages – I even remember hearing him conversing in Latin.'

In 1960, I was amazed to discover that Bon's father was still alive, still living in Eastbourne in a silted-up antiquarian shop and in need of rescue. A handsome hawk-faced man, he arrived at our small house in Jericho in his only suit and wearing the hat he always wore out of doors. His three suitcases contained an extraordinary number of coat-hangers and alarm clocks, a complete edition of Kipling's works on India paper, bound in limp calf, a number of saleable semi-pornographic etchings by Félicien Rops (1833–98) and his small brown teapot, but no clothes at all.

To Bon's astonishment, he became a doting grandfather to our baby son, Christopher, always willing to babysit and buying special sweets for him to suck, insisting they were made only of pure fruit juice – forget the sugar!

An Italo-Slovene originating (I think) in Carniola and educated in Germany, he had lived much of his early life in Trieste. Coming to England in 1914 (to 'strike a blow against Austria-Hungary'), he joined the army, where he met an Englishwoman – his military driver – married her and stayed on in England to become an antiquarian bookseller, specializing in natural-history books. He spoke excellent English with a strong middle-European accent. His humour was wry, critical and understated.

To me, he was always courteous and usually he ate my cooking without comment, though once, when I made pizza (an exotic rarity in Oxford in those days), he said, 'Vot is this? It reminds me of something very poor people used to eat in Naples, you could buy it on street corners.'

His treatment of his son was distressing to observe. Bon was forever trying to impress him with an interesting purchase – 'good buys' were after all what we lived on. His father never let fall a word of praise, recognition, even mildly favourable comment or appreciation of his son in my presence. This became a family joke when Bon bought an astounding *art nouveau* hatstand: huge cast-iron lilies rose up on twisted stems to offer their great stamens as hooks. When Bon staggered in with it, his father's only comment – after a long pause – was 'Vell it's *bainfully* utilitarian' – which in his terms meant that it was not in any sense a work of art. Bon laughed, but he minded.

Clearly he inherited much from his father: a gift for languages, an emphasis on learning, the use of reference books, a level of knowledge of books, pictures and *objets d'art* that cannot be accounted for by his formal education. Above all, he inherited a pressure to succeed and a lack of satisfaction with any success. When Karli speaks in his grandfather's voice, perhaps he is speaking with the voice of Bon's father. He issued his son with two rules of conduct, perhaps intended to make it easier for him to be an Englishman: 'a gentleman never wears a brown suit' and 'a gentleman never carries a parcel'. These theories of correctness may come from his time in the army.

He left behind some sayings, but as far as I know no writings.

Of Yugoslavia, he would say 'there's no such country' – a statement proved tragically correct in recent times. He had a great admiration for things British and an insistence on their stability, once maintaining that if you were to go to Cairo you would still see the British Tommies marching up and down outside Shepheard's Hotel in their scarlet uniforms. When Bon deferentially questioned this, he said firmly: 'Things like that don't change.'

In letters to Ian Lowe, Bon records three of his father's sayings:

I hear my father's ghostly voice saying 'He must be a very busy man, he answered my letter by return of post.' The ghostly voice sometimes said discouraging things in German.

He also used to say, when I had won a prize at school or whatever, '*Der dümmster Bauer hat die grösste Kartoffel*' (sorry, I can say it convincingly but I never learnt to spell in German: it's supposed to mean 'the stupidest peasant grows the biggest potatoes'). More to the point; he always rubbed my nose in this: '*Hundert Freunder sind nicht genug aber ein Feind ist schon zu fiel*'. Again the spelling is shaky but it's supposed to come out as 'a hundred friends are not enough but one enemy, that's already one too many'.

Bon was very fond of my father – who treated him with complete acceptance, something Bon never seemed to expect – and would give him signed copies of his science-fiction magazine as they came out.

References to 'My Father' in the novels are probably not to Bon's actual father but rather to Charlie's father, Lord Mortdecai, whose life story was partly derived from a life of the great art dealer Joseph Duveen.

My father always warned me against lying where the truth would do; he had early realized that my memory – essential equipment of the liar – was faulty. 'Moreover,' he used to say, 'a lie is a work of art. We sell works of art, we don't give them away. Eschew falsehood, my son.' That is why I never lie when selling works of art. Buying them is another matter, of course.   – *Don't Point that Thing at Me*, p. 137

. . . flushed with the glory of young fatherhood, it seemed to him that the sight of his grandchild might gratify – even cure – the old man.
                                                            – 'The Gombeen Man'

A memory of his father's delight in our baby, Chris, seems glanced at here; the effect of seeing the baby on the Gombeen Man is the reverse and explosive.

Bon's father as an old man. Sketch by Peter Wardle for a projected family portrait

Fiction and friends

I never in fact, use real people in fiction (every author hates people who say, 'Oooh, you'll be putting me in one of your books') and I reckon it's a poor writer who cannot make up his people from his own head.

The exception to what I've just said is that I usually put in a little cameo as a present to a friend; in the novel enclosed I complimented a Mrs Simms-Hilditch of Melbourne House who does indeed possess a splendid cellar of wine – she read the book twice and didn't notice herself. In the one I'm just finishing now the optometrist is real and will be delighted, but I'll have to get a waiver from him nevertheless.

– from an undated draft of a letter to 'Pat' from Ireland

'To worry without a friend to confide in is a lonely business and wearing, wearing.' – *All the Tea in China*, p. 204

Without friends, Bon would not have survived as long as he did. Many of them have supplied recollections and material for this book.

Film In the sixties we lived near the Scala, an independent cinema that showed old classics and foreign films; there we saw *Rashomon*, *The Seven Samurai*, *The Magnificent Seven* and Powell and Pressburger's *A Matter of Life and Death*.

Once Bon left Oxford he probably saw more old films on television than new ones in the cinema. James Bond's adventures, which Bon read as they came out in Ian Fleming's books, gave him an appetite for their film versions and alerted him to film as a possible medium for his own writing.

In 1972 the American film-maker Carl Foreman read an advance copy of Bon's first novel and that December wrote expressing his and his wife's enjoyment of it, but saying 'I am not sure about its prospects for a film, because the bulk of its humour seems to be literary rather than visual. Obviously I may be wrong, which would not surprise me at all.' A few months later, Bon became enthusiastically involved in a project to collaborate with Michael Powell on a film treatment based on the lives of the Kray brothers. A flurry of letters were exchanged, and the two met in Jersey and

London. Energized by this possibility and with his usual zest for scenes of violence, the wrestling world and criminal jargon, Bon began researching the Krays and the criminal fraternity. Although always visually aware, he took his inexperience of writing for film seriously and felt the need to analyse and work with the idiom of film and above all to visualize scenes as strongly as possible. His reactions to film became, in his view, a kind of qualification for this new field of writing, as this section of a letter to Michael Powell shows:

A. Please let me reiterate: do not, I beg you, be vexed if I seem to poach on preserves not my own, or pre-empt or presume or merely jump the gun. I am a child in these matters and it seems to me that at this stage, it is most productive if I simply pour at your feet any fruit which my brain-tree grows, sweet or sour. There is an advantage to my innocence; hitherto I have been a mere audience-unit and I write what *I* would like to see. Venice and Cannes may deplore the corny but the lumpen-proletariat doesn't. Do tell me, if you think fit – is this a film to make money alone, or is it to be a work of art and to hell with the box-office or are we aiming high at the double crown? If you decide that I am more useful not knowing what is in your mind in this respect, don't hesitate to say so: I respect your judgement absolutely. As far as I am concerned you are the Maestro; I will sit at your feet, I want to learn; this is the first time for years that I have had something I want to do and I will go to all lengths to get it *right*. Naturally, I reserve the right to argue!

B. *Comprehensibility and Trendiness*. Being a *desdichado* and, in England, classless, I can truly say that I mix happily and freely with everyone – I like it. Judith [Todd] always twits me that if I meet an amusing lavatory attendant I ask him to stay. (These are my credentials as an audience researcher.) What I want to say is that I believe huge slabs of the audience have very little idea of what is going on in present-day films. I will cite you chapter and verse one day if you don't believe me. Everything is so fast, so allusive, so trendy, so stirred-about; and so aimed at the critics, the festivals, the confrères in the profession that the audience says, 'Eee, wot a foony fillum!' Now, do you want a sort of kaleidoscopic, part-comprehended, impressionistic montage which leaves people aware that they have seen something exciting happening – rather like a Swinburne poem which leaves one with a magic fragrance but simply will not stand parsing and analysing – or do you want everything explained, spelled out, taken step by step? Or don't you think this a good question?

Powell replied: 'I adore the corny and I hate the obscure & the pretentious.'

Despite Powell's evident pleasure in the synopses and treatments Bon wrote and some preliminary indication that Peter Sellers and David Niven might be interested in taking parts, their collaboration did not result in a film, possibly because – or so something in the papers suggests – Bon managed to offend all parties at a late stage by offering his treatment to Steven Spielberg. However, the stimulus to conceive scenes of action in film terms showed up well in 1979 in Chapter 21 of *After You with the Pistol*, when Charlie escapes his captors, one English and one Dutch policeman, who are driving him at gunpoint through London to an unknown destination sinisterly called 'Home'. The escape through a meat-processing plant is vividly realized and full of surprises. The core of this complex scene had been sketched out for Powell six years earlier.

One of them ushered Johanna and Jock into the kitchen and locked them in; the other didn't rip out the telephone cord, he unscrewed the mouthpiece, took out the diaphragm and put it in his pocket.

'Extension?' he asked.

'No.'

'Where is it?'

'In the bedroom.' He walked me there and repeated the procedure. He was *good*. Then we went. Their motor-car was a sensible, Rover-like vehicle and I was made to sit in the front, beside the Dutchman who was driving. The English copper – well, I was still not sure that he wasn't – leaned forward and said that I must not do anything foolish because his pistol was pointed at my left kidney. Now, every schoolboy knows that if a man means to shoot you he does so there and then, without shilly-shallying. Clearly, they wanted me alive, so the threat was idle. I hoped it was idle. I craned over my shoulder for a glimpse of the sidearm in question: he snarled at me to face the front. The pistol was there all right and I had had just enough time to see that it was one of those monstrous US Government Colt .45 automatics which can blow a hole through a brick wall. What was nice about this particular weapon was that it was not wearing a silencer; to let off such a thing in a car would stop the traffic for miles. That was the third mistake they had made. I applied myself to thought.

'Where are you taking me?' I asked idly.

'Home,' said the Dutchman. This was probably meant to be a joke. We sped eastward. As we passed St Paul's I courteously pointed out its beauties to the Dutchman.

'Shot op,' he said.

We sped further eastward, now in parts of London quite unfamiliar to me.

'Where is "home", please?' I asked.

The Englishman answered this time. 'Home's where the heart is,' he said with all the jovial smugness of a large man holding a large pistol. 'We're just taking you somewhere nice and quiet where they can ask you a few questions, then if your lady wife delivers Mr Ree to Gerrard Street within twenty-four hours we let you go, don't we?'

'Shot OP!' said the Dutchman. He seemed to be in charge . . .

When we came to a complicated road-junction, crammed with traffic and well populated with uniformed policemen, I murmured to the Dutch chap that we drove on the left in England. He was, as a matter of fact, doing so but it gave him pause and the wheel wobbled. I snatched the ignition keys; the car stalled in the midst of a welter of furious traffic and I sprang out. Sure enough, they didn't shoot at me. I ran over to the nearest 'Old Bill', gabbled that the driver was having a heart attack and where was the nearest telephone. He pointed to a kiosk, then stamped majestically towards the car, which was now the centre of a tumult of block traffic.

In the kiosk I frantically dialled my own number and rammed in a wasteful 10p piece. Johanna answered from the dressing-room extension which had not been noticed.

'Look,' I said, 'I'm in a phone-box, corner of . . .' I read off what it said on the instrument '. . . and I've got away from them but not for long. I'll be . . .' I frantically looked out of the kiosk, saw a great, grubby, warehouse-like building opposite with a name on it '. . . Mycock's Farm-cured Bacon,' I read out.

'This is no time for jokes, Charlie dear.'

'Just get Jock here; fast.' I replaced the receiver, did not even spare the time to check the returned coins box. I ran towards the excellent Mr Mycock. Inside the door an elderly slattern, redolent of Jeyes' Fluid, pointed to where the guvnor would be. 'He's probably having his dinner,' she added. 'Out of a bottle.' As soon as she was out of sight I changed direction again and again, diving into the abattoir's labyrinth. The pong of scorched pig became excruciating; I longed for that Jeyes' Fluid. The air was split by an appalling shriek – it was the dinner-time whistle but it gave me a bad moment. I pulled myself together, affecting the arrogant stroll of a Ministry of Health official looking for the germ *Clostridium botulinum*. The workers who thronged out past me did not even spare me a glance, they were off to chance paratyphoid from beef pies at the Bunch of Grapes; they wouldn't eat *pork* pies, they'd seen them being made. As I stalked proudly through the corridors, turning randomly every now and again in a purposeful sort of way, I was doing feverish sums in mental arithmetic concerned with how quickly Jock could possibly get here . . . Twenty minutes was how I had the race handicapped. I had to survive for just twenty minutes.

I squeezed past a cluster of bins marked PET-FOOD ONLY: WASH HANDS AFTER HANDLING and was about to thread my way through another lot marked IRELAND AND BELGIUM ONLY when I saw a large chap about thirty feet away, holding a pistol with two hands. He was the Dutchman. The pistol was pointed at me. The two-handed grip was perfectly good procedure according to the book they teach policemen with, but it seemed to me that if he was any good with that thing he would, at that range, have been holding it in one hand, pointing it at the ground a couple of yards in front of his feet. All the same, I froze, as any sensible chap would.

'Comm, Mr Mortdecai,' he said persuasively, 'comm; you have donn the teatricals. Yost comm with the honds behind the head and no one will hort you.'

I started to breathe deeply; in, count ten, out –

I went on hyperoxygenating; the Dutchman's pistol roved up and down from my privates to my forehead. He was the first to become bored.

'Mr Mortdecai,' he said in a dangerous voice, 'are you comming now?' Well, I couldn't resist a straight line like that, could I?

'No,' I said, 'just breathing hard.' While he was thinking about that I feinted a dive to the left, then, for my life, plunged to the right, behind the friendly bins of pig-pieces. 'Rooty-toot-toot-toot' went his shooter. One round went howling off the wall, the other pierced the bins.

I durst not give him time to change his magazine so I shed my jacket and slung it over the bins. 'Rooty-toot-toot' went the Browning. That made seven rounds expended, seven to go; even I could tell that. The floor sloped down in a gentle ramp towards him. I kicked over a couple of bins which rolled down the slope dripping pig's blood and goodness knows what else. He shot at them, for the Dutch are cleanly folk. Ten rounds gone, four to go. I raised an unoccupied bin-lid and slammed it onto the floor; he fired two more rounds, quite wildly.

Where I had kicked the bins away I saw that there was a monstrous iron door with a lever instead of a handle. It looked like an excellent door to be behind.

'Jackson!' I bellowed – it seemed a plausible sort of name – 'JACK-SON! Don't use the bombs: I'm coming out to take him myself.' Hommel can scarcely have believed that, but he must have dithered a bit because I got that great iron door open and scrambled through it without a shot being fired at me. The room inside the door was cold as the tip of an Eskimo's tool: it was, indeed, what the meat-trade calls a Cold Room. The lever on my side of the door had a position marked SECURE in red paint. I made it so. High up on two walls were those rubber-flap kind of entrances you see in hospitals; between them and through them ran an endless belt with large hooks. (Yes, just like a dirty weekend with a shark-fisher.) A pistol roared outside and a bullet spanged against the splendidly solid iron door. I sat with my back to the door and quaked, partly with cold, for I had discarded my jacket in that little *ruse de guerre*, you remember. The secure lever beside my head wagged and clicked but did not allow admission. Then I heard voices, urgent voices: the Dutchman was no longer alone. An unpleasing sort of whirring, grating noise made itself heard; evidently they had got hold of some kind of electrical tool and were working on the door-handle. Had I been a religious man I should probably have offered up a brisk prayer or two, but I am proud, you see: I mean, I never praised Him when I was knee-deep in gravy so it would have seemed shabby to apply for help from a bacon-factory.

The grating noises on the other side of the door increased: I looked about me desperately. On the wall was one of these huge electrical switches such as American Presidents use for starting World War Last. It might well set off an alarum, I thought; it might turn off all the electrical power in Mr Mycock's bacon-factory – certainly, it couldn't make things worse. I heaved with all my might and closed the contacts.

What happened was that pigs started trundling through the room. They were not exactly navigating under their own power, you understand, for they had all crossed The Great Divide or made the Great Change; they were hanging from the hooks on the endless belt, their contents had been neatly scooped out and were doubtless inhabiting the PET-FOOD ONLY: WASH HANDS AFTER HANDLING bin. They were the first truly happy pigs I had ever seen.

The eighth – or it may have been the ninth – pig wasn't really a pig in the strictest sense of the word; it was a large Dutchman fully clothed in what would be called a suit in Amsterdam. He was hanging on to a hook with one hand and seemed to have all his entrails. His other hand brandished the Browning HPM 1935, which he fired at me as he dropped to the floor, making his fourth mistake that day. The shot took a little flesh off the side of my belly – a place where I can well afford to lose a little flesh – then he aimed carefully at the pit of my belly and squeezed the trigger again. Nothing happened. As he looked stupidly down at the empty pistol I kicked it out of his hand.

'That was fourteen,' I said kindly. 'Can't you count? Haven't you a spare magazine?' Dazedly, he patted the pocket where the spare magazine nested. Meanwhile, I had picked up the Browning; I clouted him on the side of the head with it. He passed no remarks, he simply subsided like a chap who had earned a night's repose. I took the spare magazine out of his pocket, removed the empty one from the pistol (using my handkerchief to avoid leaving misleading fingerprints) and popped it into his pocket. I cannot perfectly recall what happened then, nor would you care to know.

Suffice it to say that the endless belt was still chugging along with its dangling hooks and, well, it seemed a good idea at the time.

It was now becoming colder every moment and I was shaking like any aspen, but even cowards derive a little warmth from a handful of Browning HPM with a full magazine. I awaited what might befall, regretting nothing but having wasted a perfectly good jacket. An indistinct voice shouted through the door.

'Eh?' I shouted valiantly.

'Open up, Mr Charlie,' shouted Jock. I opened up. Had I been one of these emotional Continental chaps, I believe I would have clasped him to my bosom.

'We got to get out, Mr Charlie, the place'll be crawling with Old Bill in about ten seconds flat.' We took off at a dog-trot. To my horror, at the turn of the corridor stood Johanna, holding my Banker's Special like a girl who knows how to use Banker's Specials. She gave me one of those smiles which jellify the knees, but the brain remained in gear. From the direction of the entrance there came a sort of crowd-scene noise and, rising above it, the sound of patient exasperation which only policemen can make. Someone came clumping nigh and we ducked into the nearest room. There were no pigs in it. What was in it was bales and bales of newly laundered white coats and overalls such as those who work in bacon-factories love to wear.

When the legions had thundered past we emerged, white-clad, and I was snapping orders about stretchers at Jock, calling him 'Orderly' . . . 'Bart's Hospital,' I snapped at the taxi-driver, 'casualty entrance. Emergency: use your horn.' At Bart's we dispersed, shedding white clothing, found the main entrance and took three separate taxis home. I arrived first – I needed that healing drink.   – *After You with the Pistol*, p. 348

Hopes of effective film or TV versions of Bon's books surfaced again in the 1980s. The actor John McEnery discovered *Something Nasty in the Woodshed* at a stressful time when his marriage was breaking up; he says that he 'clutched it to his heart' and that the book made him 'laugh against all the odds'. He was inspired to make an offer for the film and TV rights, to write some episodes himself and to renew the option a year later.

Still hopeful, perhaps, Bon put a compliment to Powell in his last novel, *The Great Mortdecai Moustache Mystery* (p. 130): 'The late-night movie was a bonus; Powell and Pressburger's lovely *49th Parallel*. Add a third bottle of *Antiquary* Scotch and you can well imagine that it was a tired, replete and happy Mortdecai who tottered to his blameless couch, moulting canaries and absentee wives forgotten for the nonce.'

See MONEY.

Finds Bon had an extraordinary flair for finds, often in the nick of time for family finances and for his growing reputation as a dealer. He was very pleased when, while still a student, he bought a small Venetian capriccio and then identified it as a Marco Ricci (1676–1730), which enhanced its value to the cognoscenti and meant something to him personally, as his researches had identified Ricci as an artist patronized by Bonfigliolis in Bologna. (A reference in the letters suggests that he sold it on to his tutor John Bryson. In 1960 the first great excitement was a fine Welsh landscape by Richard Wilson (1713–82) painted not long after his return from Italy. This was sold to Richard Booth (subsequently of Hay-on-Wye fame). Next came a shoebox full of letters in among piles of books that Bon had hastily unloaded all the way up the narrow stairs of No. 66 Cranham Street. Intrigued by the handwriting and the purple ink, I was amazed to find the signature of Charles Lutwidge Dodgson and also an unpublished poem of his. The letters were invitations and comments on the visits to his rooms paid by the two little girls addressed – sisters who had to the end of their lives kept them among their books, which Bon had just bought from their house on Boars Hill. Better known as Lewis Carroll, Dodgson, the respectable mathematician of Christ Church, offers his little friends a choice of jokey exotic alternatives to tea, including ink. In playful and arch tone, he wonders if Mama will forbid kissing next. We went to the Cobra restaurant to celebrate with friends, and the letters were put at casual risk of curry stains before going through the London salerooms to a private collector in the USA.

After May 1962, when we had moved into a huge house in Norham Gardens, wonderful and large pieces of furniture came into our house for short spells – to be enjoyed but not relied on to stay for any length of time. For a while, I had the use of an elegant bombé Dutch marquetry desk. Two magnificent architectural screens were with us for a while, the most exceptional about eight-foot tall in Dutch marquetry, specially designed to mount a collection of blue and white Chinese porcelain. The effect of the cool blues of the porcelain against the warm harvest colours of the wood, with its inlay of delicate patterns of flowers and leaves, was very striking. The screen was sold for £400, which seemed a lot at the time.

The research trail that finally inspired Bon's historical novel *All the Tea in China*, first published in 1978, began here.

One of several remarkable cabinets that we had at different times points towards the Mortdecai novels. It was inlaid in ebony and ivory with scenes from the adventures of Don Quixote and his faithful servant, Sancho Panza – prototypes of Charlie and Jock. The inscription on the cabinet states that it was made for Cervantes himself (see QUIXOTE).

Smaller finds were useful and depended on noticing the unusual. In those pre-recycling days, Bon spotted an aged college servant passing with a wheelbarrow full of bottles. The empties were being cleared out of the cellars of All Souls. Bon saved the man the trouble of taking them any further and gave him a pound or two, having noticed that they were eighteenth-century wine bottles specially marked for the college with a moulded glass stamp on the shoulder of each bottle – highly saleable.

The true story of Bon's last and greatest find begins one morning in 1964. Nudged into early rising by a fellow dealer, he drove off to a country house sale in Hampshire. The catalogue listed a Titian and a Tintoretto Resurrection. Dealers who could see that the Titian was a copy ignored the next painting, murmuring, 'Tintoretto schmintoretto.' Bon had looked more expertly. 'None of them bought it so I picked it up quietly for 40 quid.' Then began the work of authentication. As with all his most significant finds, he had Thomas of Oxford take first-class photographs to send to the Fondazione Giorgio Cini in Venice, where three Tintoretto experts confirmed the picture as genuine. Subsequently it was sold through Colnaghies and went to the Wernher collection at Luton Hoo. In storage since 1991, this collection will once more be on display to the public at the Ranger's House in Blackheath from early 2002.

Bon's 'Pictures of Stock' file with its Thomas photographs stayed with him through all his changes of residence, showing what impressive treasures they were to him even if his ownership was brief. I believe them to be identifiable sources of imaginative inspiration in his writing, working at less conscious levels than the more obvious literary sources.

Bon's alertness for a find, the accuracy of his visual memory, a kind of antiques reference library in his head, combined with his research techniques, sometimes seemed phenomenal. Mere luck does not account for these skills adequately. However, they fostered a Micawber-like confidence that neither he nor anyone sharing a bank account for him should have relied on.

Firearms and French *sang-froid* One day a pair of lightly rouged French dealers came to the house to buy pictures. When dealing was done, Bon began to show them other treasures, including a pistol. One accepted a challenge to stand by the door holding a sixpence between finger and thumb. The shot was fired, the dented sixpence flew and the Frenchman put his hand in his pocket. We all went out to a Chinese restaurant to celebrate. After a little while, Bon noticed the dealer having trouble with his chopsticks and he typically offered kindly instruction – perhaps he was using the wrong hand? 'Yes,' he said, 'I am right-handed,' and drew his – until then – concealed hand from his pocket, wrapped in a very blood-stained handkerchief. Aghast silence. Then more drinks all round.

Fires and floods We had two fires and one flood in our first house and a flood in the second, all contributing to the sense of living in a constant state of emergency that was my new way of life married to Bon in 1959. The first fire was caused by me using a sheet of picture backing-card to draw up the fire, leaving it in the grate and not realizing that it was still smouldering and next to a wastepaper basket when we went out for a child-free meal in the local Indian restaurant. We heard the fire engines go past and joked that they were heading in the direction of our house. Most people in the neighbourhood at that time did not have private telephones, and an old lady approached a passing friend of ours near the Jericho telephone box asking for help deciphering the number she'd been advised to ring – she'd left her glasses at home. She showed him a crumpled piece of paper on which someone had helpfully written 999. We strolled home to find clouds of smoke, fire engines and a crowd of people staring at the house, saying things like 'There's little children in there.' Fortunately Bon's two boys were away with friends. The dogs in the house had burrowed to the bottom of the bedclothes in an upstairs room and were perfectly safe.

The next fire was much more serious. Bon had put his pyjamas to warm on an electric clothes dryer in the room next to ours, where the baby, Christopher, was asleep in his cot. He went downstairs to make a late-night sandwich. I vaguely heard a strange cracking, snapping noise, then I heard Bon call my name, the most resonant urgent shout I have ever heard. As we opened the door, flames leapt across the cot, the window curtains caught fire and all the panes cracked. The whole room was roaring with flame intensified by the new draught. Bon caught hold of the cot and pulled it near enough to the door for me to snatch Christopher out of it. Quickly we shut the door on the flames and Bon rushed out to the phone box to call the firemen. They doused the room and chucked every loose burning object outside into the garden. Next morning, we found Christopher's teddy bear lying on the grass with its fur burned off, its eyes melted into two large golden discs. When Bon arrived a bit late for his work with Professor Wind with visible marks of the fire on his face – singed eyebrows, a burn on his nose – still coughing from smoke inhalation, the Professor said he had heard every excuse for lateness, but a fire in the house was too much.

Both floods were caused by frozen pipes. We came back from a comfortable Christmas in London with our centrally heated friends the Harrises. We drove down the steep slope of the Chilterns towards Oxford; the ice-bound landscape gave us a slight warning of what was to come. A massive trunk of ice went up the side of the house to the bathroom overflow and every liquid inside the house was totally frozen. As it all thawed, we waded about in six inches of water throughout the ground floor. Walking down the road to a New Year's party in a house with lights, fitted carpets, warmth and hot food, we felt like members of another species dazzled by a world of unbelievable comfort.

The next flood happened in the next house, No. 18 Norham Gardens, which had a form of Gothic central heating called Early English Partial. I was lying in bed listening sleepily to Beethoven's Ninth and found myself amazed at how it suggested endlessly flowing water. Suddenly I realized the water was in the next room. Despite the fact that the huge boiler in the basement had been endlessly stoked, the pipes in the sitting room had frozen and then burst. An endless supply of water flowed through the floor to the room below, where Bon stored his entire print stock. I phoned Bon, who came rushing from his gallery, where he had been working late. He dug through the foot of snow in the backyard to find the stop cock and hastily shovelled hot coke out of the external boiler fire into the snow before the rapidly draining system exploded.

Imagine a scene of urgent activity fit for Turner: snow, ice, hissing coals, steam, the glow of the hot boiler and, struggling within it, Bon in an old sheepskin coat and me in my leather thirties motoring coat worn all day for the next six cold weeks.

See ENGLISHNESS. The snow-clearing letters of January 1963 are reticent about what was going on back at the ranch. And that's only the half of it. It's never really cold in the Mortdecai novels and the emergencies of life are quite different.

Flyting 'The Flyting of Dunbar and Kennedie' by the poet William Dunbar, 'the Scottish Chaucer', was a favourite poem of Bon's for reading aloud with a much relished Scots accent. The two poets attempt to outdo each other in insults, traditional and new-coined. A 'flyting' is a poetic celebration of verbal fisticuffs, a genre suited to Bon, which he brings back into subtle use in prose in *The Great Mortdecai Moustache Mystery*. He loved the idea of single combat between near equals and collected insults and terms of abuse (alphabetically) for future use. Some of his relationships were based on the friendly exchange of insults.

ABUSE dish-rag mop-cloth (Lancs.), lickspittle, toady, smell-feast, caitiff, churl, dastard (see Rabelais/Motteux), pisspot, dotard, pilgarlick, jobbernol
kapper xxxx-teaser hoyden tomboy jillflirt hussy round-heels woman journalist
In France – *député* is vilest
In USA – President
here – Tax Inspector
Old women: bag, hag, dripper, mother-in-law, ogress, duenna, raddled harridan   – from one of Bon's lists of useful words

Folders Bon's loose-leaf folders, some ochre, some brown, some full, some empty, some turned inside-out for reuse and misleadingly labelled, are the source of much of the material in this book. Fragments of notes fall out of them only too easily; some have travelled more than once between England, Jersey and Ireland, while others date from a sorting of papers which he undertook towards the end of his life in Jersey.

The most frustrating of all is labelled MOUSTACHE DISJUNCT *WHOLE* CHAPTERS and turns out to be the seal-culling folder ('SEAL CULLING – *rites de passage*'), containing information from the Canadian government via the Canadian High Commission in London in reply to a letter from Bon written from Jersey in January 1983.

Two folders are particularly interesting in a cryptic sort of way, as their covers are elaborately decorated and annotated: SEVEN DEADLY SINS & ARTISTS' ADDICTIONS and THE GREAT MORTDECAI MOUSTACHE SCANDAL. The latter carries a kind of self-portrait with bristly moustache, surrounded by notes on poker hands and epigraphs drawn from the poems of Sir Thomas Wyatt, used as endpapers.

Bon investigates the fish trade in Lancashire

Food Bon was notoriously difficult to feed. Put before him steak and kidney pudding, his favourite hot dish and long in the making, and suddenly a sandwich was imperative instead. Feasts were anticipated, but appetite vanished; this characteristic of Peter Stevenage in *All the Tea in China* was closer to Bon than to Karli and his perpetual keenness for nosh.

Bon wrote an article in the *Visitor*, a Morecambe paper (29 April 1970) that relates to the photograph above. 'We inhabit an island completely surrounded by fish. Fish are cheap, plentiful, nourishing, delicious. British fish are the best in the world. So of course we never eat them.'

Food references seem particularly likely to trigger an autobiographical response, as may be seen in CHILDHOOD and CHIPS and also in the following passage:

Harry Harrison, when he is in affable mood, which is always, likes to tease me with the title 'Baked-Beans King'. I am, indeed, a dedicated baked-bean eater but that is not the reason for his gentle taunt. I am, you see, a zealous if erratic amateur cook with a strong historical bent. One day I reasoned, plausibly, that the common baked-bean of commerce is but the bastard child of the Pork-and-Beans of my childhood (let us say the late thirties) when each tin contained a token scrap of belly-pork. This clearly derived from the Boston Deep-pot Baked-Beans, which, to my mind, is a dish imported by the intrepid Jersey-cod fishing skippers of two centuries ago: a transatlantic mock-up of the Jersey bean-crock, or *jatte de pais* (beans are called peas in Jersey, naturally: the Jerseyman is a Celt). The Jersey bean-crock is again a bastard child of the superb cassoulet of the Languedoc, a dish whose very name moves me to tears of happy nostalgia.

Well some well meaning idiot forced into my hand a very very genuine recipe for the old-time Boston Baked Beans. I followed it. I bought imported Navy beans at great cost, American Molasses (would you believe Fortnum's?), bullied my butcher into producing a sheet of pork-rind and set about my historic task. Thirty-six hours later (yes truly!) I set upon the table a steaming, savoury crock with a smirk. (No, the smirk was not on the table.)

My wife ladled it out on to every plate in sight and many a spoon dipped in unison, for I had been boasting all day.

'Delicious,' said my wife, for she is loyal. 'Why it's almost as good as . . .'

'Hey,' said my son, 'that's really nice! It reminds me of . . .'

'Darling Daddy,' said my little daughter, 'you are clever! It's very nearly the same as . . .'

This is a written version of an often told baked bean story that still crops up among reminiscing friends. For me the surprise is the way he represents himself as paterfamilias cook at the heart of a friendly but slightly mocking family. By the time he wrote this, it was a rare scene in his life and absent from his fiction. It's true he shows a concern for nourishing food for children in Karl's feeding of the foundling in *All the Tea in China* and in his letters to his adolescent son Chris.

Food thoughts were a pastime for him and his antique-dealer friend Alan Mobey on their long drives to country sales in Bon's early dealing days. Together they would work up a dialogue, taking the parts of Mr and Mrs Beeton and translating the vegetation, farm animals and game birds of the passing scene into substantial recipes described in fruity accents with special lip-smacking noises. They would arrive home laughing and ready to do the Beeton performance for Joan (Alan's wife) and me.

Bon continued to collect food jokes in his folders: 'Have some wurst?' 'No thanks, this is bad enough.' He was working on a Shakespearean series, e.g. 'Never know what you're eating these days. The Raven itself is horse.'

Forgeries Apart from literary pastiche and playful impersonation, the nearest Bon came to forgery, to my knowledge, was to take a pencil and write in a rather antique hand on the back of a picture of children playing: 'A game at hoodman blind.' 'That'll make it sell,' he said to the watching dealer friend who recounted this to me years later.

Each novel has one 'palpable forgery' among the chapter epigraphs, written as a pastiche of the poet chosen for that book and signed acrostically by Bon. He loved an art forgery story of his father's and recounted it with variations – here is the Mortdecai version:

His ears pricked up and the car wobbled.

'Crivelli? No. What Crivelli? Did he have a Crivelli? A good one?'

'It was a very good one, Bernardo Tatti said so. Your father bought it somewhere in the Veneto in 1949 or '50. You know how they sell Old Masters in Italy – the important ones hardly ever go through commercial galleries. As soon as someone with serious money makes it known that he's in the market for serious works of art he will find himself invited to a palazzo for the weekend. His titled host will very delicately indicate that he has to pay a lot of taxes in the near future – and *that's* a joke in Italy – and may be forced, even, to sell an Old Master or two.

'Your father bought the Crivelli like that. It bore certificates by the greatest experts: they always do, of course. *You* know. The subject was the Virgin and Child with a bare bottom and lots of pears and pomegranates and melons – quite lovely. Like the Frick Crivelli, but smaller.

'The Duke or Count hinted that he wasn't *quite* certain of his title to the picture but he could see that your father wasn't a man to fuss about such trifles – it had to be smuggled out in any case, because of the law against export of works of art. Your father took it to an artist friend in Rome who gave it a coat of size then daubed a piece of Futurist-Vorticist rubbish on top. (Sorry, forgot that was your field.) Boldly signed and dated 1949, it went through the customs with no more than a pitying glance.

'Back in the States, he sent it to the best restorer in New York with a note saying, "Clean off modern overpaint; restore and expose original." After a few weeks he sent the restorer one of his cables – you know – "REPORT IMMEDIATELY PROGRESS ON QUOTE MODERN UNQUOTE PAINTING."

'The restorer cabled back, "HAVE REMOVED QUOTE MODERN UNQUOTE PAINTING STOP HAVE REMOVED QUOTE CRIVELLI UNQUOTE MADONNA STOP AM DOWN TO PORTRAIT OF MUSSOLINI STOP WHERE DO I STOP QUERY."'

Dr Krampf didn't laugh. He looked straight ahead, his knuckles tight on the wheel. After a while I said diffidently, 'Well, your father came to think it very funny indeed after the first shock. And your father was not easily amused.'   – *Don't Point that Thing at Me*, p. 146

See also EPIGRAPHS.

Freemasonry

The way I had phrased my remark about having been taught prudence was tentatively Freemasonic. Guardedly he asked me another question. I breathed a sigh of relief to the Great Architect and answered, translating freely from the Dutch. He sent his wife out of the cabin and invited me to share a certain word with him . . .

This is one of several coded exchanges between Karli and the ship's captain in *All the Tea in China*. At last the captain calls him 'young Lewis', the latter being, I understand, the term for a son in

Freemasonry. (It is also the name Chaucer gives his son in his book of instruction in the use of the Astrolabe.)

Bon told me that he was a Mason when he lived in Scotland. I simply do not know what contacts he had with Oxford Masons or whether his father, on whom Karli is partly based, was a Mason. It was important to him that Masons are a brotherhood. His eldest son, sorting Bon's belongings after his death, found he had the apron and other kit. Once, when we were desperate for a carpet for half of our huge drawing room, Bon appeared with a rather worn but very striking-looking carpet from a local lodge. Large, black and white check, and with a blue border showing Masonic symbols, it was much admired by visitors. Its reflection is just visible in the John Creasey Memorial Glass in the photograph on p. 220.

Garlic

'I am a Garlic, I will 'sterminate you!'

This was once the alien cry of the smaller Dalek-owning children in the family. In a period when English cooks still thought it daring to rub a cut clove of garlic round the salad bowl, Bon was remembered for a recipe requiring twenty-two cloves of garlic.

Still exploring how to be an alien in *After You with the Pistol*, and having studied Somato-Ethnic Ambience-Values at combat school, Mortdecai finds a secret weapon:

. . . when it came to my turn I was able to do a pretty convincing imitation of a Levantine, for I had begged a clove of garlic from the kitchen, the Instructress fell back in disorder when I came bellying up to her, whining and waving my hands and gurking out great, poisonous gusts of that prince of vegetables.   – *After You with the Pistol*, p. 266

This deals with the instructress, but immediately afterwards he has to persuade his fanciable lunch companion to chew a clove herself so that she will not reel away likewise.

Garlic still has its non-culinary uses in the home life of an older Mortdecai:

'And your usual is by your gloves on the hall-table.' Splendid chap he'd remembered that I make a practice of chewing a clove of garlic just before visiting fashionable dentists: it cuts down your time in the torture chair amazingly. Try it.   – *The Great Mortdecai Moustache Mystery*, p. 131

Gestures and generosities   Bon's present-giving had an aesthetic of matching the unusual present that he alone could give to the person who would most appreciate it. Examples abound. Many of the people I've talked to while researching this book have shown me something special and unusual given them by Bon. He often enjoyed a certain theatricality in the presentation. When I was recovering from a general anaesthetic after having four impacted wisdom teeth removed, there was a terrific commotion at the door flaps of the hospital ward as Bon struggled through with an enormous, brilliantly coloured modern embroidery that he knew I had admired at an exhibition he had had to miss of work by students at Goldsmith's College. My heart rejoiced to see it. The frame was five foot wide and two foot plus tall; getting it through the door flaps was the cause of the commotion that turned all heads in the ward. Despite his knack of getting round nurses, he was not allowed to leave it with the flowers and cards by the bed.

Maggie Noach, the literary agent, tells the story of how one hot summer's day, when she worked at A. P. Watt, Bon turned up to have lunch in a smart restaurant with the publisher Tom Rosenthal. He was wearing a lovely cool cotton paisley shirt that she much admired. 'Do you like my shirt! You shall have it!' he said as he stripped to the waist. 'I've always wanted to give you the shirt off my back.'

Though he loved the flamboyant gesture, Bon's private and quieter generosities and kindnesses were many.

His engagement presents to me were a seventeenth-century folio of Thomas Fuller's *Church-History of Britain* – I was doing a BLitt on Fuller at the time – and a thirties leather motoring coat, a great standby in those courting days when I was sometimes marooned between Oxford and Cambridge at Bletchley Station. His wedding present was a Chinese carved amethyst pendant symbolizing fruit-fulness.

Two amber necklaces, a smooth honey-coloured one of graduated oval beads and one that looked like rough-cut chunks of barley-sugar toffee, came to symbolize the rough and the smooth of our marriage. When both had broken I mixed the rough with the smooth and made a remarkable necklace slightly too heavy to wear.

Having bought a set of large, Victorian rust-prone steel knives to be cleaned with Vim massaged on with a cork, he imagined I would be delighted to be given a huge knife-cleaning machine: a great drum shape on an almost immovable cast-iron stand obstructing our large larder, it had to be fed with graphite and should have come with a needy orphan to turn its handle. Some presents one would rather do without.

Impatient egoist though he was, he could be sensitive to other people's sadnesses and depression and had his own schemes to cheer by laughter and mayhem or to give employment to people in a discouraged state. In his gallery, when not under the pressures of hanging an exhibition, he was generous with his time and attention, often the listener, even the therapist. Over-indulgent to time-wasters, some business colleagues thought. He stood character witness in court for a local villain friend; was he foolish, nobly quixotic or acting from a sense of a brotherhood in trouble?

Terry Hampton's obituary of 'Karl Bellamy' in the Jersey Angli-can monthly, the *Pilot* (vol. 40, no. 11, 1985), recalls Bon's gen-erosity:

Bon was one of the most generous men I've known. I have a treasured copy of Basil Humes's *To be a Pilgrim* which Bon gave me. I'd just seen the book on his table, said I meant to read it ere long, and a day or so later he left me a copy (but didn't stay to be thanked; he disliked fulsome expressions of appreciation). He also gave me a small statuette of a dog which came from Sumer, or was it Babylon? He'd lost the paper with the details! One day I shall take my dog to the British Museum and see what they can tell me about him.

Getting up in the morning

I embarked on the quotidian *schrecklichkeit* of getting up. With occasional help from Jock I weaned myself gingerly from shower to razor, from dexedrine to intolerable decision about necktie; arriving safely, forty minutes later, at the bourne of breakfast, the only breakfast worth the name, the *cheminot*'s breakfast, the great bowl of coffee laced and gadrooned and filigreed with rum. I had not been sick. The snail was on the thorn, to name but one.   – *Don't Point that Thing at Me*, p. 19

This is pure autobiography as far as the feel of the experience goes . . . once again morning had broken.

Ghost Train   Bon planned *Ghost Train* as a vehicle to accommodate the short stories he was writing. Chaucer-fashion, each tale was to have an appropriate narrator, as the following outline, sent to the agent Hilary Rubinstein in 1977, makes clear:

True to Bonfig form – or perversity – this doesn't fall into any known category. It's a kind of a novel but it is richly studded with eerie stories.

Charlie Mortdecai (remember him?) is in a luxury train (suggestion of the Blue Train Jo'berg to Cape Town) which is hi-jacked by Palestinian terrorists. Everyone is chucked out except those carrying British passports: the men are imprisoned in the club-car, their women in the restaurant car. Terrorists fingering triggers; British chaps behaving in assorted British ways. Horrid tensions as terrorists dicker with authorities; they want a top terrorist released from prison for starters. Authorities agree to release top terrorist and, at end, he approaches the train, beaming. Ah, but, the leader of the train-terrorists only wants him for a little matter of personal revenge, wants to kill him. Ah, but, again, the top terrorist has sold out to the authorities and has agreed to kill the train chap. They meet, embrace lovingly, and shoot each other simultaneously. Curtain.

That's what holds it all together but, in the meantime, the British prisoners are interplaying their personalities like little mad things. Moreover, since they are all too frightened and hungry to sleep, they relate Eerie Stories from their personal experience, each one in his own idiom.

Of the stories, I have so far done the Adjutant's Tale (which I think I showed you, Hilary), the Barrister's Tale (printed as 'Jersey Granite'), the

Irishman's Tale (which is a deliciously nauseating story about the Great
Hunger of 1846/8), the Publisher's Tale (printed in the anthology *Winter's
Crimes* as 'Catch Your Death'), the Interpol-man's Tale (a fiendishly
ingenious detective story with supernatural grace-notes) and the Canon's
Tale. To come are Mr Mukerjee's Tale, the Commercial Traveller's Tale,
the Novelist's Tale, the Engineer's Tale, etc. and *quant. suff.*

I can hear you shrieking from here but you'll love it.

'The British chaps behaving in assorted British ways . . . interplaying their personalities like little mad things' produced a number
of pages of delicately observed speech habits and gestures: a bishop,
a doctor, a commercial traveller.

A story commissioned by the *Tatler*, 'The Liar's Tale', has
developed a mythical excellence – Bon refers to it as 'the best thing
I ever wrote'. It was intended that it should be a part of *Ghost Train*.
Craig Raine, who commissioned it for a Christmas edition, tells
me it never happened and that the commissioning was more a
matter of having a good lunch at the Sorbonne, Bon's favourite
Oxford French restaurant, to discuss it.

Bon's Jersey bank statement shows a credit of £150 from the
Tatler for September 1980. Letters to his agent suggest the story was
never printed but that Bon believed it to be sitting complete and
unused in the *Tatler* archives. Drafts of the first page and the last
two are in the *Ghost Train* folder and are all that I have traced of it
so far. Its length was to be 5,000 words. I include these pages
here for their autobiographical content. Mental-health warning:
remember curious reader that the author/liar is Bonfiglioli putting
himself directly in his fiction, as observed by his creation the
fictional Charlie, who is the 'I' of the telling.

The Liar's Tale

'Well, then,' said the Commercial Traveller jovially, 'we seem to have
survived again, gents. Who's for a nice cupper and a bag of crisps?' We
seized the cheering cups, wax cardboard though they were, and drank
gratefully. I had not yet sunk so far below my station in life as to claim
my ration of crisps although I derived great inward pleasure from watching
the others with theirs; it is not vouchsafed to many to watch – to hear –

a Bishop and a Brigadier sharing a bag of Mr Smith's best and crunchiest.

When the noise had abated the Commercial Traveller, who had some-how – and unchallenged – elected himself Master of our grim Revels, turned to the portly writer-chap with the unpronounceable name.

'I believe you said you were a writer of fiction, sir,' he said invitingly. 'Bit of an author, eh?'

'I said nothing of the kind,' he replied stiffly. 'I claimed only to be a creator of fiction. I am, to speak plainly, a professional liar. Being, nowadays, financially independent, I chiefly exercise my art for pleasure alone, although I confess that I have sometimes felt bound to commit one or two of my choicer *chefs d'œuvre* to print, for I should not care to be remembered after my death as nothing more than a loving husband and father.' He shuddered delicately.

'Then, perhaps,' I ventured, 'since you clearly will have no true experience to relate to the company, we may hope to be favoured with a lie or two to help while away the time?' . . .

[*The middle of the tale is missing, and might never have been written.*]

'My word!' cried the Brigadier. 'What a whopper!'

'Thank you,' said the Liar.

'It's the way you tell 'em,' explained the Commercial Traveller.

'Naturally,' said the Liar.

'Young man,' said the Bishop, 'it is a great comfort to me that you, with your great and unusual, ah, talent, are so clearly a man of honesty and rectitude.'

The Liar thanked him with a grave little bow and an enigmatic glance.

'Ever come across an old chap called Mulliner?' I asked.

'Yes, oddly enough he's an uncle on my mother's side. Strange you should ask that.' His eyes twinkled at me.

'Not very strange,' I said, twinkling back. 'In fact I shouldn't be surprised to learn that you were also related to old Jorkins . . .'

'You are very kind,' he said.

'You know,' said the Barrister, 'you ought to read for the bar. Never too late, you know. You could be at the top of the tree in ten years and make a million in the next ten.'

'Thank you,' said the Liar, 'but I already have a million. My profession is not unremunerative.'

'Tell me,' said the Policeman, leaning forward from his chair and bursting with professional curiosity, 'what made you throw up your career and enter this rare and remunerative profession of lying?'

The Liar stared at him pityingly. 'I thought I'd made that clear,' he said.

'You mean women?'

'That's right.'

Later in the lavatory, I was sharing a wash-hand basin with the Brigadier.

'These writers, now,' he said. 'Not like us at all, are they? They live in a world of their own; can't tell truth from lies, wouldn't you say?'

'No, I wouldn't say that. He didn't tell a word of a lie just now; it was a parable, sort of. I rather fancy the Bishop understood.'

So what autobiographical material can be discerned in this coded and intertextual writing? There is some Woostering, a bonding code between characters, but it could come in useful: they are in danger and need to convey messages under the noses of the Palestinian terrorists who have taken them prisoner. Jorkins is a character from Dickens's *David Copperfield*. Or did Bon write Jorkins for Jorrocks (from his treasured volume of Surtees), his favourite fictional Victorian?

The mannerisms are recognizably Bonnish (though 'I wouldn't say that' is pure Betjeman) and, yes, women were a reason he turned from art dealing to earning his living as a writer. His attitude to truth and lies in everyday life cannot be explained simply. There are the 'lies' that make a good story and lies intended to deceive. I remember that, when I became aware of the extent to which he was deceiving me, I experimented with telling him a few lies. As he always thought *him* liar, *me* truthful, he believed me without question. I found this extremely disturbing: it was as if we were both sinking in the same quicksand and could not help each other out. In his dream poem *The House of Fame*, Chaucer gives himself a speaking part. He has been 'swap' up into the air by an eagle to learn how fame works in the world. He sees a Truth and a Falsehood struggling to get out of the same narrow aperture in a rotating structure that will whirl them about the world. In the fierce struggle in the restricted space, they emerge for ever entangled.

God Holed up in a cave at the end of *Don't Point that Thing at Me*, Charlie is able to say '*Donc, Dieu existe*' as he contemplates an incomparably beautiful Goya painting of a naked woman. The same novel has as one of its epigraphs some significant lines from Browning's poem 'Andrea del Sarto':

> And, thus we half-men struggle. At the end,
> God, I conclude, compensates, punishes.
> — *Don't Point that Thing at Me*, p. 148

Troubled by the idea of God, often referring to priests and parsons as God-botherers, Bon makes Mortdecai too proud to pray in adversity when he is trapped in the cold store of Mycock's bacon factory in *After You with the Pistol*. His fear of judgement was stronger than his belief in forgiveness. He found it impossible to forgive himself, and Mortdecai, describing the character of George in *Something Nasty in the Woodshed*, slips in a sharply accurate piece of self-recognition: 'The inability to see any flaws in oneself is a branch of pottiness, of course, but much less harmful than being unable to see any good in oneself.'

George believes in God, but the C of E brand, as advertised on television by virtue of the Equal Time Agreement, although he has an Open Mind because he has seen some pretty Queer Things in India and places like that. His manners are too good to let his religion show, which is as it should be. — *Something Nasty in the Woodshed*, p. 379

Nothing really had happened in the newspapers that day, either, except that some Arabs had murdered some Jews, some Jews had retaliated on some Arabs, some Indians had perfected an atomic bomb for dropping on some Pakistanis and various assorted Irishmen had murdered each other in unpleasant ways. You really have to hand it to God, you know, he has terrific staying power. Jehovah against Mohammed, Brahman against Allah, Catholic against Protestant: religion really keeps the fun going doesn't it. If God didn't exist the professional soldiers would have to invent him, wouldn't they? — *Something Nasty in the Woodshed*, p. 406

A Gombeen man was a thing that God himself would hate.

> – 'The Gombeen Man' (see 'Short Stories' section)

Bon knew by heart the Donne sonnet 'Batter my heart, three person'd God' and recited it to his daughter Catriona when she visited him in Ireland. He saw himself in it: as needing God's active force, as never chaste 'except you ravish mee'.

Donne was the great love poet of students in the fifties. 'The tender well-armed feeling braine', Donne's words about himself in 'Of the Progress of the Soule', could have been Bon's. How many students were in the habit of preaching against themselves through a thundering sermon of Donne's as I remember Bon doing?

A folder entitled 'Space Ship God' gives no evidence of a complete plan for a story but contains notes from the gospels on Christ's healing miracles that emphasize Christ's instructions that people not speak of them.

See PRIESTS, SILENCE and SUNDAYS.

Going to bed at night This was exceedingly difficult for Bon. Day or night, but especially at night, he used a repertoire of means to make guests stay far longer than they or their wives or girlfriends had intended, filling a tumbler with whisky as people got up to go; inviting several people to call at the same time, having told each that he wanted to see him alone (this led people to try to outstay each other); telling funny stories; starting a new game of poker or gin-rummy; crying 'the night is young yet. There's still some in the bottle / I've opened another bottle'. He hated to be left; he hated to be left alone with his ghosts.

But sleep when it came was a blessing to him. See ZIZZ.

Graves, Robert Hilary Rubinstein (literary agent):

Maggie Noach invited him to a party to which Robert Graves, who was also a client, came. And Robert Graves must have seen him looking in the dumps, which was quite a frequent expression, and he said, 'Oh, you look very unhappy, young man.' 'Yes, I've been disappointed in love once again,' Bon said. And then Robert Graves must have given him some line of poetry and Bon said, 'That's Robert Graves, isn't it? I wonder whether the old bugger's still alive.' 'Young man,' said Robert Graves, 'both of us are going to dine out on that.'

Guilt

Let other pens dwell on guilt and misery.   — Jane Austen, *Mansfield Park*

A tragic burden of guilt accumulated through a series of events, which were not in fact his fault, coloured Bon's view of life. His view of priests as 'Godbotherers' and psychiatrists as 'Trickcyclists', a kind of pride about asking for help, a fear of losing some of his essential nature — all these were factors that left him no effective means of easing the burden except oblivion.

Guns

'There cannot be too many guns for my taste,' I said frankly.

— All the Tea in China, p. 77

With that he opened his gun-case and assembled his beautiful Churchill XXV with a brutality that made me wince.

— Something Nasty in the Woodshed, p. 409

See ARMS AND THE ART DEALER and WEAPONRY.

Hangovers

(It has often been remarked that men about to face death on the field of battle or, indeed the very gallows itself, frantically seek solace in the sexual act. The same is true of the common hangover: a raw egg beaten up in Worcester sauce or Tabasco is a useful placebo for the hungover novice; a pint of flat and tepid ale is a kill or cure specific/emetic for those with leaden stomachs, while a brace of large brandies marks out your seasoned boozer who knows that he needs an emperic to get him back into the human race as quickly as may be. You may depend upon it that the only sovereign cure for us men of iron is a brisk five minutes of what Jock coarsely calls 'rumpy pumpy'. It is positively warranted to scour the cobwebs from the most infected skull; no home should be without it.

Try some tomorrow. I shan't pretend that you can buy it at all reputable chemists but you will find a registry office in most large towns. I digress, I know, but usefully: these words of mine alone are worth the price of admission.)

This digression from *After You with the Pistol* (p. 316) occurs in the middle of a scene of violence and torture.

Happiness

Above me and to my right shone the lights of the honest bungalow dwellers of Silverdale: I found myself envying them bitterly. It is chaps like them who have the secret of happiness, they know the art of it, they always knew it. Happiness is an annuity, or it's shares in a Building Society; it's a pension and blue hydrangeas, and wonderfully clever grandchildren, and being on the Committee, and just-a-few-earlies in the vegetable garden, and being alive and wonderful-for-his-age when old so-and-so is under the sod, and it's double-glazing and sitting by the electric fire remembering that time when you told the Area Manager where he got off and that other time when that Doris . . .

Happiness is easy: I don't know why more people don't go in for it.

– Don't Point that Thing at Me, p. 160

I find myself transcribing this passage from Bon's first novel just a few days after what would have been his seventieth birthday – 29 May 1998. The wonderfully clever grandchildren he never met are just coming back from the village school.

In the novel the passage has great poignancy: Mortdecai is on the run and has just lost his best mate and manservant, the immortal Jock, in quicksand.

It is also poignant for any of the friendly inhabitants of Silverdale who knew Bon after the collapse of his happiness and hopes in Lancashire; his love departed, the house to be sold, bailiffs at the door. Two families came to his aid at this point; the Martlands and the Turnbulls. Ann Turnbull has described to me the sad comedy: the house had been emptied except for Bon's possessions piling up in the study – he had refused to deal with it. She particularly remembers him at half past the eleventh hour carrying out a tuba and attempting to fit it into a Mini and then staggering along with a huge bust of Byron. He suddenly disappeared from sight as he fell sideways into the bushes.

Pursuit of happiness an inconceivable concept except when absent.
> – a note on the cover of Bon's 'Seven Deadly Sins' folder

Stevenson's poem 'The Celestial Surgeon' was one Bon frequently quoted. He always felt he *ought* to have been happy.

The Celestial Surgeon

If I have faltered more or less
In my great task of happiness;
If I have moved among my race
And shown no glorious morning face;
If beams from happy human eyes
Have moved me not; if morning skies,
Books, and my food, and summer rain
Knocked on my sullen heart in vain: –
Lord, Thy most pointed pleasure take
And stab my spirit broad awake;
Or, Lord, if too obdurate I,
Choose thou, before that spirit die,
A piercing pain, a killing sin,
And to my dead heart run them in!

Health Bon subjected himself to a punishing way of life. Always searching for an explanation for his lack of well-being, he attributed his symptoms variously to malaria, stomach ulcers and a rare form of brucellosis. Richard Booth remembers Bon saying liver cells were floating about his bloodstream, yet speaking as if about someone else. Apart from diagnosis of a heart-murmur in a bout of pneumonia in the sixties, which he recovered from speedily with the seemingly magic aid of penicillin, it is hard to say – given the strong constitution he was born with – exactly when he was first forced to take his health seriously. Some landmarks in this process follow.

Some time before Christmas in 1977 Bon sent a £2 contribution to Miss Noeline Kenny, Hon. Secretary of the Irish Brucellosis Society. Her two-month delay in responding meant to him that she too might be a sufferer. He wrote back describing his own condition: 'Luckily as a professional novelist, I have a good relationship with my typewriter and if I can bring myself to wind a sheet of paper in I can usually start a letter although I often lose heart before the end. I'm sure this is a recognizable symptom . . .' He thanks her for her papers from the Society, which he has read with interest, and continues:

I'm afraid I score very high on all signs and symptoms, except the ear, heart and sexual disorders. I may say that I am a pretty objective thinker (MA Oxon.) and *not* one of those who reads medical encyclopedias and convinces himself that he has every disease from alopecia to zygodactylism.

This is a couple of hours later. I plucked up the energy to go upstairs to fetch a cigarette, for which I had been pining for *an hour* and, predictably, had a nap.

And, oh dear, this is now tomorrow. I went 'blah'.

To me, the worst symptoms are the irrational sweating bouts, the terrible, almost narcoleptic fatigue, the impatience of uncomprehending friends and, above all, the apathy. There isn't anything I want more. If you gave me a hundred pounds to buy myself a present I know very well I'd wander out in an agony of indecision and finally come home with nothing except, perhaps, a bottle of whiskey.

Last week I was invited to a party: influential people, lovely girls, gourmet dinner &c. Having accepted, I started dreading having to organize shave, shirt, suit, transport and rang back lying that I was starting 'flu' . . . The Christmas before last I was in Moscow for a weekend holiday; the tour of the Kremlin and its treasures was timed for 10 a.m. I stayed in bed. Couldn't be bothered. Imagine being in Moscow and not crossing the road to see the Kremlin! It frightens me.

He then includes a reference to the Stevenson poem (quoted under HAPPINESS), finds that some twenty days have passed and it is now Easter Day and, with thanks and good wishes to Miss Kenny, goes back to his own state:

Am presently going through a very bad 'ramshackle' period, sleeping twelve to twenty hours a day and I have taken nothing but whiskey, cigarettes and one bacon sandwich in the last four days. Have started dosing myself with massive quantities of vitamin C as suggested. Luckily, I have a book coming out on 10 April so mere curiosity as to what the reviews will be like is enough to keep me away from the shotgun. I know that you will know that I am not dramatizing.

This letter, combining a bid for sympathy with an in-built expectation of its not being sent, remained unfinished.

The characteristically paced punctuation of a voice speaking to someone runs through art. Neither the touching belief that we Oxford MAs are objective thinkers nor the thought of a book coming out are sufficiently cheering to keep him going; the letter becomes too autobiographical, too much of a soliloquy to remain anything but a painful private reflection.

The book mentioned is *All the Tea in China*. Its dedication, recalling T. S. Eliot's 'I am not Prince Hamlet', reveals a submerged train of thought: that he is not important enough to take his health more seriously in a practical way. 'For Rubincrantz and Rosenstern – two princes without a Hamlet' makes princes of Hilary Rubinstein and Tom Rosenthal, while he bows himself out as a Hamlet or as anyone worthy of a tragic fate.

A consultant psychiatrist from Manchester Royal Infirmary wrote to him thus on 28 October 1982:

Either you were inaccurate in your report of the amount of alcohol that you have been consuming or your liver has become extremely susceptible to the effects of alcohol. When you were in the ward your gamma GT liver enzyme fell from 900 and something to approximately 300, when you left the ward. It now stands at 565, which is serious damage.

He concludes: 'I do not think this result should be ignored.'

Despite attempts to dry out in hospital, about which he was very secretive at the time but which he drew on in his fiction, serious doubt remained whether the will was there. Doubt in the mind of Professor David Goldberg (his friend and a professor at the

Manchester Royal Infirmary) and indeed in Bon's mind too, but for different reasons. Bon feared sobriety.

Among his papers is an article, 'Drinking and Creativity: A Review of the Alcoholism Literature', concerning the links between genius and illness, particularly in writers and painters.* An alphabetical list of some forty-five distinguished writers who drank heavily has Bonfiglioli inserted between Berryman and Boswell in his hand and a marginal question: 'At what ages did these die? – Check.' Carefully highlighted are the following statements about writers and artists:

writers have chosen to accept an image of themselves as tragic, lonely, doomed, outside society . . .
writers whose mental problems invade their creations . . .
writers who drink heavily certainly do write about drinking in their books . . .
The function of drinking being to reduce sensory overload to which all writers are prone. If preventing the drinking can be seen as interfering (possibly to ill effect) with the artistic productivity, then writers have a case for arguing that they are at least an occupational group whose drinking is indeed part of the job.

The complexity of the relationship is admitted but the conclusion is that drinking and writing are inextricably connected.

Bon's writings show drinking as part of the rhythm of life, a key social accessory and sometimes part of an occasion for wondrous bonhomie. Mortdecai's failures of perception are never due to drink, it seems.

For as long as possible Bon refused to admit the role of booze in his life, relying on the idea of himself as essentially a survivor. Sometimes a casual comment pointed to heart-sickness as much as to the state of his liver.

Hell

Why this is hell nor am I out of it.　– Christopher Marlowe, *Dr Faustus*

* *British Journal on Alcohol and Alcoholism*: Marcus Grant referring to research first presented in June 1980.

Mephistopheles's reply to Faustus as to the whereabouts of hell fits both Charlie's and Karli's perceptions in a variety of situations.

The first Mortdecai novel ends as if Charlie were a type of the fallen angel Satan:

> . . . then one of the others will kill me and I shall fall like a bright exhalation in the evening down to hell where there is no art and no alcohol, for this is, after all, quite a moral tale. You see that, don't you?
> — *Don't Point that Thing at Me*, p. 176

More lightly in the second novel of the trilogy it is experiences of school and army PT that provide references to hell in a scene much enhanced for Charlie and the reader by the presence of girls:

> PT was hell. People made me prance absurdly, climb up and down wall-bars, hurl myself at hateful vaulting-horses and try to do press-ups. Then they threw monstrous medicine-balls at me. I panted and groaned my way through it until a bell rang and we all trooped into the showers. They were communal, unsegregated showers. Kitty twinkled at me as she soaped her luggage-like carcass and the younger girls played *pranks* on me.   — *After You with the Pistol*, p. 262

For Karli in his young days it is shot-gun pellets in his left buttock that burn like a foretaste of hell as he runs away from an angry uncle. Hellish experiences on shipboard increase in power and significance as Karli's first captain becomes increasingly rash and demonic in his failure to shoulder the guilt of having lured a rival ship to a certain wreck.

We scrambled across the 'brow' between our ship and the sampan alongside it, under a glare from the Captain. In an instant the men at the sweeps were bending to it with a will and we were amongst a flock of vessels making best speed towards the open sea. I knew enough by now to keep out of the way. The men at the sweeps were pulling like galley-slaves and needed no whip to urge them.

'Typhoon,' snapped Peter as he ran past me, 'get oilskins and get below!' I got both.

Later I crept out to the break of the poop, for nothing seemed to be happening. On the poop stood the Captain and all three mates. Captain Knatchbull and Peter were discussing something heatedly, the First Mate was growling ignorantly and the Second was looking white but holding his peace.

(Afterwards, I pieced together the burden of their argument: a typhoon in the Northern hemisphere moves north, you see, and rotates anti-clockwise. The western side or half-circle is navigable but, clearly, blows south – dead foul for us. The eastern semicircle is dangerous, for the wind there blows at unimaginable speeds – few have attempted to measure these speeds and very few have survived to record them. But that side blows northwards, towards the 'country-trade' part of the Coast where, sooner or later, we wished to be. The Captain's great experience and insanity told him that, by a dashing use of sail, we could make use of the south-western part of the rotatory storm, claw ourselves free on its eastern side and use the residual fringe winds to carry us safely north.)

I did not, thank God, understand anything of what was said, but I heard the Captain close the discussion with a roar of command, saw Peter throw up his hands in a gesture of despair and was jostled by the First Mate as he thrust by me, eyes terrified, to give orders for making sail. The sky was now a rich reddish-brown, full of bizarre menace. I crept below again. There was some cold food in the cabin but I could not touch it: I confess that I was alarmed.

This alarm was nothing to my feelings when the wind first hit us: the impact was such that I thought we had struck a great rock. But the blow was from behind: the ship leaped forward like a maddened horse, I could hear the water roaring against the skin of the ship, the yelling, then the screaming of the tortured rigging and above all the demented bellow of the prodigious wind. Again and again I was sure that this was the climax, that nothing could exceed such violence, no force on earth make a more deafen-ing clamour, but again and again I was proved wrong as the clamour grew more intolerable. At last, insane with the noise and the terror, I clapped my hands to my ears and rushed on deck, determined to confront death sooner than later – and not in that rat-trap of a cabin. As I emerged the hellish din was heightened by an explosion or so it seemed – as the fore staysail burst into tatters. We lost steerage-way, yawed, and in an instant we were pooped by a cliff-like wave which had been pursuing us. A thousand tons of grey water thundered the length of the ship, lifting me as though I were a fragment of paper and burying me oceans deep. I knew that I was a dead man, there was no question of it, my eardrums cracked, water spurted into my nostrils and, as I opened my mouth to scream, my lungs were instantly so gorged that I could feel them begin to split with the pressure. In the few instants it took to die the whole of my past life flashed in review across my inner eye: this was a disgusting experience.

I awoke in hell, which did not surprise me, all things considered.

A black, glistening demon, ten feet high, was tormenting me excruciatingly, crushing my agonized ribs with his great hands. I spewed a gallon of sea-water at him. He turned me over and attacked my chest from behind. It was intolerable – and I knew that the torments would continue through all eternity. I vomited another gallon.

'Din't eat yo' nice supper, did you, Maz Cleef,' said the Doctor reproachfully, making me sit up and forcing my head between my knees. 'Don' tell me different: I seen you brung up nothing but sea-water. Might a gone to glory on a empty stomach; ain't no sense in that now.'

As my eyes cleared and the shards of my wits reassembled themselves, I became amused at the sense of disappointment that I felt. I began to cry, then to giggle idiotically. The Doctor smacked me hard across the face and I sank into a happy sleep.

What had happened, it seemed, was this: the great mass of water had wedged me into the bowsprit-rigging – in the angle between the martingale-backstays and the dolphin-striker, to be exact – and, as the ship stood on her tail after the wave had passed, gravity had thrown me on to the fo'c'sle, along the deck, where I caromed off the mainmast bitts and fetched up against the galley. The Doctor had plucked me inside, just before the next pooping.

'Were many drowned?' I asked when I could speak again.

'Of course not,' said Peter. 'Everyone else had the sense to be lashed to something stout – or to stay below when told to.'

– All the Tea in China, p. 163

Karli's narrative ends with an even more demonic captain:

A door opened and blinding sunlight made me blink. Black against the sun I made out the shape of a huge man.

'Get up,' said a voice I thought I had heard before.

I rose to my feet and staggered towards the figure rubbing my eyes and trying to focus. There was a snake-like thing dangling from its hand.

'Where am I?' I whimpered.

'You're in the *Rose of Boston*, loading for Sydney. And you call me Sir,' said Lubbock.

I gaped. The rope's end flicked out and my groin jumped in agony.

'Aye aye, Sir,' I said . . .   – end of *All the Tea in China*

These images of shipboard-hell under demonic captains are significantly contrasted. The first is a hell of recovery: the black figure is no demon but Karli's rescuer, ship's cook, doctor, healer and friend, a kindly black man of subtle intuitions. The second is a true hell: Karli has entered a new circle of hell, deeper than the young man's experience that begins the book. I am reminded that the first exhibition of pictures we had at Norham Gardens was a series of huge oil paintings of Dante's *Inferno*. Bon also had a copy of Coleridge's *Ancient Mariner* with illustrations by Paul Gustave Doré. As a reader he had met many hells, from Marlowe to Sartre, and knew well that the mind is its own place and can make a hell of heaven or a heaven of hell.

Heraldry

'I tickled him up by asking wilily why *or* and *argent* were juxtaposed in those arms contrary to all the laws of '
                    – *The Great Mortdecai Moustache Mystery*, p. 97

Bon himself and his referees for college entrance in 1955 list heraldry as one of his interests. It is a visual and symbolic language of great precision and once considered among the essential accomplishments of any seventeenth-century gentleman. The beauty of its colour vocabulary appealed to Bon and he was proud that as a soldier in Scotland he had restored the painting of the coat of arms in the Gordon Highlander's barracks, a photograph of which he treasured.

One of the possible titles for the sequel planned for *All the Tea in China* was *A Hand Proper Argent*, a phrase in the language of heraldry that implies a clear visual image. (See SILVERHAND.)

Bon also did little sketches of the arms of various branches of the Bonfigliolis and noted two of their heraldic mottoes: one backward looking, the other forward looking:

Prinz ne puilz; Bon Filz suis – I cannot be a prince; I am a good son

Only in his romantic imagination could he be the Prince of Aquitaine, yet he was a good son, though I saw no sign that he or his father ever acknowledged this. In contrast Charlie's embittered comments about his parents never suggest any interest in being a good son. It should be remembered that Bon brought his father to our tiny house in Jericho and that like *pius Aeneas* carried him on his back, economically speaking, restoring to him as much dignity as he could by giving him a role in his business and setting him up in a shop of his own in Eynsham until he became too ill to manage it.

Fuimus et sub Deo erimus – We have been and by God we shall be

This one seems to speak of Bon's hopes for his children.

Hidden jokes There are a great many hidden or half-hidden jokes in Bon's writing – it's hard to tell how far he wanted them to be decoded or whether they were little legacies for friends who might remember them from convivial times with him in those old joke-telling days. An example is the following:

I shall never say another harsh word about that sainted woman.
                                    – *Don't Point that Thing at Me*, p. 67

Triggered off by a reference to Queen Mary's blend of tea in the previous lines, this has a second level of reference to antique dealer's gossip about old Queen Mary – the present Queen's grandmother – who was notorious among the antiques fraternity for acquiring choice articles from their shops without suffering the indignity of having to pay for them.

When a little girl skips past the window crying *Umgawa umgawa*, or words to that effect, she seems to recall the ever passing Pippa (and to understand *her* role fully you need to have read your Browning). Otherwise the reference is mysterious except to those who know the Umgawa story, which goes like this:

A smug Socialist politician visiting Africa with a mission to encourage native independence movements believes himself a great success when he addresses a large crowd gathered to hear him. They stamp their feet and their assegais rhythmically on the ground shouting 'Umgawa! Umgawa!' – Freedom! Freedom! – with every sign of enthusiasm. His host the chief, who was so helpful in setting up the rally, now escorts him courteously back to his hut, pointing here and there with his staff, saying, 'Be careful not step in umgawa.'

In other words it's another way of suggesting that Mortdecai is as usual in deep shit.

Bon waited till his last novel to unravel this clue: Karli, as a would-be anthropologist, is sitting round a fire of *umgawa* and discovering that dangerous misunderstandings are going on between him and the natives. Shit again, bullshit this time.

See also JOKES.

History

The only Britishers with a sense of History are the Irish, with them it is a disease. He was mouthing the words painfully, hatingly, as though history were an abscessed tooth which your tongue cannot resist tormenting . . .   – 'The Gombeen Man'

A. L. Rowse once said that making a really important historical discovery is very like sitting, inadvertently, on a cat. I felt, at that moment, like just such an historian – and, indeed, like just such a cat.

– Don't Point that Thing at Me, p. 148

Bon's army referee Colonel W. J. F. Craig mentions discussions with him on world history and says he 'formed the highest opinion of Sergeant Instructor C. E. G. Bonfiglioli's erudition in the fields of History and Literature'. Bon was always glad of an excuse to research something. Each place he lived in was just such a stimulus.

All the Tea in China involved him in the politics behind the Opium Wars, trade in tea, Delft and porcelain, the nefarious sides of the British Empire as well as the lore of ships and shipping. Preparing to write *Lord Mortdecai* and *Silverhand* involved him in historical research, and he was good at finding contemporary sources both pictorial and written. He was adept at bringing to bear all the accumulated knowledge from his years as a dealer.

See *SILVERHAND* and UNFINISHED WORK.

Home

I have just been in my old bedroom which is always kept ready for me, never altered or disturbed; just the kind of false note my brother loves sardonically to strike. He often says, 'Do remember that you always have a home here, Charlie,' then waits for me to look sick.

– Don't Point that Thing at Me, p. 163

The painfully ambivalent attitude Bon had to the idea of home is repeatedly expressed through Charlie's brother Robin with his repeated phrase of false welcome. It would be hard to assess which of the places Bon lived in he would have, at least briefly, called home.

Sylva

I see old forest trees as men so wise
That films of cobweb grime their patient eyes.
Too wise they always were to budge;
To stray, they always knew is but to bleed;
Where the wind blew their fathers' seed they are content to lodge.
The ant who walks their sweetheart-carven trunks,
The drunks who water their impassive roots
(Or their own boots)
The bird that couples in their cracking hair
Is prisoned deeper than they ever were
And to be deeply Earth-fast they are glad.
Or so *they* say.
I think perhaps they're mad.

This poem dates from when Bon was still living at No. 18 Norham Gardens, which looked out back and front on huge well-established trees. His printing press was in the cellar. I picked this poem off the floor when I moved out myself. Bon had intended to publish a small hand-set volume of his poems under the title *Poems of Prejudice* – a plan to make something more permanent of his writing and to print it himself. This was to be the first poem, a reverie on rooted-ness, undercut sharply in the last two lines. It was written in the last home he could call his own. Or perhaps his rented cottage in Ireland was one. It was not shared with anyone.

Idiocy and cowardice

Look, I think it is only fair that I should set out for the innocent reader the limits and parameters of my idiocy and cowardice, these two heaven-sent gifts which help a chap to survive into what I choose to call early middle age. Reader, are you over the age of eight? Good. Then you must have found yourself embroiled . . . in some frightful catastrophe, such as an outbreak of fire in a theatre. Being the shrewd and sturdy chaps that you must be (having pursued my simple narrative so far), you will have observed that in such an imbroglio three distinct kinds of idiots can be seen by the naked eye.

First: the staunch, officer-type idiot (usually sporting one of those absurd little moustaches which – unlike some I could name – are scarcely worth the mulching) who leaps on to a seat and in staunch officer-like tones commands everyone to keep calm, stay in their seats and on no account to panic.

Second: the idiots who listen to him, keep calm, stay in their seats and get incinerated.

Third: the idiots who, seeing no survival-value in keeping calm and not panicking, rush to the exits and get trampled to death. Unless they happen to be among the leaders at the exit.

I am happy to say that I belong to this third class of idiot and, being pretty fleet of foot for my age, have always contrived to be among the first three out of the exit. I'm not saying this is entirely creditable, nor that my mummy would have approved, but I am alive, am I not? Perhaps this is a good thing. I'm sure my Life Insurance Company thinks so, although again my mummy might raise an objection, not to mention an eyebrow.

What I'm leading up to in my diffident sort of way is that when the Mortdecai second-sense (no, I don't mean sixth sense, I was never a braggart) when I say, the Mortdecai second-sense tells me that large, rough men are about to bonk me on my valuable skull, I tend prudently to trip away in an opposite direction and a rapid silent fashion.

– from draft of The Great Mortdecai Moustache Mystery

At this point in the plot Mortdecai has just congratulated himself on having taken some outwitting steps when . . . I don't want to spoil the story for you. Charlie gets it wrong again. Survival is the prime value. Bon was not a coward in any real emergency (see FIRE), but he did feel that British *sang-froid* was an overrated virtue.

'I think he considered himself a very ridiculous person,' said the publisher Tom Rosenthal in a BBC radio programme about Bon.

Ireland

I must thank all my new friends in County Cavan, whose unquestioning kindness to their new neighbour has carried me through a long dark winter: the fact that I cannot list their names here is a measure of their number.   – acknowledgement in *All the Tea in China*

Long before he ever went to Ireland, Bon liked to think that the Irish with their gift for language were likely to say things like: 'The tea was so strong that you could trot a mouse on it.' In encounters with my Irish mother, he invariably ritualized their mutual antagonism in an argument about Roger Casement in which he played a rather bigoted British role stressing Casement's homosexuality and treachery.

My mother's role then was to defend Casement as a hero of the struggle for Irish independence who had been an instrument of British colonial rule in Africa long enough to receive a knighthood, but in the process had also learnt enough to see the Irish question from a different side for ever afterwards. He was executed by the British for his part in the Easter Rising of 1916.

The Irish government's tax advantages for writers and artists, and Bon's need for escape, isolation and economy, were among the reasons for his choice of a small cottage in Cavan as his home between 1977 and 1981 when he was there as a full-time writer. Irish generosity, hospitality and love of good 'crack', jokes and stories and understanding for a drinking man were heartwarming.

I sat back and realized that Rembrandt was an Irishman. Not by birth of course, but by his nature. A compulsive self-searcher, an inveterate rebel, a man who would snub a king to sup with a beggar, a man who spent his life balancing spirituality against sensuality and measuring the result against his own decay; a shrewd but careless businessman; a man whose reaction to triumph and disaster was to examine himself with an enigmatic smile – and to put down the results on paper or canvas without bitterness or self-pity.

               – from a review of *Rembrandt* by Kenneth Clarke, in the *Irish Press*

Bon with shillelagh outside a shed full of empties in Shercock

An imaginative fusion has taken place – one of the Irish Bons has appeared.

Tara Heinemann's photograph of Bon with shillelagh is another.

My publishers sent me a beautiful she-photographer to do a mug-shot of me recently, she had a plump little she-assistant. I said that they should ask for me at Hughie McEleary's pub which is 5 miles from the cottage. I was there when they came in and asked if Mr Bon was there. An impressive silence fell, everyone staring into their glasses of Guinness. Me too. (The rule here is never tell any stranger anything except the time.) Hughie finally said 'I might know him or again I might not. Who's asking?' Two young women, you see, is a known IRA formation. When they said who they were I chirped up, otherwise they'd probably have been courteously set on the road to Castleblaney or Ballybay or, god forbid, Crossmaglen.   – from a letter to Tom Braun

After he had settled in he joined the Irish Brucellosis Society (see HEALTH) and took an interest in local folklore, crafts and natural history, exchanging letters on these subjects with local worthies, including a poet–lighthouse keeper. Press cuttings of October 1981 show him present, standing just behind Charles Haughey (leader of Fianna Fáil) at the official opening by Brian Friel of Annaghmakerrig, the Tyrone Guthrie Centre. Run by the Arts Councils of North and South, providing bursaries and 'a temporary home for Irish writers and artists wishing to work in peace and seclusion', for Bon it may have meant some hope of stimulus by the company of fellow writers.

(As a matter of fact I spend about £3 a week on keeping orange squash, lollipops for the countless raggedy kids in this lough-side who are always popping in to see that I'm all right. All other considerations apart, I'm glad of these visitations because if I broke a leg getting out of the bath, for instance, I might not otherwise be found for days and all the kids know that if my car's there and I don't answer the door, then they must run to their father and tell them. No telephone, you see.)
                                         – from a letter to Tom Braun

He became fascinated with the Irish way with language, and his first fictional Irishman is O'Casey, who appears in *All the Tea in China* as drinking companion when Karli is feeling desperately lonely because his other shipboard friends have their own reasons for not wanting to share talk about the dangerously deteriorating conditions caused by the new captain.

'Tis a shockin' tarror of a life dese times, is it not Sorr?'

'I'm afraid,' I said in a benign Peter-like voice, 'that I cannot discuss the failings of any of my superiors with you. Pray keep the conversation general.'

'Of course, Sorr. I was just t'inking of a lieutenant I sailed under wance . . .'

He goes on to warn Karli with tactful obliqueness of all the dangers ahead, including the captain's character:

'It was not dat terrible a lot of years ago, Sorr, and the only difference is that in them days he still had a few marks of the gentleman about him. Today he's a man that would tear Christ off the Cross.'

— *All the Tea in China*, p. 87

Karli's foolish class prejudice and anti-Irishness put him in danger as he fails to benefit from this kindly warning or to appreciate O'Casey's gift of reading the future.

Living in County Cavan, near the border, Bon found himself a suspect person. In a letter to Tom Rosenthal, he recounts a conversation that took place in his presence.

Ah, yes, well, it's all very well to talk of knee-caps in peaceful, pastoral London, but they take that sort of thing seriously here. I am not jesting when I say that last week I was quietly told by well-wishers that there is a faction in the village which is convinced that I am an SAS spy. No, really! Of course I roared with laughter but they looked very grave. 'Forst,' they said, 'yez seem to have plenty of money' – well naturally that set me off again. 'Bot no vusuble means of support,' they went on. 'Would you believe Secker & Warburg, Pantheon and Penguins?' I asked weakly. They looked graver. 'Foreigners,' they seemed to be thinking. 'Den, yez have an Egyptian name,' I am quoting verbatim, 'bot a Jersey passport and ye speak loike an English officer.' That enraged me: 'Your actual English officer today,' I told them, 'speaks like a counter-jumper.' 'Worst of all, ye've hidden yerself out at Kilmacaran.' I lost patience.

'What the $&^%+! am I supposed to be spying on out there?' I roared. They looked at each other. Decided I really didn't know. Told me. My cottage, it emerged, overlooks: (a) the farmhouse of the local IRA bloke and (b), in the other direction, a deserted building where a year or so ago the army discovered the biggest explosives and ammunition dump ever seized.

In another letter, written shortly after his arrival in Ireland, Bon reports: 'No one has shot nor bombed me; I must say it seems a bit *stand-offish* of them.'

Japonaiserie Japanese prints were readily to be bought in Oxford in the fifties and sixties. Bon had a successful exhibition of Kuniyoshis in July 1962. The Ashmolean collections and the expertise of Oliver Impey there and of our Cranham Street lodger Derek Grigson all added to his knowledge.

Samurai and their kit fascinated, with all the artistry and vocabulary of their sword furnishings and training. He could do a terrifying imitation of the faces in theatrical prints of warriors from Noh drama, with their fierce expressions. *Seven Samurai* was a favourite film.

See also WEAPONRY.

Jersey Bon took refuge in Jersey when he left Lancashire. He received much hospitality there, having at least eight different addresses in eleven years; he did some tutoring in art history and Shakespeare and inevitably some dealing and drinking. His Jersey novel, *Something Nasty in the Woodshed*, is dedicated to a long list of Jersey friends (Christian names only) with thanks for their patience and tolerance. Terry Hampton, a dedicatee, says 'it was a typical Bon touch' that he 'asked me not to read it, as he thought I'd be offended by the language and the plot'.

Its beginning is almost a specialist guide to Jersey's most idiosyncratic customs and language, which must have offended some and amused and informed many. For a while he enjoyed many aspects of Jersey life. Thanks to Jersey hospitality his children were able to visit him and we all spent one Christmas there with the Johnston family.

Writing from Jersey in July 1976 to John Bryson, his old tutor at Balliol, he shows signs of feeling cut off: 'I have the Island disease: I pounce on any word from the Mainland as though it were an antidote for snakebite and a letter from you is rare medicine.' Later in the letter he says that he is 'fitting out a van for a reconnaissance of Ireland'.

In the last novel mainly written in Jersey, Mortdecai is reluctant to leave the lavish comforts of home for detective work in Oxford, especially as the imperious Johanna insists that Jock must stay behind this time.

Bon returned to Jersey from Ireland in 1981 and remained there in declining health till his death (q.v.) in March 1985.

Jewishness Though Inez, Bon's sister, says she is not aware of a Jewish strand in the family, I am fascinated by this possibility and by the question of how much the uncircumcised Bon seems to have considered this himself. He knew that in Ferrara there are Jewish families with the name Bonfiglioli. In some moods he would have liked to be a Jew and certainly during his writing life he became progressively more interested in the history of the Jews and collected books on the subject. The great families of Rothschild and Duveen are part of the background to his fiction. Having created Charlie Mortdecai a Jewish hero or anti-hero for his first novel, he then invented an ancestor for him: Karli Van Cleef, a Dutch Jew, the protagonist in *All the Tea in China*. His main projected novels would have fleshed out this family background and traced out branches of the fictional family tree. (See SILVER-HAND and UNFINISHED WORK.)

He greatly valued staunch Jewish friends from his Oxford days, such as the financial journalist Anthony Harris, Professor David Goldberg and Thomas Braun, Fellow of Merton; he was also conscious that both his publisher Tom Rosenthal and his literary agent Hilary Rubinstein, who laughed with him, drank with him and also showed him great patience and practical generosity, were both Jewish.

Tom Rosenthal says, 'I always assumed he was a Jew.' Maggie Noach, the literary agent, says she took it for granted he was Jewish.

There are literary precedents for choosing a Jew as a vehicle for universal human experience as the persecuted and wanderers on the face of the earth. James Joyce, an Irish exile living in Trieste – that city of territorial dispute and home to Emmanuel Bonfiglioli for part of his life – makes Bloom, a Dublin Jew, his Ulysses. There is a Jewish visionary called Mortdecai in George Eliot's *Daniel Deronda* and further back still there is a haunting appearance of the Wandering Jew in search of death in Chaucer's 'Pardoner's Tale', which Bon knew well.

Strangely it came to me with great certainty that they were all recalling that I was a Jew. They knew just how Peter Stevenage would behave in such a case but they could not guess how a Jew would comport himself. This helped me.   – *All the Tea in China*, p. 175

Hatred of Jews is a sin in Bon's analysis; he listed it in his folder in the Seven Deadly Sins under *ira* and connected it with *invidia*. He did not think such hatred derived

from the practice of usury or jealousy of Jewish success but because they, by their terrible Old Testament which should only be read, really, as background matter for the New Testament – to show us what Christ, Xtianity was up against – have saddled us Scandinavians, Latins and Teutons with the frightful burden of Mosaic morality and Levitical Law suitable for desert nomads but utterly wrong for us. That is why we persecute not only Jews but other Christians, why sects and heresies multiply, why hordes have been slaughtered in the name of gentle Jesus meek and mild.

Bon told Jewish jokes but liked best to hear them told by Jews. The following dialogue is a variant of one told by Bon's father:

Hymie sees Abe crossing himself with extravagantly large gestures.

Hymie: Vot you doing, vot you doing? you're not a Catholic already!

Abe: Just checking: spectacles, testicles, vallet and vatch.

He owned a copy of Josephus in the last phase of his life and Karli from time to time remembers that he is supposed to be reading it. Bon had certainly intended to include more of the history of twentieth-century Jewry in projected novels and went to considerable trouble in correspondence with Ian Lowe, his Ashmolean friend, to try to obtain information on the Jewish cemetery in Prague with which to flesh out research on the Golem.★

Jock

Johanna went to bed; kissing me but not fondly.

Jock was up brewing 'Sergeant Major's' which is the sort of tea you used to relish when coming off guard duty in a January dawn; it is the cheapest Indian tea boiled up with sugar and condensed milk. It is not at all like tea as you and I know it but it is very good indeed. I gazed at it longingly.   – *Something Nasty in the Woodshed*, p. 143

Was there a 'real' Jock? He is Bon's best-loved character and this question matters to readers. 'Lord knows who he knew in the army' is a close friend's response. Turning over a group photograph of the Royal West African Frontier Force taken in Freetown, Sierra Leone, during Bon's military service there, I find 'Jock' is among the other names pencilled in on the back, identifying a rather good-looking square-jawed man of middle height standing in the back row with a resolutely straight face. Before the Americans introduced the full toothy smile to formal group photographs, this would be the norm for a group of soldiers; however two or three soldiers in the group are twitching amiably at the mouth.

The literary antecedents to Jock, 'thug and anti-Jeeves', are legion and go back to Gilgamesh and Enkidu, Achilles and Patroclus. Cervantes with Don Quixote and Sancho Panza

---

★ In Jewish folklore, the *golem* is a human image fashioned from clay and brought to life by magic. Legend has it that the *golem* is animated by God and sent to help them in times of great need.

developed the modern ironic possibilities of two men with contrasting views of life sustaining one another through adventures dire and ridiculous, with happy reunions and near-death experiences . . . Bon had certainly read *Don Quixote* more than once, as well as rereading and collecting P. G. Wodehouse's books. These were an obvious key source, giving readers the pleasures of recognition spiced with irony. Morse and Lewis belong in the same bag.

Further developments of Jock's character that occur in *After You with the Pistol* were received with delight by John Blackwell at Secker & Warburg: 'I infuriated the other denizens of this incomplete building by locking my door the minute the MS arrived, and emitting squeals of glee at unpredictable intervals. What a perceptive bugger the irreplaceable Jock can be, to be sure, when he grows vocal.'

The Great Mortdecai Moustache Mystery opens with Jock's words advising Mortdecai against a certain project. His indispensability is made clear for new readers on the first page:

Perhaps I should explain that I have a fully comprehensive Accident Protection Policy which guarantees that if anyone even looks as though he's going to be horrid to me he will be cured of all known diseases. Permanently. The Policy's name is Jock.

Jock, in short, is my large, dangerous, one-fanged, one-eyed thug: we art dealers need to keep a thug, you understand, although it isn't always easy to persuade HM's Commissioners for Inland Revenue that it's a necessary expense. Jock is the best thug that money can buy; he's quality all through, slice him where you will. When I decided to conserve my energy-resources – who'd want to become fossil-fuel? – and gave up art dealing in favour of matrimony I tried to pay him off but he just sort of stayed on and took to calling himself a manservant. He is not quite sane and never quite sober but he can still pop out seven streetlights with nine shots from his old Luger while ramming his monstrous motor-bike through heavy after-theatre traffic. I've seen him do it. As a matter of fact, I was on the pillion seat at the time, whispering promises to God that if He got me home safely I would never tell another lie. God kept His part of the deal, but God isn't an art dealer, is He? (Don't answer that.)

Jokes

'Then call me a cab!'

'Awright, Mr Charlie: you're a taxi.'

'How d'you mean?'

'Well, I couldn't hardly call you 'ansom with that bleeding moustache, could I?' With that he started to stagger about the room, helpless with guffaws and cannoning into pieces of fragile furniture as antique as his jest. — *The Great Mortdecai Moustache Mystery*, p. 46

Telling jokes was an evening's entertainment in Bon's circles in the fifties and sixties. Simple shaggy-dog stories had peaked and required elaboration and Spooneristic endings. Bon credited his sister Inez with winning a prize from the *Beano* for creating narrative and scenery for a little creature from a raree show to cry as he fell, 'It's a long way to tip a raree.' Oxford produced the tourist story advising against getting all your Basques in one exit. There were more Basques about then.

Bon's most retold and original contribution to the genre was spontaneous. He was carrying two glasses of whisky through a crowded pub, pushing between a fine pair of bosomy women. Some of the drink slopped over and he cried, 'A Haig on both your blouses!' There are those who believe that the opportunity for this quip was set up more than once.

He was good at accents and had a repertoire of Scottish stories centring on a questioning character called Hamish. There were also three Welsh stories, one of which may be found under YARNS.

Considerable analysis of the circumstances of joke-telling fills a folder marked LAUGHTER BOOK (which also includes a lot of page numbers from Montaigne).

See also HIDDEN JOKES.

Junk In some people's view our house was full of junk. Even the not-so-ancient Rolls standing in the drive at Norham Gardens prompted someone to complain to the council. As becomes ever more evident last year's junk is this year's collectable. The Smith brothers of Thame told Bon that the Duke of Marlborough had given them the job of smashing up his pre-war cars for scrap; Lord

Montague of Beaulieu had not yet formed his collection. Seeing what is about to become saleable and spotting the non-junk in the junk shop is part of the art of buying and the foundation of a dealer's success. Bon did not always get the timing right. He acquired an enormous collection of photographs (which might since have become saleable, but where are they?) – he saw it as foundation material for an imaginary thesis called 'The Semiotics of Irish Provincial Photography'.

King of the Boeotians

I was attractive before I died.   – Offenbach's Orpheus

So John Styx, late King of the Boeotians, sings dolefully, explaining that he who now is the gaoler of souls in hell was once King of the Boeotians, famed through the ancient world for their dullness of intellect. Bon simply loved a record of Offenbach's *Orpheus in the Underworld* and especially the wonderfully lugubrious baritone part, the King of the Boeotians, with whom he identified. Anthony and Alison Harris had fought our prejudices against opera and dragged us to the Sadler's Wells production playing in Oxford in 1960.

Bon came home singing. I have many times played the remains of the tape Bon made from the record. It speaks to me so strongly of Bon and his identification with stupidity.

Kipling

In our trade we be all felons more or less.   – Rudyard Kipling

Kipling whose missing letters to P. G. Wodehouse would have been the find of the century for a Bonfig, Kipling who coined the expression 'It' to signify sex-appeal, Kipling who invented the Janeites, Kipling who was almost completely out of fashion at the time when Bon was a devoted reader of his works – how can I write an adequate note on Bon's involvement with Kipling?

He owned more than one set of the works, bound in red cloth with illustrations by Kipling's father, John Lockwood Kipling.

A Kipling Companion was a project for which he was collecting materials in a folder with that title. He had written notes on the story 'The Big Drunk Draf', of special interest to him because of its army background and his interest in Kipling's use of characters with Irish accents, like the soldier Mulvaney. It is a story of the making of a man and a soldier. Bon remarks, 'It is not hard to see why some people resented Kipling's "side" at this time: a 23-year-old reporter should not speak quite so wisely about how 19-year-old subalterns can be turned into leaders of men. But we were all 23 years old once. Indeed most of us were once 19.' At nineteen Bon was a soldier in the Royal West African Frontier Force (see ARMY and WEST AFRICA) and at twenty-three married with one son and in the army in Scotland. He too was certainly resented for 'side'.

There are detailed annotations of several other stories. Two Bon-typed copies of 'Proofs of Holy Writ', the Kipling story that has Ben Jonson and Shakespeare in friendly argument about their life and works, exist. Shakespeare is unabashed by complaint that he stole most of his plots from others and reveals his contributions to the Bible in English. Bon, defending Shakespeare's knowledge against critics of *The Winter's Tale*, adds a signed footnote: 'Yet Bohemia *did* have a sea coast in the 16th Century: in Venezia Giulia.'

Brian Clark, who has dramatized a life of Kipling, suggests that his interest for modern readers may be 'part of a wide-spread public rumination about identity, a continuing effort to knit together past and present free of embarrassment and polemics, and to understand exactly what being British means nowadays'. This describes for me one of the many aspects of Kipling's work, apart from his sheer brilliance and subtlety as a writer, which chimed with Bon's scepticism about the British Empire. In common with Kipling he had endured a damaging childhood and had a sense of multiple identity.

In his *Science Fantasy* editorial on p. 235, Bon discusses Kipling as a writer.

♌

Landsman at sea Anthony Harris, who had a boat and enjoyed sailing himself, says that Bon hated and feared the sea. When he arrived in Jersey in his boat Bon was not at all keen to come aboard. A great deal of the fun and the fears in *All the Tea in China* come from personal experience combined with well-researched historical detail.

Lord Peter Stevenage roared with laughter as he saw Orace staggering up the gangplank that afternoon; the child was so heavily burdened that I was having to push from behind to keep him upright. Had I not so recently become an English gentleman I believe I would have carried some of the parcels myself.

'You luxurious bugger!' cried Peter merrily, 'is this the last of your stores? Your dunnage has been streaming aboard all day, quite altered the ship's trim, burst me if it hasn't! Come to the cabin if that child can still walk, and let's overhaul this gear of yours.'

He seemed taken aback at my choice of clothing and, since he was now free of the watch, offered to take me to a ship-chandler's slop-shop. There were many such places within a stone's throw of the docks but Peter led me unerringly to one where, he said, the proprietor was too intelligent to rob one more than was reasonable.

He made me buy two suits of oilskins, two pairs of sea-boots and some huge slabs of smelly, greasy wool which he said would prove, when unfolded, to be warm underclothing. I protested that my duties were to be mercantile rather than maritime and that I had no intention of scrambling up and down masts and riggings in the wind and weather-oh – why then should I need such things?

He looked at me strangely.

'Well,' he said, 'you never know. It might come on to rain or something, d'you see.'

If the wind in the English channel veers far enough to the west you may be sure that it will back again just so soon as the barometer rises. The Second Mate told me this while I nodded sagely, for, clearly, it meant something. What happened in the event was that the rain stopped the

next day, the wind changed from the SW to the S and then to the SSE
and soon we were battering our way down-Channel close-hauled on the
larboard tack, the sails booming and rigging screaming and sheets of spray
knifing across the deck. It seemed a frightful storm to me, a very act of
God; I did not want to drown like a rat in my cabin, I fled out. From the
Second's cabin, next door, came a noise of snoring – should I rouse him
and give him time to make his peace with his Maker? The crash of a sea
hitting our side made me selfish: I rushed on deck, looking wildly about
me, threaded my way between thinly-clad sailors who, all oblivious of
our peril, were heaving at various ropes, chanting strange words as they
stamped the deck with their bare feet; and after many a drenching with
spray fetched up in the shelter of the galley. Inside the doctor was fisting
out great lumps of salt pork from a keg and roughly slicing them into a
pan full of frying onions. He was braced against the side or bulwark of
his galley and deftly tilting the pan each time it threatened to spill over,
singing a deep-voiced and barbarous song.

The snack given him by the doctor is twitched from his fingers by
Peter, who proceeds to tease the naive landsman Karli:

I fumbled in my tin box for a Thin Captain's biscuit to gnaw while I
asked him whether our frail barque would survive the dreadful tempest.
He spluttered a little: I believe that, had his mouth not been full of hot
bread crammed with fried onion and delicious pork gravy, he would
have laughed.

'I think,' he said gravely, having swallowed the last exquisite morsel
and pulled on a fresh pair of drawers, 'I *think* that we have ridden out this
particular Act of God. Indeed, for some twenty or thirty hours we may
have little more than a fresh wind until we sight Ushant.'

'Ushant?' I quavered. 'What is that? I supposed that we were bound
for the Indies and the China Coast. Why are we going to this Ushant?'

'We are not going there, Karli, we are looking for it. So soon as we
see it we shall know where we are and shall leave it, God willing, on our
port quarter. It is merely a headland which we must weather, d'you see.'

'Ah,' I said in an intelligent way.

'After Ushant we shall drive sou'west across the skirts of the Bay, of
course.'

'Of course, Peter. This Bay is . . . ?'

'Biscay,' he said solemnly. 'Biscay. The weather there is often calm, mild and a joy to sailors.'

'Capital!' I cried.

'But never at this time of year,' he went on. 'At just this season the seas are as high as mountains, the winds seem the bitter enemies of man and many a tall ship has sunk without a trace, dragging all hands down with her to Davy Jones's Locker.'

'But, surely . . .' I began.

'Yes, surely, our little ship is well found, well officered and well manned: we shall probably cross Biscay with the loss of but a few of us – and we can replace the spars which will be carried away with a few weeks of labour.'

'I see,' I said nonchalantly, fumbling in the tin box for another Thin Captain's. My voice was perfectly steady.

'That is, of course, unless we fall in with the Portuguese sardinha-fishers,' he said.

'And what might they be?' I asked, my voice still steady. He lowered his voice, leaned towards me, his eyes wide.

'*Fiends incarnate!*' he whispered.

'Promise me, Karli, that you will put a bullet in my head rather than let me fall into the hands of those fiends!'

'I promise,' I quavered, a fragment of Thin Captain's falling from my nerveless lips. He burst into laughter and staggered about the floor, incapacitated by mirth. Slowly I realized that this had been an English joke. I retrieved the piece of biscuit and munched it sternly. When Peter had recovered he saw my expression and was at once contrite, for he had a kindly nature, except in dealings with his own heart and health.

'Forgive me, Karli,' he cried, 'we sailors reckon that we have a right to tweak the tails of landsmen: It helps us to endure our hardships, don't you see, and it helps you to come to terms with the sea.'

– All the Tea in China, pp. 86, 99–101

Laughter

He's a lovely laugher and that ranks him high in my rating.

– letter to the Goldbergs, 30 August 1981

(Can you chortle, by the way? I can giggle and snigger but chortling and chuckling are quite out of my range. It's a dying art. Some modern Cecil Sharp should go round recording the last few practitioners.)

— *Something Nasty in the Woodshed*, p. 426

This brief digression in the novel is prompted by an academic who chortles while taking a cool view of rape and religion.

One of his folders shows that Bon was planning a book on laughter, and he wrote to David Goldberg proposing that they collaborate on it:

Look, I have what seems to me a lucrative notion which costs nothing but the time in small doses. You must have noticed that books about humans are bestsellers these days; they outsell fiction enormously. I mean books like *The Naked Ape, The Human Zoo, The Ape's Reflection,* &c.

What I have in mind is a popular/scientific book about laughing. I have a file full of questions and some answers on the subject and the more I consider it the more interesting it seems.

Like, is laughter innated in the precise sense of the word? What makes babies laugh or cry? Why are so many professional comedians self-destructive — impossible marriages, booze, giving all their money away and dying in poverty or simply doing a suicide? Why are the verbal jokes good when told to an audience, goodish when told to 3 or 4 people, poor when told to one listener and quite dud when written down? On the other side of the coin why are some passages in a book capable of making you roll about helplessly — but when retold flat? Why do kids go through a period of compulsive joke telling? Why do women not tell jokes or, if they do, make their faces writhe hideously — and tell dirtier jokes than a man would in mixed company? Where do jokes come from? The only funnies which can be precisely attributed are puns: we do not laugh at them, we wince and say 'oww'. Where lies the boundary between wit and moria? Is the Wildean epigrammatist simply an intelligent moria-patient? Why are some subjects forbidden — incest, cancer, menstruation? Why, in Catholic countries can you make jokes about priests, Jesus and God but must never bring the Virgin Mary into play? There are dozens of questions.

I think the whole thing needs looking into; more to the point I think you and I could make a nice piece of money. I see it just now in the form of a dialogue between you and me and the logistics could be arranged to give you minimum trouble: I'd post you a set of paragraphs, you send me back – on tape if you like – your remarks, refutations, castigations. I'm thinking in terms of years desultory to-and-froing and, say, three personal confrontations. Look, I'm not talking about pie-in-the-sky: I'm sure my agent would handle it (his name is Rubinstein, he can't be all bad) and we could sell it on the strength of a sample chapter and synopsis.

Think about it, do. (You would of course have the final say on any aspect of the thing which would militate against you professionally.)

Lies

Bon's perennial preoccupation.
Why I was puzzled was because Johanna was using the warm, true, real voice which she only uses when she is lying. Which isn't often, naturally; with all those looks and all that money why should she bother.

– Something Nasty in the Woodshed, p. 412

See GHOST TRAIN.

Luger In the fiction it is Jock who has the Luger, in Lancashire it was Bon. One night he came into the room demanding the bullets for the Luger. Judith Todd, whose house it was, said she really couldn't tell one bullet from another, but any she'd found lying around she'd have put in the ashtray and please if he was going to shoot himself could it be in the lobby, not the drawing room – think of the mess – she for her part was going to bed. Bon's theory of how to deal with a potential suicide was to offer to fetch the rope – it always puts them off.

Marriages

Married again and again; one died; one I deserted; one threw me out. You can't really want to know their names even if I could remember.

– Bon's author's questionnaire for Pantheon Books, 1977

On 16 June 1950 he married Elizabeth Smith in Marylebone

Register Office. She was an assistant nurse at the St Marylebone Hospital. He was twenty-two and she was two years older. They had two sons, Aeneas and Roderick. Elizabeth died in 1953, when Roderick was only a few months old.

On 25 March 1959 he married me, Margaret Slater, in Oxford, and we had three children: Christopher, Catriona and Amanda.

'You married me for insecurity' was a quote from the film *A Suitable Case for Treatment*, which Bon seized on with delight because it explained why I had married him. He also invented a remark to attribute to my mother: 'I always knew you were waiting for Mr Wrong.' His youngest daughter says, 'It was because he was drop-dead gorgeous, wasn't it, Mum?' The impact of his personality on mine was beyond my previous experience. Being married to him was never boring.

We were divorced in 1969.

It is not certain whom he considered to be his third wife, as he did not enter into lawful matrimony again. However, he did fall passionately in love with Judith Todd, with whom he moved to Lancashire in 1970. The breakdown of their relationship was tragic and painful to both of them.

A number of liaisons followed, and he ended his life sharing the home of a Scottish widow about the same age as his first wife would have been by then. I came to know and like her at the time of his funeral and to see that together they had been trying to create some order in his books, his papers and his life.

May

Nothing was new except that it was the First of May, which was Pinch-Bum Day when I was at my dame-school but is now known as Labour Day, when portly, well-paid Trades Union officials persuade lean, ill-paid Trades Union dues-payers to march about the streets saying 'hooray' for excellent reasons of their own. They carry beautiful woven banners each of which would keep a starving docker's wife in Bingo cards for a week. But I digress.

This is the fifth of a sequence of six paragraphs each beginning with the word 'nothing', which opens Chapter 5 of *Something Nasty in the Woodshed*. The whole month of May was tainted for Bon by being his birthday month; each paragraph is laden with cynicism and disappointment with the way things are.

In swapping the facts of conception and birth around between himself and his fictional hero, he gives Charlie a birthday at the end of September (the time of his own conception) and a conception date of Christmas: Charlie, who is generally bitter about his father, says that he was drunk at the time. Every May, Bon found himself entangled in a Gordian knot of feelings with no sword to cut his way out.

In 1958, the year we met, on his thirtieth birthday he read in a cowboy book: 'I was riding into town, thirty years old and I didn't even own a good watch.' He promptly went out and bought himself a watch. (The following year when we were married he bought me my first new watch for my birthday.)

In May 1973 he was cheered by a phone call from the film director Michael Powell, followed up by a birthday postcard expressing a wish to meet and eat:

> Now some eat ham
> And some eat lamb
> And some eat roly-poly
> But I will grab
> A spider crab,
> A Jackson Pollock,
> Skate, or dab,
> With dear Bonfiglioli

In May 1981, at fifty-three – only three years before his death – he dates a letter to Ian Lowe, his old Ashmolean friend, in a thoroughly Bonnish way: '29th of May (Oak Apple day, the anniversary of the fall of Constantinople, and more to the point my birthday!)', reflecting the moody thoughts his birthday always brought him. He goes on: 'I do think a man should be allowed to mope just once a year, don't you?' He recollected from time to time that devastating quote from Sophocles: 'not to have been born is best' and could easily be reduced to a state of maudlin self-pity at Christmas and on his birthday and start counting his cards.

Mayhem An army friend remembers Bon as a high-spirited practical joker with a love of explosions, sometimes nicknamed 'Bomber'. Creating mayhem of one kind or another relieved boredom and depression, producing a kind of painful fun and sometimes explosions and loud noises.

In the fifties he had played tricks allegedly in the interest of providing a young man in the same lodging house with a girlfriend. He would tell the only single woman in the house, a fiery Spaniard, that A was a mass of unacted desires and perversions so that she would pounce on him unexpectedly . . .

As one of the managing directors of Sanders of Oxford, he returned to business after a liquid lunch and disappeared into the basement. He reappeared dressed in a gaudy military uniform playing a mighty euphonium to the astonishment of the antiquarian books manager and a print-buying customer. The euphonium came home and in an attempt to re-create Kay Kendall in a scene from *Genevieve* he plied a stockbroker friend's wife with drink until she was persuaded with much laughter to produce massive farting sounds from the instrument.

At home once, late at night, I found a pale figure in Y-fronts had somehow crept into my bed, sneakily and without waking me. Suddenly, with great commotion the door was flung open and Bon stepped into the room, pistol pointing, shouting at the 'bastard' to 'leave Margaret alone forthwith' or be shot. Dumb creature that I was, or so numbed by a constant diet of the unexpected, I didn't analyse or question this incident but went back to sleep again, relieved to have been 'rescued' from this tiresome friend.

At Yewbarrow, Judith Todd's home in Silverdale, he announced a surprise birthday party for her and (typically), having announced it, he disappeared for the day. Come six o'clockish Judith decided there'd be no supper if she didn't do something, so she put a joint of lamb in the oven and sent Roderick – number two son on holiday from school – to pick raspberries. The first unexpected arrivals were invited to join her and Roderick at the kitchen table. Each time the doorbell rang more people turned up – old friends of her parents, complete strangers, the local butcher – and all were successively ushered into the drawing room. Meantime in the kitchen Roderick had accidentally dropped the bowl, scattering raspberries on to the middle of the kitchen floor.

A loud commotion in the hall was Bon arriving with champagne – not enough for the accumulated guests, not a glass for Judith. Whisky was somehow found, the party proceeded; someone's wife locked herself in the downstairs loo and passed out. Bon challenged people to join him in the kitchen and help him make the world's largest sausage roll; the prototype was to be three yards long and to squelch the idea that there were any good reasons for making lots of niggly little sausage rolls. Back in the drawing room an egg-breaking competition had broken out in the hearth – someone had said a freshly broken egg instantly swallowed was sovereign against drunkenness. Somebody went home for more eggs. Roderick appeared in the doorway to say another lady wasn't feeling too well so he'd layed her out in the bathroom upstairs. The party melted away at about 4 a.m. Coming down next morning Judith found Roderick picking up eggshells.

Maggie Noach, the literary agent, who enjoyed Bon's company enormously in London while consistently refusing all his proposals of marriage, went on a number of amusing outings with him. Here is her story of one of his embarrassment tests:

One time he took me to the theatre to see a play the name of which I've forgotten and it was obviously not very exciting because Bon took out his copy of *The Times* (we were sitting in a box almost above the stage) and he propped the newspaper on the edge of the box and started doing the crossword, which he was very good at doing and very keen on. And at one moment there was a loud noise on the stage and Bon jumped and dropped *The Times*, which fluttered page by page into the auditorium. The actors stopped and stared at us and then he wrote me a wonderful letter about it some time later in which he said, 'Your small tight understanding smile was exact to the last millimetre. Cooking, sex, laundering, childbearing, all these are the common coin of womanhood, but a woman who can remain poised while a *Times* flutters down unfolding itself forty feet on to a rapt theatre audience, that woman is a pearl beyond price.'

Medievalism In the early fifties Bon seems to have been planning an Arthurian Romance.

Six sheets of half-foolscap paper in his hand show his characteristic approach to writing. The germs of scenes of verbal combat lie in a list headed 'Expletives and Abuse'; landscape and local colour would have sprung from the following:

flagged, pollard limes, quicksets, heron's feathers, lightly armed in soft leather, town at knees of castle, wry-necked, scrub of wild plum, slowly dragged a snake's way down his face, colour of a bullfinch's breast, white cloak over armour, drawing of Caernarvon, swart, within draught of bow, the camp-sickness – a crawling galloping disease . . .

A fragment of narrative in typescript suggests the state of mind of a hero setting out on pilgrimage and adventure, and carries a shadow of personal poignancy:

This same uncle and King presently says to him 'Come out of your dream boy; these are old tired matters and the hurts are past mending. Rolaund, Count of Ermonie, is dead and there's an end; Tristrem, the King's nephew of Cornwall, is born today . . .

A dull, plaster-work sky with a smouldering gap in the West where the sunset glowered angrily . . .

There are notes on Caerleon as Arthur's court, on Ermonie, on Pilgrim Badges and an attempt to list the objects that would identify seven English Saints in sculpture or church window. Another page lists names for knights and ladies, giving seven variants on the name Yseult.

The paper and hand suggest that this belongs to the time when he was recently widowed and aiming to get into university. Colonel W. J. F. Craig, one of his army referees, mentions having read his 'romances': perhaps this is a fragment of one. The genre inspired no further writing, but from time to time Bon offered to kill dragons for people.

After completing his degree in English, Bon's ambition was scholarly research in medieval iconography. To this end he had collected and classified images from many sources, taken his own photographs of carvings and stained glass in churches and owned Mrs Jameson's illustrated classic on Christian iconography, *Sacred and Legendary Art*. Lack of means frustrated him, however. A mature state studentship had financed his first degree; aged thirty, he discovered that state funding for postgraduate degrees was not then available to people over twenty-five.

A photograph from Bon's research collection

Medicines

To this day I never travel without a cake of such soap; it is as sovereign as Dr Collis Browne's noted Chlorodyne, which is saving so many cholera-stricken soldiers in the Transvaal today.

— *All the Tea in China*, p. 124

Just as Bon sought diagnosis, so he sought medicines to stop him feeling bad.

Still available in the sixties without prescription, Dr Collis Browne's chlorodyne was widely thought to contain opium; Bon favoured a slug of it while shaving in the late morning. Kaolin and Morphine was a normal stomach settler for all ages. A rather dodgy non-practising doctor, not otherwise a friend, used to call on Bon occasionally to provide repeat prescriptions for various 'uppers and downers' to help Bon cope with a life externally and internally stressful. In Ireland he was prescribed Ritalin. But laughter and good company were always the best medicine.

See also HEALTH.

Memory

> 'Nice to see you Mr Charlie,' he growled.
>
> 'And it's nice to see your honest face, Jock; as refreshing as a glass of cool water.'
>
> 'You got a bloody lovely memory, Mr Charlie.'
>
> 'Eh?'
>
> 'I mean fancy you remembering what cold water tastes like.' And he unleashed the grin again. – *The Great Mortdecai Moustache Mystery*, p. 170

Bon could almost rely on being complimented on his excellent memory, but here Jock undercuts Charlie's pleasure. A little joke, a little warning from Bon to himself.

> All the time Lord Peter was pouring facts and measurements into my ears; I coiled them away into my memory like a jolly jack-tar stowing an anchor cable. – *All the Tea in China*, p. 88

There is no doubt that Bon's memory for both the visual and the verbal was strong, had perhaps even been eidetic. It was an aspect of himself that he took for granted. Constant use of quotation in his writing is not showing off so much as a desire to share the overflowing richness of memory. Somewhere out there he is hoping for a reader who will recognize the original quotation *and* enjoy his modification of it.

When I last spent time with him there were curious signs of slippage in his short-term memory as well as paranoia. He would tell me something and then, as I replied, an expression of intense alarm would come into his face and he would say, 'Who told you that?' in an accusing voice. When I said, 'You did,' he would calm down for a little until the same disturbing pattern repeated itself.

Mentors Three younger men regarded Bon as a significant mentor in his Turl Gallery days. It was a role that he took seriously himself and that brought out a gift for teaching noted by his army referees but that he could not easily exercise with his own sons without causing distress.

Richard Booth still speaks of him with enthusiasm as someone who changed his life and inspired his remarkable career as the man who made Hay-on-Wye a book town. Richard describes himself then as a naive and inexperienced young man coming to Oxford from a very sheltered background: 'I needed another fantastic reality.' This alternative reality – so different from the accountancy firm Richard entered – seems sometimes to have been connected with Bon being 'a sensational drunk' but also with his 'unbelievable talent in things like pictures' and 'his being a kind of refugee from Oxford who knew about Indian restaurants'. Richard first encountered Bon in his Little Clarendon Street shop, led there by a friend, Hugo Vicars, to see a wonderful watercolour by the nineteenth-century landscape painter David Cox. Richard rapidly became a good customer and also worked with Bon sorting a massive book purchase. Richard felt confident that Bon's 'superior taste' would ensure that money paid for a watercolour would be well spent. He paid £100 for the David Cox and sold it at a considerable profit to Jeremy Maas in Bond Street.

Richard's first coup as a novice bookseller came from selling a bee-keeping library that came to him through Bon.

Andrew Skirving, who became managing director of a sister gallery, Bonfiglioli Nottingham, learned much picture lore from him but rapidly became independent.

The Hon. Christopher Lennox-Boyd, who got to know Bon while still an undergraduate at Christ Church, moved from being an escapee from his background to a place where his quirky humour, his sophisticated knowledge and his love of children and comics could find a home. He is now a distinguished collector and has developed his specialist knowledge.

For writers Christopher Priest, Keith Roberts and Grahame Hall, Bon was briefly a mentor. As fellow writers Priest and Bonfiglioli renewed their relationship through letters in the late seventies. 'Avuncular' is Priest's word for their relationship.

Who Bon would consider his mentor I can only guess. I remember him speaking of Ridley Lewis, who taught him Latin after he had left school. At Balliol, the Master Christopher Hill, Ted Gang, Russell Meiggs, John Bryson and the librarian Vincent Quin were all men he admired greatly. Reg Alton, Bursar of St Edmund Hall, with his acute eye for a picture and his gift for reading signatures, and the architectural historian Howard Colvin were valued as much as consultants as picture buyers.

Misogyny

Bon's contempt for women was very deep but I think he depended on his ability to charm them.   – Margaret Parsons

Odi et am. Excrucior. – I hate her, I love her. It hurts.
                    – Catullus, quoted in *All the Tea in China*, p. 119

'See, Blanche,' I said, pointing at the sky, 'a kite or vulture!'
'They call it an *aasvogel* here,' she replied, smiling. I was not pleased with her. From women one wishes loyalty, not information.
                              – *All the Tea in China*, p. 226

Calling Bon a misogynist provides no adequate description of his relations with women. Soon after I'd met him, he took me for a drink at Balliol buttery and introduced me to an ex-officer straight out of the army, a man he seemed to admire. I was simply staggered by the bad manners of their conversation and the range of words referring to women as commodities. It was a mode I had not met before and I had no concept of what might now be called institutional misogyny.

Sometimes Bon's actions and words to women went so far beyond normal bad manners as to embarrass his men friends. He seemed to want to behave unacceptably *and* want to be accepted.

One could easily find in current and admired writing a kind of taken-for-granted misogyny that I find pathological although it does conform to some kind of norm.

In Bon's writing there are traces of a stronger and more personal hostility, particularly towards mothers.

He liked women to be sexy, witty, intelligent and beautiful, and celebrates these and other qualities in Johanna, Charlie's wife – she is, for instance, seriously rich.

Knowledge or qualifications in a woman alarmed him or disturbed some category or made him insecure. He took a vicious dislike to my elderly, distinguished woman doctor, which I could never fathom. Yet I could name two older women dons he loved, admired and joked with.

Women provoked him into behaviour he could not admire in himself. The ultimate betrayal was to die on him like his first wife and his mother. A woman's place was in the wrong if he could contrive it. Bon would have liked not to need women.

I had thought of calling this piece 'DOWN WITH WOMEN – UP WITH MEN' but I showed the title to a woman friend and she squealed, 'Oh sooooper, you podgy darling, I thought you would never get round to thinking about me like that . . .' so I scrubbed it out. (Sooner or later every woman I know goes to Italy and sends me a ribald postcard from a place called Poggibonsi – pronounced 'Podgy Bonzy'. I've become used to it but I don't have to like it, do I.   – from Bon's papers

Money

. . . the same principle ensures that you cannot borrow money from a bank unless you don't need any.

> – *Don't Point that Thing at Me*, p. 126
> (a variation on a remark attributed to Bob Hope)

It is an exquisite irony that Bon is quoted in several modern anthologies on the subject of money, the thing he was least good at. Kevin Jackson included a passage by Bon about money laundering for his edition of the *Oxford Book of Money*.

Olive Bevan, who worked in Bon's Oxford galleries as his secretary, found it so difficult to get him to sign cheques for purchases from small dealers, who left unpaid would soon cease to bring in useful replenishments to stock, that she adopted the habit of converting cash from the till into postal orders and using them to pay the bills. She also remembers Bon ringing up every day to know if the Tintoretto cheque had come in yet. On the whole he didn't think the bank was the right place to keep money. Somewhere he comments on a rich man ringing the bank every day to find out how rich he is; in Bon's case it was to find out which debts he could pay.

Writing to his elder daughter in 1981, he says:

Pay the whole term's rent and other fixed things in advance. Join one of the banks which offers a no-charge service to undergraduates and keep your account in credit: a good record at your bank will be a great help in future years, whereas a lousy one will stick to you all your life and damage your chances of getting an overdraft, mortgage or whatever when you really need it. End of paternal sermon.

Impeccable advice from a father to his nineteen-year-old daughter, written at a time when Bon had been running a continuous 'sanctioned overdraft' on his account in Ireland starting at £300 in November 1980 and rising in September 1981 to £500.

Bon's army service was the only time when he had a reliable regular income; any capital sums he ever acquired were already committed to debts. As a widower with a grant to study at Balliol, he received an allowance for his two children that was so pitifully small that his tutor and others wrote letters on his behalf to have it increased. When we married we had my state studentship and his skills as a dealer to rely on.

See FINDS.

From May 1962 the big house in Norham Gardens provided a roof and an income from lodgers that kept us fed and clothed and provided me with a way of life after he left. Buying the last years of its 99-year lease had given us the advantages of spacious high-ceilinged rooms, but this was based on a gamble that the Leasehold Reform Act would put us in an advantageous position for buying the freehold. This was a gamble that did not come off. When the Leasehold Reform Act was finally passed, it included a clause, argued strongly for by ducal London property owners, that set a ceiling on the value of the houses it would apply to. Our house was above this level. Bon's departure for Silverdale in Lancashire and embarking on his career as a writer coincided with his becoming liable for a huge sum for dilapidations, so that half to one third of any subsequent earnings from books went directly from his agent A. P. Watt to Freshfield's solicitors acting for St John's College. I now know that Hilary Rubinstein expended considerable energy and eloquence in trying to modify this dispiriting burden for Bon. His never-ending financial difficulties were well understood by Tom Rosenthal, who arranged that money due to him would be paid in the form of a monthly allowance in the years 1978 and 1979 to give him something to live on while he completed his contract for Secker's. It is hardly surprising that only the first three maintenance payments awarded for the children by the divorce court at £58.68 per month were ever paid, something about which I felt bitter for many years. But the break-up of our marriage left Bon with the dilapidations to pay for and me with the house as an income-provider for the next eighteen years.

The only capital he had for his art dealing was his talent and expertise; even the Tintoretto money was already committed by the time he received it.

In January 1983 he wrote to Hilary Rubinstein thanking him for a cheque from the actor John McEnery: 'You, I am sure, must fret from time to time at the problem of scraping up an extra thousand for school fees; try to visualize the misery of scraping up (I am not exaggerating) the price of a packet of gaspers PLUS a postage stamp. If I were a religious man I'd say a prayer tonight for McEnery. I can pay my newsagent!'

In January 1984 McEnery renewed his option for film rights (for *Something Nasty in the Woodshed*) with another cheque, which drew the comment that it 'came most timely at a moment of sheer panic'.

Bon was remarkably successful at living on credit and even conveying the impression that he was rich or used to being rich. He sometimes and without irony expressed the belief that rich people were simply nicer.

I am amazed at the power of fiction or the naivety of readers when people ask me about Bon with complete confidence that he was a rich high-living connoisseur who spent most of his time toddling about St James's and certainly not one who had earned his living.

Mother

Motherless – a journalist's word for drunk.

– from Bon's word notes

'Oedipus-shmoedipus! What does it matter so long as he loves his mother?' – Jewish mother's exclamation after the psychiatrist has explained a certain complex to her.   – Bon's Jewish joke bag

Dorothy Annie Pallett was born in 1900. She seems to have learned to drive early if she was Emmanuel Bonfiglioli's military driver in or shortly after the First World War. This suggests a background affluent enough to have owned a car in an era when few people of either sex could drive. She married a man fourteen years older than herself and in 1926 gave birth to their first child, Inez. Cyril was born in 1928 at No. 57 Dudley Road, Eastbourne – his birth certificate gives his father's profession as natural-history bookseller.

Five years later, on 26 June, their third child, Christopher John Audubon, was born. His birth was not registered until 3 August. The family seem to have been in financial difficulties.

Many mothers in that pre-Spock era followed the guru of infant care Dr Truby King, whose extraordinary book is hot with fear and jealousy of the newborn intruder who is to be dominated as fast as possible. The mother must not weaken or respond to the baby's cry or the fullness of her breasts. The clock, not hunger or crying, dictates the action; above all there is to be no picking up, no feeding on demand. In the forties these instructions were frequently followed to the letter, even with a sense of pain and sacrifice considered worth while in the cause of good mothering. I cannot claim to know whether this had any bearing on Bon's feelings about his mother, saying as he did more than once: 'She hated me.' There is no evidence that this was the case. It is certainly true that demand feeding was something he was ever in search of in daily life (if daily is the right word for such a night feeder). Jock, of the Mortdecai novels, is the great provider of food on demand and often brings it instinctively and unasked at exactly the right moment for the young master.

Gerald Denley, a schoolfriend, remembers Bon's mother on a visit to Hitchin as 'a very good-looking woman, elegant, well-dressed – very English, always very smart, especially for wartime'. A small photograph shows her smiling in a hat at a dashing angle. These are the inadequate clues as to what she was like. Only Bon has added to this limited picture, with the wartime detail of his mother's irritation at not being allowed to own a bicycle because of being married to an 'enemy alien' (although I think his father was by then a British subject).

'Such a mother as I have!' I cried with real affection, clasping her in my arms so far as the fatness of her little body permitted.

So Karli writes of his warm, practical alternative mother in *All the Tea in China* (p. 12). She is the provider of chicken soup and chastisement, shrewdly knowledgeable about Delft china, porcelains and bargaining. She provides him with the necessary funding and advice to set up in business when he reaches London. She provides comfort and realism:

. . . my mother thrust a soft bundle inside my coat . . . 'It is the blanket your grandmother wove before you were born. You well know you have never been able to sleep without it. People you don't need, not even me after the milk in my breasts dried. I understand you, my son; I looked into your eyes ten minutes after you came out of my belly. You will never understand yourself, thank God. Take the blanket and run.'

Karli, putting away childish things, leaves the blanket for the little dog who has befriended him across the channel. But later in the novel we find him experiencing an extremity of seasickness and fear:

'I no longer cared. A fear formed in my right eye; the room was smoky from the slush-lamp. I wiped it away with a corner of the blanket. I began to think of my mother, God knows why, and found that I needed the corner of the blanket again.' Peter his messmate brings cheering food and ignores the tears; repressed and heavily understated emotions end the chapter.   – *All the Tea in China*, p. 102

Bon had a tender concern that his children should have soft blankets and be cosily but firmly wrapped as babies, so that they should not be startled and wake suddenly.

    See also CHILDHOOD.

Motherhood An awareness of the sufferings of mothers is a notice-able strand in Bon's writing that sits a little oddly among the machismo and occasional misogyny. There is a kind of ferocious bitterness to it in the story fragment 'Freddie', more gentleness and empathy in 'Blast Off', where Christ's mother is the subject of reflection, and again in 'As Simple as That'. I remember Bon telling me how moved, baffled and astonished he was when Elizabeth (his first wife) only just after the ordeal of childbirth said with radiant face 'When can we have another?' To have his first two children lose their mother at an even earlier stage of life than he had lost his own and without the accidents of war was bitter indeed.

Music Bon loved Purcell, Handel, Haydn, Bach and above all Mozart's clarinet concerto. I remember him playing the music for Queen Mary's funeral and *Pavane pour une infante défunte*. He also loved jazz and folk songs, Bessie Smith's singing, Acker Bilke's 'Stranger on the Shore' and in Ireland collected 'wallpaper' music from the radio to while away long hours alone as well as taping Haydn's *Salve Regina* and Bach's *Magnificat*. Charlie plays Amelita Galli-Curci singing 'Una voce poco fa'.

    At one time Bon thought he didn't like opera, but Offenbach's *Orpheus* was an exception and a much played tape of *The Marriage of Figaro* was among his last possessions.

    Bon loved to attempt any musical instrument and, according to a Jersey hostess, ruined a cocktail party by wandering about making noises ranging from the obscene to the musical by blowing down the spout of a tea-pot.

Mustard

We dined in the hotel, which spares me the trouble of saying how good the dinner was. The waiter, who to my certain knowledge has been there since 1938, murmured into my ear that he could recommend the mustard: a statement that has never failed to charm me. Indeed those were the very words spoken by that very waiter, which first opened my eyes on the enchanted landscape of gastronomy, long, long ago. (Few men and almost no women understand about mustard, you must have noticed that. They think that mustard-powder and water mixed five minutes before dinner makes a condiment; you and I know that this is merely a poultice for sore feet.)   – *After You with the Pistol*, p. 208

Is there an allusion to a Bateman cartoon here? Yes, he was fussy about mustard and his main contribution to a dinner party was to try to remember to mix the mustard himself at least half an hour before guests arrived. He would certainly have rejoiced in the range of mustards now commonly available.

𝔑

Names At school he had to fight a boy in the latrines every day for calling him a 'wop', and when Aeneas went to school, Bon warned him he might have to fight on account of his name and taught him some elementary fisticuffs.

It was only in 1958, at the age of thirty, that for the first time in his life his own name became an asset and not a disadvantage, when he set up as an art dealer in Oxford as Bonfiglioli Limited. An early customer, writing Bonfiglioli Limited on a cheque, was astonished to find it was his name: 'I thought it meant Fine Arts,' she said.

In practice everyone called him Bon. At school he was known as Cyril (or George, to one schoolfriend Peter Bowyer) or by his surname. He entered Balliol as Cyril but shifted to Kyril, which became his official name for the rest of his life. He reflects on the subject of authors' names here:

Authors themselves change or manipulate their own names apart from nom-de-pluming; Joseph Kipling, William Maugham, George Shaw, Thomas Eliot, Robert Stevenson, Neil Norway, Herbert Wells – some of these metamorphoses may be like those of the butterfly: no schoolfellows can make fun of James Chase – and if he joins one of the professions he remains James Chase but should he prove 'artistic' – off comes the dull cocoon and the interior 'Hadley' bursts forth – a new image indeed.

Uriah Heep, had it not been pre-empted for 'your very 'umble', might very well serve for a Cromwellian general or a rawboned New Englander but, except through perversity no novelist would have dreamed it up for a ballet-dancer or a Bengal Lancer.

These coded names – Cheeryble, Gradgrind, etc., are no great sin; an innocent device to etch the outline of the character firmly in the reader's mind. Another level a clue in a *roman-à-clef*, a kind of in-joke.

– notes from Bon's Kipling folder

Bon's fictional use of names includes names provocatively borrowed from friends (Blackwell, Braun, Jaggard, Martland, Rosenthal), names that suggest friends' names (for example Dr Farbstein, whose character is a tribute to the real Dr Goldberg), names that are suggestive in a Dickensian way and perhaps more than one anagram (Gloag is an anagram of 'gaol' with an extra *g*).

The naming of his children was of importance to him. Aeneas's and Roderick's naming has been mentioned above and was not without its problems for them (see BROTHERS). Bon and I readily agreed on the names of the next three. Christopher Kyril Owen picks up his father's and my father's first names and was called Christopher at first sight after his godfather, Christopher Fildes, but in fact also after Bon's brother. Catriona Mary Frances's second and third names come from two sides of my family. Soon after her birth Bon met John Bryson in the street and was asked the new baby's name. Bon stammered out that she was called Robert Louis Stevenson. Bryson smiled in perfect comprehension. Catriona is the feisty self-reliant heroine of the novel of that name. The name suits her. Amanda Margaret Alison has my name (also my Irish grandmother's name) and the name of a godmother figure, Alison

Cobb. She was born when the marriage was disintegrating and it was Bon's firm choice to give her the name Amanda to signify that she was to be loved whatever (Amanda means 'lovable' in Latin).

Abusive names and affectionate nicknames are all part of Bon's sense of the emotional and imaginative power of names in life as well as in fiction. These can be seen in the letters too, especially in the endless variations he played on Secker & Warburg.

Noises Much as he liked to create loud noises he also startled easily at unexpected ones. He turned his own voice into a vile noise for a while when he set up an intercom, a friend's cast-off baby-sitting device I think, between the basement kitchen at Norham Gardens and his study so that he could lie in bed and call up a sandwich; he could not hear from his end of it the distorted grating sound it produced. All below stairs agreed it was intolerable and persuaded him to dismantle it before his last shred of reasonableness disappeared or we humble kitchen folk went mad.

Ships, in these nasty nowadays, are made of iron and propelled by coal. This may be a good thing, I cannot say. What I do know is that the ships of those days, real ships, wooden ships, were alive: they manifested their life in a thousand ways which at first irked – sometimes frightened – me, but later became a reassuring cradle-song when I had learned to single out each noise and understand its origin. The gurgle of the running tide past the ship's strakes, the gentle schlipp-schlopping of the wavelets created by a passing vessel, the soft, grinding bump, more felt than heard, of a fender nudging the quay-side and the moan of standing rigging set vibrating by the wind – all these I had heard before, although on a smaller scale, but now there were countless other noises new to me. In particular I recall from that first night the placid straining and grunting of great timbers which had learned to live and work together, the rattle of the gangplank and boom of feet on the deck-planks which told of Johnny-tars rejoining ship at the last moment before midnight, the sudden clangour of the ship's bell marking the watches and once, the squalling scream of the ship's cat locked in a death-struggle with some unhappy rat.

– All the Tea in China, p. 87

See ALKA-SELTZER and MAYHEM.

Norham Gardens

. . . with his Rolls-Royces decaying before his 27-room house in North Oxford – which was once tenanted by a bishop, the bishop's brother, and a shared mistress, a North German princess. Oxford fantasy had struck again.

So Brian Aldiss pictures Bon as editor of *Science Fantasy* in *Billion Year Spree*, his history of science fiction.

We moved there in May 1962. It was a large, superbly built Victorian house; to get twenty-seven rooms you would have to count lavatories, bathrooms, the three compartments of the cellar, a boot-room, a huge larder with slate shelves and a rail of meat-hooks and a conservatory off Bon's huge study. There were out-buildings, a large garden with a habitable shed at the bottom. Besides Bon and me and our five children it was home to nine lodgers and an au pair and was as much a way of life as a house – site of some amazing parties, scenes of fear and loathing, scenes of company and laughter, full of books, prints, pictures, large some-times exotic antique furniture. Bon had statuary, plants and tropical fish in the conservatory – a place of privacy and calm for him – and first a darkroom and later a printing press in the cellar.

Breakages occurred there, not all in anger. 'Take a look at this,' Bon said as he threw a beautiful antique Roman lamp for a friend to catch. It shot past her and shattered irretrievably against the marble mantelpiece. Gone for ever was a delicately sculpted scene of a mature satyr leaning luxuriously back between the legs of a nymph, who was stroking his hair, while another nymph leaned amorously forward over him.

One afternoon four or five of us were sitting quietly having tea when, in the far corner of the room, a heavy stone bust of Burns fell off its plinth – suddenly and unprompted – and crashed through a very pretty small Regency table with ormolu mounts. We stared at the heap of sticks with Burns's head on its side in the middle. It was as if things could break in Bon's presence without visible cause. Of course plates broke if we threw them at each other.

Oddly enough it was very rarely the children who broke anything.

During Bon's time there and even more so in my subsequent life as an Oxford landlady, No. 18 Norham Gardens was a remarkably rich and talented community, nurturing future linguists, doctors professors, adolescents in trouble at home. A now well-known soprano practised in the attic; a distinguished black yoga teacher mended bicycles in what had been Bon's study; a bagpipe-playing Arabist sounded his native wood notes wild on the first floor. Scientists, anthropologists, arts administrators, people in advertising, writers, painters, Buddhists, etc., sprang from its attic, basement, even the garden shed . . .

See MAYHEM and MONEY.

Oxford Bon lived in Oxford from 1955 to 1968, first at No. 99 Woodstock Road, then No. 66 Cranham Street and No. 18 Norham Gardens. Each of these places had very different social contexts. His love–hate feelings about his Alma Mater the university come out strongly in all his pictures of Oxford. It is a place Mortdecai returns to and moves about in with wonderment, presented with sharp satire and amused affection.

During vacations Bon worked as night porter in the Randolph Hotel, which provided some very useful perks for a man with children and friends to feed. Night life there contrasted strongly with daytime life in the Ashmolean Museum opposite, where he also worked.

As the overstretched managing director of three businesses – his Turl Street gallery, Sanders of Oxford and the Drawda Hall Bookshop – he knew yet another Oxford. Bon, who had a genuine turn for scholarship, found himself awkwardly straddled between tradesman and scholar in the complicated crossing snobberies of the Oxford of that time. This accounts partly for his many faces and voices.

His rooms are the best set in Scone; there are *boiseries* and a pair of bookcases rivalled only by those in the Pepysian Library in Cambridge ... Moreover, he has a bathroom of his own, an unheard-of luxury in Scone, where the *corpus sanum* – or *vile* – runs a very bad second to the *mens sana*. (The story goes that, long ago, when it was first proposed in the College *concilium* that bathrooms should be provided for undergraduates, an ancient life-fellow protested in piping tones that the lads couldn't possibly need such things: 'Why they are only here for eight weeks at a time!' But then came the strange late-Victorian epoch, shot through with obscure guilts, when the English – whom Erasmus had named as the grubbiest race in Europe – found that nothing would do but that they must scrub themselves from head to foot whenever they could spare a moment from smartening up Fuzzy-Wuzzy and other Breeds Without The Law. There are three times as many undergraduates in Scone now, and the bathrooms are just as few, but now no one seems to mind any more.)   – *Something Nasty in the Woodshed*, p. 425

Parrot Bon's second-most destructive pet remained nameless. It would sit on his shoulder and chew systematically along the shoulder seams of his best tweed suit or along the top edge of our dining-room chairs and was totally charmless except for the brief moment when the children believed they had discovered that it spoke French: they said '*Parlez-vous français?*' and the parrot said '*Oui!*' with some force and convincingly enough for beginners. Its master hoped to teach it to talk and enjoyed feeding it. If it got too uppity he would frighten it by showing it a flat coil of rope, which it reacted to with hysterical screams as if confronted with a poisonous snake. He was extraordinarily indulgent about its depredations, owning it in imitation of his father and recalling it in *All the Tea in China*. He left it behind with me in lieu of maintenance when he moved to Silverdale, assuring me that it was highly saleable. I advertised it in the local paper – never have I felt more ready to excuse dishonesty in myself than the moment when I assured the purchaser that its out-of-condition look was normal in a moulting bird – perhaps it was, perhaps it was pining.

***Personae* and impersonations**   Bon shared with his hero Charlie a tendency to move in and out of being someone else. For Charlie it's Sir Percy Blakeney-Mortdecai, often a cowboy: 'I tried . . . to earn a reputation for being the fastest chopstick in the northern Mid-West, an Englishman, a ghastly middle-European lodger, even a priest.' His need for disguise is recurrent.

Robert Browning, Tennyson, Swinburne and Thomas Wyatt all speak for Bon in their own words in the epigraphs and also offer themselves as temporary disguises through pastiche.

In exchanges of letters Bon is an impersonator and prompts others to join a game of impersonations. Writing as Norman Douglas (someone in Jersey had called him the poor man's Norman Douglas) provokes a camp reply from Tom Rosenthal, who played this game the best.

Norm, Darling,
How simply bliss-making to get your billet-doux from Capri. Ah, how it brings everything back, not to say up, to recall that simply divine *pissoir* at the bottom of the cable car.

I did in fact see Darling Martin only the other day and for someone of ninety-four he's in remarkably good shape . . .

He tells me that the firm which he founded, which is run by some huge bearded beast whom I suspect to be of disgustingly heterosexual tendencies, is doing reasonably well these days and is planning a biography of me by a man called Mark Holloway. I suspect that Holloway is in fact a pseudonym based on the author's previous life in prison and since the author is undoubtedly male, it is a transparent disguise for the wonderful times he used to have in Pentonville.

Don't, darling boy, whatever you do, have any dealings with David and Charles, I am told they are simply gorgeous to look at and have an exquisite maison de tolerance at Newton Abbot, but my dear, Newton Abbot is so terribly suburban these days. I do think it is essential to remain in Soho, which has so many *interesting* buildings.

Back to more important things. I thought the review of my autobiography quite quite beastly. If it wasn't for the fact that the House of Lords has the most capacious lavatories in the palace of Westminster I would have told Harold and Jim what they could do with their bloody Bradwell title, but you know how frightfully straight they are.

Yours with lots of hugs etc. etc.

Tom also writes as Freud expressing some concern about Bon's relations with his publisher. A letter from Bon to Judith Todd is written to her dog as if from his Irish terrier bitch Gershal O'Bonfiglioli (see DOGS).

Photographs of Bon show him borrowing likenesses including Robert Morley's and Harry Harrison's. As Bon Quixote he was always ready to ride to the rescue.

Persuasive powers Being fatally persuaded himself that stuffed birds were a good thing and marketable, he had to persuade others. Paul Rich, a dealer colleague, laughingly told me how he once found himself leaving behind pictures he had gone to purchase in Bath and struggling instead to get a stuffed bird in a large case into his car. As he glanced back to the shop he'd left, he saw the door hastily locked and the CLOSED sign turned to face him.

See also SEDUCTION.

Pictures The *Oxford Mail* ran the following article by Bon under the heading 'Picture, Picture on the Wall'.

As recently as 1950, although the prices of art on the international market were rocketing, pictures were considered a Bad Thing in the ordinary English middle-class home.

It was the age of the Festival of Britain – probably the biggest set-back to English taste since the Royal Academy was founded – and pre-war Bauhaus notions of stark beauty arising from functional efficiency had swept the country with a terrible, Beatle-like momentum.

To own a Constable was 'camp'; a Fernand Léger lithograph was barely permissible clutter; only in the adolescents' bedrooms did the prints of Van Gogh's curdled sunflowers leer out from between the Chianti bottles (lethally newborn as table lamps) at the *corrida* poster on the opposite wall.

I remember the period with pain. Owners of lovely Guardis would mumble apologetically that they had been left them and that they were supposed to be worth a lot of money – as though that was an excuse. Converted-cottage dwellers would strip their interior walls to the functional bricks or spatter the wattle and daub with samplers, horse brasses, anything but the dreaded picture. Meantime, quietly and lucratively, the art dealers were packing England's pictures into stark and functional packing cases and shipping them to Sweden, Canada, the United States and other backward places that didn't realize that pictures were out.

That's all over now, of course: a piece of wood that Constable once wiped his brush on costs the same as one of his easel pictures did fifteen years ago – and worth it too. An original chalk drawing by Burne-Jones is at last worth as much as a colour reproduction of a gaggle of Russell Flint never-never girls dressed for pneumonia.

But the point is that this is what we have now to settle for – oil sketches and charcoal drawings. The pictures we would like are gone – or are out of our range. Every art dealer is asked at least once a day for 'just an ordinary English landscape, you know, about the size of a tea tray, painted before 1850, blue sky, white clouds, green trees, distant hills, not too many cows, and we wouldn't mind paying as much as £40'. A bitter laugh is all the dealer can offer; a picture of this description by one of the less ham-fisted of Constable's imitators – F. W. Watts for instance – costs about the same as a moderately inconvenient country cottage. There are three choices: pay through the nose, put up with bare walls or buy something else. Assuming that the third is the only unacceptable choice, here are some suggestions.

Compared with the ridiculous pieces of painted tin we trundle about in, all art is still cheap. Anonymous art is absurdly cheap: you can buy a dozen dazzlingly skilful anonymous English drawings for the price of one minute scrap of paper scribbled on by Turner and signed. Train your eye by looking at what is good (the Ashmolean is one of the finest collections in the world); trust your own judgement and back your own taste. The man who doesn't know much about art but knows what he likes is well on the way to being the owner of some good pictures and is certainly better off, both financially and spiritually, than the amateur pundit who wears himself out seeking unrecognized Rembrandts in junk shops. Try the less popular media. Pencil drawings are by far the cheapest original works of art today; a perfectly genuine David Cox sketch can be bought for about £10 whereas an equivalent piece in watercolour would fetch £20 to £40.

Black and white engravings, too, are seriously undervalued and only fetch a fraction of what they were worth forty years ago. Like pencil drawings, they react rather well to a rather daring treatment with mounts and frames: instead of the traditional cream mount and frame, try mounting several small ones in a single bright pink card mount, surrounded by a deep box-like white frame. This sort of treatment brings rather dim little engravings or drawings to life in a most surprising way and forms one strong unit of decoration instead of a straggling flock of little oblongs.

Consider the possibility that you are quite wrong about what you think you want. While you are hunting for a landscape about 18 inches by 30 inches to go over the fireplace and a pair of upright flower pieces 28 inches by 12 inches to go in the alcoves, you have probably missed all sorts of pictures the 'wrong' size and shape which you would have enjoyed looking at very much. A picture is not a dado or hearth rug or any other kind of fitment; it is a work of art for looking at, not for completing a scheme of décor. When you buy curtains, you should consider the colour of your carpet; when you buy a picture you should consider the colour of the picture. If it clashes unbearably with the carpet, then throw away the carpet. Carpets are made by carpet-making machines; pictures are made by men who, if they do not possess genius, at least have chosen to spend their lives to make beauty.

Bon had himself begun to collect horse brasses and was to become an expert on how to differentiate genuine antiques from modern reproductions.

See also ART DEALING, BARGAINS and FINDS.

Plots Bon's life could be seen as a progressive losing of the plot, some sense of strategy, in which major gambles had a part, giving way increasingly to tactics, to being just about quick-footed enough to dodge debt, depression and death. He had too low an opinion of himself to consider this a tragedy, which requires a noble hero.

Some critics complain of lack of plot in the novels, some might feel there is too much plotting. Aficionados of Bonfiglioli books think the plot need only be an adequate excuse for all the wit, observations and mayhem. Mortdecai is a reactive hero, more plotted against than plotting, often misunderstanding what plots he is involved in, who his real enemies are and from what direction they will strike next.

However the novels are certainly not formless. Bon became a master of the chapter as a unit of form. Whole series of leitmotifs are woven together to produce rhythm and pace and iterative imagery. The writer does not lose track of days and nights, and with the assistance of Jock, the rhythmic recurrence of tea, meals and drink-times is held to much more firmly for Mortdecai than it ever was for Bon in a life where he delighted to disrupt any regularity created by anyone else while not being able to create any of his own.

Writing to Michael Powell he describes the plot movement of a projected film based on the lives of the Kray brothers:

I see it as a sort of escarpment: the long, pleasant rise towards hubris, the stout Cortés surprise at the top when the Mafia are given the boot, the leap into space when they spring the axeman – then the long, sickening plunge to earth. Only Barney lands more or less soft: the rest never knew what hit them; indeed they never really knew where they were *going*.

Poem   In a poem Bon wrote for a woman friend as their relationship disintegrated, he explores the troubling theme of confused identities:

> *A Few Questions*
> You the bright thief from whom last week I stole
> Any love left and all small peace of mind,
> Last night played fast
> Loosely; and lust left
> Leaving you whole,
> Me bereft.

Who when what stole
From whom? Who was left whole?
Who lies where, thinking?
Who is lying now, who drinking?
Who drank my drunken spirit?
(Have another? –
Have my spirits no brother?)

The magpies sharpen silver beaks for
Fresh thievings. Not me.
Crows polish coy plumes – thief-sneaks for
Others' leavings. Not me.
What's left to steal?
Integrity?
Who's likeliest to heal?
You? Me?

Bon knew well a love poem by Robert Graves and often quoted the first few lines:

Lovers in the act dispense
With such meum-tuum sense
As might warningly reveal
What they must not pick or steal,
And their nostrum is to say:
'I and you are both away'.

Whereas in Graves there is a comfortable enjoyed mutuality in loss of identity: 'To the act again they go / More completely not to know', Bon in his related poem is expressing a more dire sense of disintegration, the puns conveying its different levels.

Poker

I gave him that look – often practised before the mirror – which I give to players at stud poker who back into the betting on the fourth card. He was unimpressed.   – *After You with the Pistol*, p. 309

We played poker fairly frequently, occasionally strip poker. At one time an antique dealer from Abingdon came over once a week for supper and to lose at poker to Bon. I have very little card sense myself but on the few occasions when I won (when I had developed some instinct for the psychology of the players) Bon always felt that a law of nature had been broken in some way beyond all explanation but his card manners meant that he had to moderate his expression of this feeling.

Chapter headings from poker hands were part of his conception of *The Great Mortdecai Moustache Mystery*. It would need a poker player less utterly amateur than I am to read their significance.

Police

. . . to an eating place where they gave us things to eat which tasted like dead policeman on toast.   – *After You with the Pistol*, p. 324

My entry on Rolls-Royce quotes Bon paying even-handed compliments to Oxford's police and Oxford's villains. Keeping discreetly in with both parties was the better part of valour. If Bon stayed late in the city centre and was too drunk to drive or couldn't remember where he'd last parked the Rolls, he would stagger home or to his gallery and in the late morning ring the police, who always knew where to find the car. Cars, parking and the police are all different now. In those days a policeman would usually be able to tell me where my unlocked bicycle had been moved to by some student in a hurry.

The police regularly sent round a list of recently stolen goods; any wise dealer who found he had inadvertently bought something stolen would return the object immediately and would have to stand the loss himself. On one occasion Bon had already dumped the worthless frames from a pair of saleable watercolours that turned out to have been stolen. He had them reframed at his expense and returned them with his compliments to the vicar who was dealing with the affairs of two old ladies in the Woodstock Road. As a result Bon was given first chance at clearing their house when they retired to a home. This yielded a great deal of useful stock, paintings and furniture, and for the household a trunk full of sheets, pillow-cases, Edwardian children's nightwear and First World War Red Cross aprons. We couldn't afford much in the way of new clothes for the children at that period, but they slept in hand-stitched garments of the finest quality.

Charlie is on the whole a goody, though often in the role of a baddy he has many an encounter with the police.

Priests

I thought of dropping in at Farm Street to catch one of those rattling Jesuit sermons but felt that might be too dangerous for my present mood. The sweet logic and lucidity of high-powered Jesuits works on me like a siren song and I have a dread that one day I shall be saved . . . Do they really wash you in the blood of the lamb or is that only the Salvation Army?   – *Don't Point that Things at Me*, p. 53

He was smart enough to notice, however, that I was becoming moody and he set himself the task of amusing me with some success. I yield to few when it comes to telling dirty jokes but it takes a seminary priest to tell a true Catholic story with the right admixture of shyness and authority. He had this art to such a state of perfection that I recall falling about a great deal.   – *Something Nasty in the Woodshed*, p. 473

. . . by late afternoon I was the proud possessor of First Class tickets on a Boeing 747 and a Vatican City passport, complete with all necessary visas and made out in the name of Fr Thomas Rosenthal, SJ; occupation: Curial Secretary. I didn't think that was very funny and said so huffedly.
                                       – *After You with the Pistol*, p. 289

Mortdecai's priestly disguise, organized for him by Johanna, gives him a Jewish–Jesuit persona. In using the name of his publisher, Tom Rosenthal, Bon pays a jokey compliment to a friend that has a double charge of warmth in that it also recalls his Jewish–Jesuit friend Peter Levi, the writer.

You can't talk to parsons, you have to shelter them from reality. Except Jesuits, of course. Worst of married priests, stops you thinking of them as neuters. The broadest might just wear your being agnostic, but atheism, which is the persuasion of most Xtians, upsets them. They don't know where to start. Atheism needs guts to possess and they know it would need guts to fight it.   – from folder notes on the Seven Deadly Sins

Each Mortdecai novel has its priests reflecting accurately some of Bon's feeling about priests. As a nineteen-year-old soldier in West Africa he was impressed that a Catholic priest drove several hundred miles to offer him Mass on the sight of his and some Irish names in the regimental list. They became friends and Bon recalled to me his admiration for the priest's work in the interior in setting up a small school and hospital and was glad to be able to send him books.

In Oxford and Jersey he sought their company. From Ireland he starts a letter to Christopher Priest 'Dear Priest' and says he feels he should go on: 'Father forgive me.'

Jesuits impressed him far more than Anglicans. Sometimes he seems to be waiting for the priest who could successfully challenge his atheism. He would have needed to be a Jesuit:

Most priests are so bad at their jobs. Jesuits are far too good at theirs. I mean, you drop in on one and ask an innocent question about, say, Pausanias of Lydia and he simply tells you the answer, whereas what you were secretly hoping for was a brisk attack on your disbelief. If you are reduced to throwing yourself on the carpet, kicking your legs and whimpering, he diffidently suggests that you might try going to church. *Any* church. He doesn't say come back in a week, he doesn't give you any little booklets or *Bondieuseries*; it's the soft sell.

– *The Great Mortdecai Moustache Mystery*, p. 92

In a late letter to a Jersey newspaper, however, Bon defended one priest for having had 'the guts to kilt up his gown and leap into the arena and lay about him with a great stick'; he went on to lament what he saw as a lack in the Church of authoritative figures, with whose help there 'might be fewer people like myself stranded on the desert island of atheism'.

Terry Hampton, the Anglican priest who conducted Bon's funeral service, wrote of his 'wistfulness' about the Christian faith – a wistfulness, perhaps, like that of Charlie in *Moustache* when he says that the optometrist 'would have made an excellent bishop; one of the good old-fashioned sort that believes in God, you remember'.

In *Something Nasty in the Woodshed*'s Father Tichbourne, Bon creates a fictional priest of extraordinary power and sinister conviction, who is called in as an expert beyond the ordinary in invoking the powers of good and evil to flush out truth.

While there is plenty of domestic comedy in the reactions of Jock and Johanna and major shifts in household dynamics chez Charlie when Father Tichbourne arrives, the Black Mass that follows works up to genuine terror and a sense of having meddled with forces beyond rational explanations, an occult purging through pity and fear.

Provenance

SCHWABE, R. Watercolour drawing of the Turl, Oxford, 1943, looking towards the High and the University Church. On the left is Lincoln College; the sunlit building is the Rector's Lodging. On the right are the renowned old Oxford shops of Walter's (tailors) and Duckers' (shoemakers). Schwabe told Rutherston that while drawing this, sitting on the pavement, he was encouraged by a don from Exeter College who had lunched copiously and pressed a half-crown into the artist's hand. Schwabe was at the time Director of the Slade School which had been evacuated and quartered on the Ruskin School of Art. Coll: Albert Rutherston (bro. of Sir John Rothenstein); Leonard Huskinson RA.

This is an example of one of Bon's catalogue notes showing the level of detailed information about the provenance of a picture he was exhibiting for sale. He enjoyed providing such information, in this case even including a typical Oxford story for a picture likely to be bought by an Oxford customer. Provenance helps establish the price and market for a picture.

Quixote

Bon the don has a bizarre adventure

Coming back here, quaking a bit I don't mind admitting, I found that my key wouldn't go into the keyhole and naturally I wondered whether certain people had been around forcing locks and hoping to collect voluntary subscriptions with a flame-thrower. When I finally got in I searched the cottage, then lit my hurricane lantern and went to the woodshed for torfs (= turves = peat). The door of the shed closed quietly behind me and I thought I heard the hasp clicking on to the tongue of the bolt. 'Rubbish,' I thought. I tried it. It was so. The woodshed door is of ¾-inch oak, each plank is attached to three oak members by 8 clenched-over nails per member. After ten minutes of bashing with a log, the hurricane lamp expired.

Of *course* I wasn't frightened. *Some* people – effete rich publishers, for instance – would have sat down and cried. I bellowed with terror. Whether or no I had been immured by certain people wearing sunglasses and berets, it occurred to me that this was Saturday night and no one would be near the place until Monday noon, *if* the postman had mail for me. (In fact he didn't come until Tuesday, by when I would have been dead, for I was thinly clad and had no cigarettes.)

I bashed away at the door until one plank was loose enough to wedge open so that I could get a hand through to the hasp. My hand was met by something cold, moist *alive*. I don't suppose I leapt more than three feet, for my hand was now trapped as the wedge fell outside the door. I scraped about with my feet and finally attracted a piece of wood to lever the plank out enough to retrieve my hand, now streaming with blood.

At least ten minutes later the whole plank had been bashed free; this was now in pitch dark, remember, and I reached out and found the hasp and emerged. An enormous white face with clown-like black-ringed eyes confronted me: it was a friendly neighbourhood bullock who had licked my emergent hand. 'Moo,' he said. I didn't bandy words with him. I am a kindly chap, fond of animals, but then I was a trifle *distrait*. I hauled off and punched him right on the hooter – he bellowed and went off straight through the barbed-wire fence like a merchant banker absconding to Barbados. I was *glad* that someone else was having a bad time. Then I refilled the hurricane lamp, stalked, still quaking, round the cottage, went in and searched the interior, sat down with a glass of Messrs Black & White's finest and – fell fast asleep for four hours. Isn't that last bit strange?

So POOH to your adventures with a bag of peat; out here getting a bucket of peat puts years on a chap. *Years.*   – letter to Tom Rosenthal

The inscription below can be read on the Spanish cabinet that Bon had photographed in 1965. All the principal adventures of Don Quixote and Sancho Panza were pictured on it in ebony and ivory. The thin and chivalrous knight with his fantasies and the tubby peasant mounted on a donkey put together would add up to a sort of Bonfig. He looked more like Sancho Panza. What an inspiration to have in the house such a work of art as this cabinet, made especially to celebrate a writer and his work!

L'ingenioso Hidalgo don QUIXOTE DE LA MANCHA Compuesto por Miguel de Cervantes sa suedr. y aqui representado por el maestro Diego de Medina En x año de 1653

Quotations Bon was ever on the alert for interesting quotations. Some of his jokes rely on half-submerged quotations and references. Whenever he read a classic like Florio's translation of Montaigne or Boswell's *Life of Samuel Johnson* he noted page numbers, sometimes with subject references, on the endpapers or on a sheet of paper. Beyond this deliberate collecting, many of the quotations that occur so thick and fast were so long remembered, so fused with his imagination and feelings as to have become spontaneous expressions of the man himself. Many a modern reader with less Latin and no Greek finds this irritating or alienating. A publisher's reader of the prototype of his first novel comments that 'a little of this high-density style is very enjoyable' and recommends that if it becomes heavy-going the reader should take a break every twenty minutes and come back refreshed. Having plucked so many quotations from their settings to make this book, I am well aware that each one glints differently in its original setting.

Bon's *mots* are quoted by others and his tales told again with many variations.

His borrowings are reborrowed and form part of an endless essentially *oral* tradition of jokes and anecdotes swapped in pubs. Bon claimed to have been told Chaucer's 'Miller's Tale' – a churl's tale set in Oxford – in the Radcliffe Arms, Jericho, Oxford.

Bon as Mortdecai is quoted in *The Penguin Dictionary of Twentieth-Century Quotations* and in other anthologies.

Inlaid Spanish cabinet showing adventures of Don Quixote and Sancho Panza

℟

Race In his writing Bon sometimes played with race in ways specifically designed to discomfort his readers and bring them face to face with their own insecurities and sensitivities – or over-sensitivities – on the subject. When, in Chapter 8 of *The Great Mortdecai Moustache Mystery*, Charlie attends a sherry party given by the Warden of his old Oxford college, he surveys the 'mingle-worthies' and then makes his choice:

It was the same mixture as before. One brace of second-year under-graduates who were being be-sherried for copying their Firsts in Honour Moderations; one All Souls pansy staring into his sherry-glass as though someone had piddled in it; one rancid portrait-painter on the make; one American Visiting Professor in a tartan dinner-jacket trying to tell risqué stories to one of those women you find in North Oxford; the American's wife, whose dress had been designed in Paris by some poof with a keen sense of humour; a clever priest; an Astronomer Royal; and, of course, the obligatory black chap being courteous to one and all. I singled out the black chap to mingle with until 7.15 precisely, when, sure enough, they all fled twittering like ghosts upon some dreadful summons.

In the following manuscript passage, which did not make it into the published version of the novel, Bon is playing with his reader at least as much as Charlie and – wait for it – 'Sambo' are playing with each other – and with just the same implicit and mutually respected recognition of both the seriousness of the underlying issues and the value of playfulness as an aid to dispensing with them:

To my intense annoyance, a motor-car or auto swept up to the gates of Scone College precisely sixty minutes later. It was some kind of a Ford which looked as though it had served in Northern Ireland; it bore Corps Diplomatique decals and the driver was as black as your hat, if not blacker. He didn't get out, he just wound down the window and favoured me with a display of big white teeth which you could construe as a civil smile or dumb insolence, according to how your liver felt that morning. I met it with a go-Home & Colonial glare.

'Your master,' I whispered murderously, 'is clearly in a frolicsome mood. To send for me in a grotty old Ford – when he knows that I'm a car-snob – and to furnish it with a black driver – when he knows that I'm a filthy racialist – oh, really!'

His smile or grin stretched wider.

'I'm a racialist, too, Bwana. Jest purely cain't abide whitey.' I eyed him narrowly. There was a twinkle of chess-playing merriment in his eye which both warned and warmed me.

Continuing the game, I said stiffly, 'I am unaccustomed to opening the doors of motor-cars.' He leapt out with surprising alacrity and opened the door, favouring me with a flourishing bow which an émigré French dancing-master would have been proud of.

'How dare you!' I said crossly. 'You primitive savages are not supposed to be able to bow like that. You are bowing above your station in life.'

'Sorry, Bwana. Jest aping my betters, I guess. That's how I rose to be real chauffeur.'

I swept into the passenger seat beside him and elevated my Graeco-Roman nose in a haughty way. He trickled us through the Oxford traffic in that easy, off-handed fashion which reminds one of Dean Martin singing. He was good, really good. Nevertheless, as we floated up Headington Hill a puzzlement was nagging at me. I cleared my throat. 'Look here,' I said. 'What's your name, eh?'

'Would you believe "Sambo", Bwana?'

'No.'

'Wrong again, Bwana. I'm Samuel Johnson Brown, Lieutenant, US Army.'

'I shall call you Rastus.'

'Call me anything, Massa; jest don't call me late for dinner – them corn fritters and hominy grits . . . mmm . . .'

'Bollux,' I said.

'Yazzuh, they're purty good toon, fried up with turnip greens an' hash-brown pertaters.'

Game, set and match against me. As usual. I began to like him: it is always good to meet someone who is just that little better than you.

Chess-players, mathematicians and fencers will understand perfectly (although I must admit that the first two categories give me a pain in the ass).

The puzzlement, however, continued to nag. As we approached the roundabout which gives you access to the swings of the motorway – after you've been circling it three times while more seasoned roundabout-users shake their puny fists at you – I cleared my throat again.

'Rastus,' I said, 'where did you set out from? I cannot find it in my heart to believe that you did Grosvenor Square to Scone College, Oxford (England), in sixty statutory minutes and in this old heap of battered tin. Pray, explain.'

'You-all heerd of manufacturers' specifications, Bwana? You did? Yeah, well this jalopy didn't. Lie back; enjoy.' Whereupon he trod savagely upon the right-hand pedal. I trod savagely on the passenger-brake as my spine hit the cushion behind me. He hummed something by Jimi Hendrix while I hummed what I could remember of the Lord's Prayer.

Rages

Now suddenly I was very angry indeed, a rare emotion for me and one which I have schooled myself to avoid since my disastrous childhood.

– Don't Point that Thing at Me, p. 129

'Insensate rages, like I said; but switching instantaneously, at will, to calm normality and charm. Classic schizo and paranoiac patterns.'

– The Great Mortdecai Moustache Mystery, p. 155

Bon's rages erupted from some deeply buried fundamental sense that life had committed an outrage on him but were baffling and very frightening to anyone who had never met anything stronger than children's squabbles and tussles and a bit of breakfast tetchiness. My first experience, after a year of marriage, occurred when I came into our small living room in Jericho carrying our baby son Chris on my left hip and a bowl of Farex in my right hand. Bon came towards me looking furious, lifted Chris from me and put him on the floor – quite carefully, I think. In the split second that I realized he was going to hit me, I up-ended the Farex on his head. Bon exploded with laughter and explained good-humouredly that he was just putting Chris out of range and that I was lucky he was laughing then instead of hitting me.

Sometimes he would come home like a thunderstorm looking for something to strike his rage against. Once in Norham Gardens – sometime after midnight – he dragged me from sleep into the kitchen shouting that the whole room was fizzing and spitting electricity because I had left the kettle plugged in and that I must do something about it at once. I stared at the bland worktop and silent kettle in amazement.

It's true that safety purists don't leave kettles plugged in at night. Was his anger triggered by fear? When Jock, the comforter and protector, is absent, he makes Charlie say: 'I shall not pretend that I would not have liked a cup of tea, but the truth is that I am a little afraid of these new electric kettles; in my experience they eject their plugs savagely at you while you stand beside them waiting for them to boil' (*Don't Point that Thing at Me*, p. 53). True also that we had had two fires in our previous house, one of them electrical. Curiously this episode also had a literary origin in Thurber's aunt, who believed electricity leaked out all over the place at night – a story we had both enjoyed and laughed over in daylight.

In the hall we had a tall chest-on-chest in which I stored fabrics to make curtains, children's clothes and mending. Out of the blue Bon emptied all the drawers out, jumbling the contents in a heap on the floor, shrieking that I was an untidy slut and must clear up at once. This time, shaking with anger and outraged sense of justice, I made for the front door. He seized the loose smocked overall I wore; one sleeve and the buttons ripped and he was left holding it as I got into the car and drove twenty miles to friends', where I stayed the night. When I came back the next day someone had taken the children to school and he had put everything back in its place. Was he playing Sergeant Majors? Neither of us spoke about it again.

Roderick tells me that after a night of shouts and bangs heard from the other side of the kitchen door he and his elder brother crept out to inspect the damage and found the large earthenware bread crock shattered and knife marks in the kitchen door. Bon liked to challenge people's nerve and on this particular evening we had been throwing knives circus fashion. I stood against the kitchen door and he threw. He was a handy thrower and liked to be trusted to aim without hurt. I don't really have nerves of steel, but sometimes I pretend. He never did throw in anger, but shortly afterwards the atmosphere changed and he broke the bread crock knowing it was a particular treasure of mine.

Writing about this leaves me as far as ever from understanding what went on between us. Could it be that he felt he hadn't frightened me enough? In 'How to Frighten Your Wife to Death' he describes a steep deterioration in a marriage through drink and hitting. He suggests that a wiser wife would have realized that 'all could have been set right . . . by packing him off each weekend with a packet of sandwiches to Dartford or Dungeness or some other bird-infested spot, there to adjust his addictive personality by watching warblers, tending terns and making Citizen's arrests on those he could catch scorning the Voles (Violation) Act 1983'. Anthony Harris says that Bon suffered from intense uncontrollable emotions of which he was bitterly ashamed. I often felt like a lightning conductor and blamed myself, hoping that if I could understand better, I might find some way of lessening his fury for all our sakes. More laughter would have helped. In his notes he distinguishes between hot rage and cold rage and gives to more than one character the capacity to switch moods at lightning speed. Reflecting on these matters in the context of much wider evidence of the commonness of serious domestic violence, I am struck by how little actual physical damage he did to me considering his size, weight and army training. So there was evidently an element of control even in the major storms and a desire to control his anger sufficiently to use it to control others. But as his elder daughter says, 'He sure knew how to be scary.'

Rape Confucius he say: 'If rape is inevitable, lie back and enjoy it.' This was the jokey way rape was talked about in the sixties when the law did not consider it possible for a man to rape his own wife.

'Lie back and enjoy it' was one of Bon's suggested titles for *Something Nasty in the Woodshed* but it was disliked by people at A. P. Watt. In the novel violent rapes are the key crimes, and the plot hinges on efforts to find and catch the rapist by bizarre and occult methods. As so frequently in real life, the rapist turns out to be someone known to the victim.

The book as published provoked one letter of complaint from a woman reader who had enjoyed other aspects of it. Bon composed an unpleasantly snide and flippant reply to this letter, which I rather hope was never sent. There is also a violent rape in *All the Tea in China*. Blanche the victim is given a few pages' rest without further reference to recover in.

Despite the violent strand in his nature and his liking for power over others, I feel confident that his hurtful acts never included rape. He was concerned to offer less frivolous and more practical self-defence advice than the Confucian to women he knew.

Reflections *Sui generis*, 'the only one of his kind', is a phrase many have used to me about Bon. He sought his reflection everywhere, not just from vanity but in a search for the company of a like-minded person, or someone whose experience could parallel his – sometimes easier for him to find in a dead writer than a living person.

Some years after Bon died I was keeping a friend's impatient children quiet in a restaurant and found myself telling the story of Narcissus and Echo. I was surprised to find that it spoke to me of Bon and our relationship. From these reflections came this poem, 'Narcissus':

> He was more alone than he knew
> Looking in that darkened pool –
> Past the unbroken surface,
> Facing another, gleaming
> Perfect.
> Fell for himself mirrored there.
> This not-self lured him
> And as he kissed cold water
> Scattering circles running

Marked briefly the depths where he died –
Death's mud-grip knew him.
And Echo?
She who'd laughed and danced in the sun
Loved long before the brink,
Narcissus never saw her – never had
As she pined behind him. –
Heard her sometimes a little
Her voice fading far out of flesh
Caught in the cry of some absurd monotonous bird,
Fragments of things he'd said –
Those chill cliffs threw back nothing whole.

Rolls-Royce A cutting from the *Oxford Mail* and *The Times* news-papers, 15 March 1966:

On his first – and last drive to Cambridge yesterday, Mr Kyril Bonfigli-oli, the Oxford art dealer and bookseller, had the Silver Lady mascot stolen from his parked Rolls-Royce while he was at dinner.

When he returned to the car after a couple of hours he found that the mascot – which will cost from £18 to £20 to replace – had been unscrewed from the radiator.

'I'd rather they had taken my tape recorder than stolen my Silver Lady,' said Mr Bonfiglioli today. 'The best they could get for it is a fiver. I have parked this car and an earlier Rolls for a total of some three years in the open in Oxford without any qualms or reason for qualms. This says a great deal, not only for the Oxford police, but also for the Oxford villains, who clearly are men of taste and dignity.

'But the first time I park in that horrible place in the fens, teeming with web-footed peasants and unsound scholarship, this nasty piece of skulduggery happens.

'Only a Rolls lover can really appreciate the emasculation, the obscene nudity of a Rolls radiator stripped of its Silver Lady.'

I mounted the Rolls, sucking my lungs full of that unparalleled smell of new coachwork, new hide upholstery. The big sad chap, knowing his place, stood on the running-board to guide me out. The Rolls started up

gently, gladly, like a well-goosed widow, and we drifted out of the Goods
Area making about as much noise as a goldfish in a bowl. I could tell by
the looks on their rough untutored American faces that, had they been
brought up in another culture, they would have been knuckling their
foreheads. As a mark of respect, d'you see.

— Don't Point that Thing at Me, p. 81

Sabres

Anyone who has ever fenced knows the feeling of scraping his foil
tentatively along the blade of a professor of arms. There is an authority
about the resistance, an especial timbre to the ring of the steel, which tells
the almost good swordsman that he is paired against a master of the art.

— All the Tea in China, p. 45

Bon was Scottish Command Sabre Champion for 1954/5 and
liked this mentioned on his bookjacket flaps.

Several friends were put to the test of being 'pinked' by Bon
demonstrating sabre passes — Harry Harrison was wearing a thick
tweed jacket and shirt and not expecting a flesh wound at the time.
Brian Aldiss had given Bon reason to suspect him of toying with a
girl Bon considered his. Brian had a sword-stick and suddenly
found its point pressed to his own throat.

Sandwiches

DO I detect a patronizing almost sneering note in today's headline: THE
DAY SANDWICH MAKING BECAME A HANDICRAFT? I know nothing of
the resourceful young man who is said to have vended his artefacts in
such and such a place and on the day or days stated, but I feel bound to
spring to his defence and applaud the magistrate Sir Graeme Finlay, whose
lucid brain recognized that an object made by hand — not that is to say
by foot, nor by machine — must of necessity be a piece of handicraft.

Speaking as one whose flagging powers have left him with only one
indoor pursuit — that of sandwichcraft — my heart goes out to this splendid
young fellow who has had the guts to display the contents of his studio

in public, and indeed challenge passers-by not only to endorse his art by purchasing but to embosom it by actually eating the product of his eye and brain.

Would you, sir, dare to say that a lovingly crafted sandwich, bursting with nutriment only hinted at by the coy wisp of lettuce peeping from its hem, is inferior to a clumsy pottery cow, a fretwork pipe-rack or a necklace of seashells? Pray remember too that the sandwich, once ingested, takes up no room in the returning holiday maker's luggage, remains a delicious memory and part of the purchaser's blood and bone, unlike the more durable and unlovely souvenirs which have to be burned, deliberately lost or, as a last resort, given away to people one dislikes.

People have carped that the young man bought in the bread, the butter, the corned-beef and other artists' materials. Why not? Did Rembrandt weave his own canvas, Michelangelo hew his own marble or Henry Moore smelt his own bronze?

Let us have more sandwiches, I say! And let them have proper respect as an art-form! Let us have a college of Sandwich-craft, let us have an annual battle of the Sandwiches; let sandwiches hang on the line in the Royal Academy and above all let the Tate Gallery confer the ultimate accolade by purchasing a pile of them for posterity!

– letter to the Jersey Evening Post, 18 March 1976

A sandwich remembered:

Bon in dressing-gown and tousselled bringing me kidneys on toast beautifully seasoned and nicely 'displayed' for elevenses while working on the catalogue.

– letter about Bon from Margaret Parsons,
who worked on his catalogue of artists' letters

There are also sandwich songs to be sung to the tune of 'La Mayonnaise' among his papers.

Sea dog The following poem comes from a folder variously labelled UNPUBLISHED PERSONAL WRITINGS and UNPUBLISHED/ -FINISHED/& POETRY. The word 'poetry' has been scribbled over. The text is roughly typed without capitals and with biro corrections in his hand, which I have incorporated.

Which Old Sea Admirable
So greatly loved to see an oak-tree grow
Not for its beauty, matey, nor because
Ecology is then not what it was
But simply to provide more wooden walls
For England's Navy next time duty calls?
Was it Rodney, Jervis, Anson, Nelson, Hood?
I can't remember. What they liked was wood:
Timbers for Frogs to shiver, Jim lad, aargh!
Good dockyard stuff to soak with Baltic tar
And blood of course.
Gouty he used to trudge the fallow field
The pockets of his half-pay boat-cloak filled
With fat and useful acorns which he'd prick
Into choice places with his walking-stick
Then hobble home to buttered scones, his duty
Still being done for England Home and fruity
Old port, blood red, of course.
Once as a boy I thought I'd do the same
Match the old barkish Sea Dog at his game
But kneeling prodding in the first acorn
A notice board above me said with scorn
Local Authority Development
Passed by the Office of Environment
Crying I punched its plexifibro face
And ran home bleeding to my Grandma's place.
Blood from my heart of course.

A sea dog was what Bon was not. He enjoyed reading C. S. Forester's historical novels and has as much fun as Golding in *Rites of Passage* with the landsman at sea trying to understand what is going on.

Seagulls

I must say I do approve of seagulls. Most petty criminals nowadays are so bad at their jobs – don't you agree? – while gulls are as dedicated as traffic-wardens and a great deal cheerier about their chosen vocation.

They (the seagulls) gather in the grey light of dawn, shouting dirty jokes at each other and screaming with ribald laughter, waking up slug-a-beds like you and me, then when they have decided what to do that day, off they fly – and how good they are at flying, not an erg or energy wasted – scrounging, stealing, murdering and generally fulfilling their slots in the ecology. At lunchtime, when we are munching our first brandy-and-soda of the day, they congregate again in some spacious field, their bellies full for the nonce, and stand there in silence, sensibly digesting and *loafing* until it is time for another worm or two (in the case of the little Black-headed sort) or a tasty dead dog (in the case of the Great Black-backed buggers). How wonderfully uplifting it is to watch them wheeling and swooping in the wake of a car-ferry, waiting for idiots to purchase British Rail sandwiches and throw them overboard after one disgustful bite! The very poetry of motion!

When all the world and I were young and people still knew their proper stations in life, seagulls were something that happened at sea, only occasionally calling in at the shore to defecate on your nice new sun-hat so that Nursey could give you a bad time. Nowadays you see them everywhere, raiding dustbins and queueing up outside fish-and-chop shops instead of swimming in their nice oil-slicks and eating up their nice, freshly polluted herring-guts. – *After You with the Pistol*, pp. 277–8

Secretaries

You are quite wrong in thinking I have a syndrome of aggression against publishers: my only grudge is that they can afford the sort of secretaries I used to be able to afford. I lust for such secretaries. In my heyday as a businessman I had many – the best of all used to stand in front of my desk at letter-signing time and meekly remove one item of clothing for each typing mistake. Poor child, she died of pneumonia, for I will not have central heating.   – letter to Tom Rosenthal

Olive Bevan became Bon's personal secretary in 1965. She recollects going upstairs to the Tudor room in Sanders of Oxford to be interviewed. The floor was covered with a tide of paper, prints, picture frames, etc. After asking her a few questions Bon said the best thing to do was to have some sherry. At this point the phone rang from some invisible part of the floor. Olive crawled about till she found the phone under a pile of prints and answered it. 'The job's yours,' said Bon. Olive successfully concealed her age: she was fifty-nine then, twenty-two years older than Bon, and stayed with the firm till a later managing director discovered that she was now seventy-two and decided she was too old. Ever resourceful, she became a freelance print dealer using all the expertise gained through working with Bon to earn her living till blindness, at the age of ninety, brought her trading to an end. She was the loyal guardian of a great many secrets.

Younger, prettier secretaries and personal assistants came and went; with one, Judith Todd, he fell seriously in love.

Seduction Bon rather prided himself on his arts of seduction and would occasionally lay bets with men friends on his chance of success. Brian Aldiss remembers a woman poet who refused Bon three times till at last: 'O come on, just a quick shag,' he said. 'O all right then,' she said. So Brian says. To me Bon said that younger Balliol men asked him for tips and that he told them it was all a matter of concentration – deeply flattering – and getting a girl to take her shoes off at an early stage. Somewhere Bon knew of a folk utopia where the girls have round heels and easily fall on their backs.

In the letters he can be found advising the writer Christopher Priest, who picking up on advice in *Something Nasty in the Woodshed*, wrote (6 July 1978): 'By the way, I read your six-point lecture on the arts of seduction with much fun and pleasure. How right you are about the shoes! Copper-bottom guarantee on that. Tell me, was it your own lecture?'

In the first three Mortdecai novels it is Johanna who is the leading enthusiast and Charlie who is always glad of the odd oyster in a series of torrid but comic sex scenes. The more youthfully lusty Karli in *All the Tea in China* takes seduction for granted, especially of the lower classes. *The Great Mortdecai Moustache Mystery* gives us an older, still lustful man disturbed when Johanna shuts the bedroom door in his face. Bon was, of course, seduceable himself.

When did you last hear anyone use the word seduction?

Seduction between equals was a lot of fun.

Self-portraits

Rembrandt's lifelong exploration of his own face and persona is the key to his whole art. The flip and the snide might put this preoccupation down to vanity: they would be very wrong. The long series of self-portraits, from the boorish, slack-lipped, hippy-haircut art student, via the resplendent painter-king in fur robes and golden chain to the wry, fat, old, widowed bankrupt in the same – now moth-eaten – furs tells a story of continual and merciless self-examination. It is the finest autobiography in the world for those who have eyes to see.

Bon would have considered it presumption to the point of blasphemy to have compared his artistry with Rembrandt's but in this extract from a review for the *Irish Press* he partly identifies with the artist. He too enjoyed images of himself in different guises. Bon's self-examination is the more merciless for being done through Mortdecai, who has been drained of almost all the living author's more endearing characteristics and given his vices in exaggerated form. Rembrandt looked at himself with compassion and acceptance in the later self-portraits, which contrasts with Bon's much more tangled and variable attitudes to himself.

The portrait of Bon taken for the book jacket of the American edition of *Don't Point that Thing at Me* by a Lancaster photographer, Peter Josclin, has all the air of being set up by Bon (see frontispiece). It seems to say this man does not take his writing seriously. He is a smoker, can tell one whisky from another and likes to do *The Times* crossword in the pub.

Shove ha'penny In *The Great Mortdecai Moustache Mystery* (p. 90) Bon returns with nostalgia to one of his most innocent indoor sports:

The White Horse in the Broad is the Mecca of ha'penny shovers; I had quite forgotten how fast its Guinness-burnished shove-h. board is, so I had lost three games at one pint per game, before I could recapture the smooth, oiled wristiness required.

Charlie playing with the porter of Scone College is Bon remembering his glory days in the White Horse and the Radcliffe Arms in Jericho (which was conveniently next door to our house at No. 66 Cranham Street). See CRANHAM STREET.

Silence

Whereof one cannot speak thereof we must be silent.   – Wittgenstein

Bon was capable of long brooding silences. He was silent about much of the pain and darkness of his thoughts and found it easier to rage than to share any inner distress. He was also fascinated by the whole meaning and implication of silence, theologically and in the detective story. The dog that didn't bark in Conan Doyle's story, the argument from silence, the eloquence of silence as used for instance when Shakespeare puts a silent figure on the stage.

As Richard Ellmann has pointed out, in a lecture on biography in a post-Freudian age, the biographer may become aware that the influence about which a writer is most silent may be the one that should be investigated. Fortunately this is not a biography, just an attempt to unravel a few clues, leaving the reader responsible for making connections according to his or her own theory of truth.

The Great Mortdecai Moustache Mystery is clearly set up to suggest that omissions of information may conceal much, as in the following conversation between Charlie and a Dominican monk. Charlie, who is doing a bit of sleuthing, has opened with a question on heraldry:

I snoozed with my eyes open. So can snakes. Then I hit him with the other question.

'I was thinking,' I said coyly 'of writing a little piece for a popular magazine about the difficult task H. H. Pope Pius XII had when it looked as though the Axis were certain to win World War II.' His eyelids drooped sleepily. When a Dominican's eyes droop sleepily it means that the Dominican is very wide awake indeed; even I know that.

'To be frank, Fr,' I went on awkwardly, 'the sort of fee I'm offered by the magazine does not warrant my doing a lot of research, you understand, and I'm told that, in fact all the relevant documents were published in 1966.' He made a fat, happy noise, like a pursuivant on a bend-sinister.

'Edited by the Jesuits?' I murmured delicately.

'"Edited" is an excellent word,' he murmured back. I cleared my throat.

'Would you advise me to study this collection? In particular, would I find in it all the Polish diplomatic memoranda to the Vatican concerning, well, for instance, liquidation of the Jews?'

He seemed to have fallen asleep. When Dominicans seem to have fallen asleep, even the hardiest Jesuit climbs the nearest tree and pulls it up after him. I waited, my hands folded in my lap to conceal the fact that I had crossed a pair of fingers.

'Tell me,' he murmured drowsily, 'what does Flavius Josephus, that meticulous gossip-writer, tell us about Our Saviour?'

'Why, nothing,' I said. 'It is a puzzling omission.' He nodded.

'And what does the New Testament tell us about Our Saviour's life from puberty until His early thirties?'

'Nothing,' I said again, puzzledly.

'And what, in the Sherlock Holmes story of *Silver Blaze*, was the significance of the dog that barked in the night?'

'The fact that the dog did *not* bark, Fr,' I said patiently.

'But now, touching on this matter of the 1966 Acts and Documents . . .'

'Oh yes, sorry, your point is taken. The old *argumentum a silentio*, what? Oh dear. Quite. Yes. Well thanks awfully, Fr. Good night.'

He waived a benign brace of fingers at me and was piously approaching the prie-dieu before I was out of the door.

— *The Great Mortdecai Moustache Mystery*, p. 97

Don't ask me how many subtexts are here, let alone silences covering significant information. I'm not sure Bon had yet decided.

Silverhand This was the working title of a sequel to *All the Tea in China*, which Bon was writing in 1979. He had returned to Jersey from Ireland and was staying for a while with a non-drinking, non-smoking Anglican priest friend, Dick Miskin, where he could benefit from Dick's kindness and his reminiscences of the North-West Frontier. Bon's feeling for the North-West Frontier originated in Kipling's stories and John Buchan's *Greenmantle*. In Dick's library he made extensive notes from contemporary memoirs to establish the historical background.

Its three provisional titles each suggested a different aspect of the writing and referred to a possibly real, possibly mythical, object of potential historical significance: the Dast I Sikander – the Silverhand of Alexander – which Bon had first come across in a copy of *Blackwood's Magazine*.

Silverhand, the antique dealer's title, is the one that appears on the brown folder. Alternative provisional titles were heraldic, *Hand Argent Proper*, and emotionally expressive, *The Heavy Hand*. This last relates to how Carolus van Cleef 'inadvertently becomes the proud but horrified possessor of the Dast I Sikander, a massive silver Graeco-Buddhist model of the hand of Alexander the Great'. He cannot get rid of it, 'frantically tries to flog it, lose it or have it stolen'. Keeping it makes him the focus of a revolution – 'he is in danger of becoming the Tartar Messiah' – and the enemy and object of attack by the myrmidons of the Governor of Herat who wants it for his own political purposes. He intended this as the main and culminating episode of the book.

Bon's preparatory researches and materials kept for this novel include a leather suitcase full of weighty nineteenth-century scrap-books of illustrated news cuttings depicting battles, landscapes and personalities of the Afghan and Zulu Wars and a collection of light-hearted lithographs about the domestic and military life of the British Raj.

In the following notes Bon sketched out the scene that would link this sequel to *All the Tea in China*. Karli, who ends that book entering another circle of shipboard hell under the dreaded Captain Dogg and the tormenting first mate Lubbock, is now visualized crucified on the mast by sheer paralysis of fear.

Karli, shanghaid (what is the origin of this word?) is put to topman's work but despite beatings is quite unable to fulfil duties because of vertiginous rigour. The solidity of this foils Lubbock's attempts to kill him thus; his limpet-like embrace of any rope or spar higher than twenty feet baffles all attempts to make him work or to make him fall to his death.

Finally the captain makes Lubbock stop trying; Karli is, quite simply, in the way of the ship's work. He is given vile jobs; captain of the heads (check earliest date of this), mucker out of pigs and other shipboard poultry, spader out of rot from the ship's nethermost bilges. Etc.

Advised by a contemptuous but half-friendly sailor to seek protection from huge Negro or perhaps heroic Wild Western figure (queer) (Ned Buntline?) (check dates for this)

Ship sinks; survivors picked up by convict boat en route to Botany Bay. Karli conned by Freemasonic tattooing to take identity of a convict.

Sold to beautiful woman who is into flagellation, submission, bondage and all that rubbish. Escapes because he just doesn't like being hurt. Meets up with gentle, timorous bushwhackers, all scholarly.

(Perhaps one day we might develop personal armour?)

Arrives at northernmost port then available; takes job on schooner to the Islands,

So far Bon's notes take us; he had not decided which route he would choose to get his hero to the Afghan Wars, but it was the part of the book he was most looking forward to writing and for which he was still collecting material. To the *Silverhand* folder he had added colour-supplement photographs of the Khyber Pass and maps of key smuggling routes. He could have described every scene with conviction and found plenty of authentically historical ways of keeping Karli on the run.

Smells Despite being a heavy smoker, Bon retained a good sense of smell and does the smells effectively in his writing.

The smells, too, remain with me, although I have long since, and often, smelled worse. Peter's hair-lotion was sharp and agreeable; it reminded me of the verbena plant in my mother's window. Tar and timber and paint are good smells; so were the mingled richnesses of our cabin-stores, especially the Stilton cheese. The London River, laden with sewage, was less good and, when the ship pitched a little as another vessel passed, our bilges, disturbed, offered up a stench of graveyards. The ship's cat had pissed somewhere within range of my nose: I resolved to take the first opportunity to boot it overside for I do not love such creatures. Dogs, yes, within reason. Overriding all, strange to say, was the smell of horses from London town. It was to be a long time until I again sniffed that smell – and with pleasure.　　　　　– *All the Tea in China*, p. 88

The doctor had bought from a bum-boat some hens and coconuts and was confecting a kari-stew of these which ravished my nostrils. (How strange it is that language has words for being deaf, dumb and blind but no word for the shocking deprivation of being without the sense of smell! To speak plainly, I would rather be dumb . . .)

　　　　　　　　　　　　　　　　　　– *All the Tea in China*, p. 147

Smith & Wesson

I had decided to give my old and beautiful .455 Smith and Wesson Military and Police Model of 1902 an airing. The men teased me about it as ever; most of them have amazingly small-bore weapons with tailored handles and changeable sights, but they know that I can still make the pop-up man-sized target look pretty sick at standard Olympic range. Although I say it as shouldn't. It weighs $2\frac{3}{4}$ pounds fully loaded and the barrel is 6 inches long; using the high-load, nickel-jacketed military ammunition it can punch holes in a brick wall and it makes a deafening and highly satisfying noise.　　– *Something Nasty in the Woodshed*, p. 407

Bon was so thrilled when he bought this gun that *I* noted it in *my* diary.

Chris says that during the police search of our house (described in ARMS AND THE ART DEALER) the Smith & Wesson remained unnoticed among the clutter on the wide marble mantelpiece in Bon's study.

Songs

> Be I 'ampshire be I buggery
> I comes down from Fareham
> My old missus has calico drawers
> And I knows how to tear 'em . . .

Bon's pleasant voice might be heard singing anything from the ribald to the holy. The lines above are from a song reserved for singing with the children in the car. The chorus was a terrible ripping noise that everyone must join in with as loudly as possible. Catriona remembers him singing Amanda to sleep on his lap one Christmas in Jersey with 'Stille Nacht, Heilige Nacht' – 'Silent Night'.

Bernard Cribbens's 'Right, Said Fred', for Bon, celebrated comic furniture-moving times with his antique-dealing friend Alan Mobey.

He loved jazz and jazz singers, listened over and over again to Burl Ives songs, Ella Fitzgerald, Fats Waller and Louis Armstrong.

Many songs spoke his feelings for him, among them: 'I Owe my Soul to the Company Store'. Above all the 'Streets of Laredo' was a kind of sentimental *memento mori* for him.

In Ireland he had taped a brilliantly funny Kenneth Williams show of folk songs, with the likes of 'Green Grow My Nadgers Oh'. To this tape he added a local man singing a poignant ballad in which a man is visited by the ghost of his lost love who promises once again to meet him on his wedding day.

Speech

'Yeah,' I said draping an extra set of inverted commas around the word, like the verbal snob I am.   – *Don't Point that Thing at Me*, p. 19

In general Bon was well spoken and eloquent. His vocabulary ranged from army slang to the most recondite language of the *Kunstkenner* and all points in between. He used a great many catchphrases, few of which appear unaltered in his fiction, where he invents a convincing and individual speech style for each character. When he was extremely drunk, his mood getting ever more trigger-happy and volatile, his sentence structure and vocabulary would become excessively formal and pedantic. In his own words this was 'the sententious phase of drunkenness'.

In particular circumstances he stammered, usually a sign of endearing tenderness and sincerity, but he also knew how to mimic this speech defect for effect.

Catriona says that 'Dad took some pains to try to teach me how to say yes in a particularly disapproving and very English way. My straightest face and flattest voice could not imitate the desired delivery.' Passing on a gift for dramatics, perhaps.

Then Blucher thanked the bobbies civilly, but in the flat sort of voice which means 'fuck off '.   – *After You with the Pistol*, p. 237

Street trading

About a year ago a gentleman of my acquaintance sought permission from the police to sell old and rare books from a wheeled cart in the St Giles parking area near the Taylor Institute – a picturesque and harmless trade, one would have thought, and not inconsistent with the character of an ancient cathedral and university city. Permission was of course refused. I am glad to see, however, that the powers are not wholly hostile to the time-honoured street trades of Old England. Every night at least two motorized barrows are there, vending such odorous traditional Oxford dainties as hot-dogs, hamburgers, frankfurters and Coca-Cola. Tourists no doubt cluster round to photograph these quaint survivals from more gracious and leisurely days.

– letter to the *Oxford Mail*, 16 December 1965

Sundays

Peter gave me a rude awakening the next day by emptying part of his shaving-water in a friendly fashion onto my sleeping face. I cried out many an obscene word in Dutch (and some in English which certain young persons had taught me) but when I could open my eyes I saw the pleasant, dissipated face of my friend, who was tying his neck-cloth and beaming at me kindly.

'Come, Karli,' he cried, 'five minutes to wash, shave, dress and be on deck. Bustle about, do!'

'Is it pirates?' I mumbled. 'Mutiny?' He laughed.

'Worse than that,' he scoffed. 'It's Sunday! Five minutes to be at the break of the poop or God forgive you, for the Captain won't.'

I could make nothing of this, nor could I ask for explanations for he had whisked out of the cabin, but I took him at his word, except that I did not shave for my beard was light – I only needed to shave twice a week. I achieved the break of the poop in the very nick of time. The ship's people were lined up in ranks and wearing their best slops; wearing looks, also, of pious respectability such as are proper to the English when worshipping their God, who speaks English Himself and prizes such clothes and looks. The Captain intoned many a resounding phrase,

commending our voyage on this, its first Sunday, to both God and Her
Britannic Majesty, but it seemed to me that his voice carried a certain
irony, a want of true fervour. I observed, whilst his voice boomed
sonorously over my bared head, that neither the First nor the Second
Mate was present. Since the ship was hove-to this seemed strange to me
but I was, of course, ignorant of the ways of sailormen. The Captain, his
tone even more ironic, commanded the men to sing a certain hymn,
calling for a man named Evans to 'fugle a note'. The man Evans, sure
enough, stepped forth from the ranks, threw back his head and delivered
himself of a note approximating to that of 'G' with all the brio of a
barnyard fowl. He then turned about and waved his arms in such a way
that the men instantly began to bellow

> 'All things bright and beautiful,
> All creatures great and small'

with every appearance of pleasure. It was, for me, a most unhappy
experience for I have ever been a lover of music.

. . . the men had derived great comfort from it and, who knows,
perhaps a tone-deaf God in an English heaven may have been relishing
it, too.   – *All the Tea in China*, pp. 90–91

On this voyage Sundays are a way of measuring time. The idea of
worship is undercut with cynicism and satire, yet the shipboard
detail remains convincing. Karli's fears, ridiculed by his messmate,
are soon confirmed as the story develops. Far stranger to anyone
who knew Bon is the news that at the time he was writing this
novel he went to several early-morning communion services – as
he himself remarked, if you stay up late enough you find yourself
up early. For six months he had contributed factual, succinct
reviews of church services in different Jersey parishes to the *Pilot*, an
Anglican monthly. He did this apparently without tongue seeking
cheek. Here follows his last contribution, published in February
1976. The tricycle was real.

Consumer's Guide to Sunday
This month your Boy-wonder reporter, 'Scoop' Bellemy, fought his way
through the undergrowth to the almost forgotten Parish of St Magloire

in the most inaccessible part of Jersey, a corner of the Isle where even his tricycle was looked upon suspiciously as a new-fangled luxury.

The Approach. Quite shocking: no parking facilities at all and the road full of mud. To my puzzlement, no one seemed to mind: everyone walked to church through the lanes and across the fields.

'Only a mile a bit more, eh?' one father of a family said to me cheerfully, kicking off his muddy boots in the porch and drawing a pair of carpet-slippers from his pockets. 'Done this little walk for at least a hundred years.'

'How many years did you say, sir?' I asked, but he was gone, herding his apple-cheeked, mufflered brood into the body of the church. 'Man must be mad,' I mused. 'Walking a mile just to go to church on a cold, wet morning?'

The Church. A beautiful little Norman building, set in a neat churchyard and in extraordinary good condition. One of the jolly churchwardens roared with laughter when I asked whether a rich immigrant had lavished money on the fabric. 'Bless you, sir,' he cried, 'they mucks in like the rest of us but it's not a question of money. The church belongs to the parish, right? And we're all of us the parish, right? When there's anything in the kitty we get paid for stone and plaster and that, but labour is our own, eh? I mean it's our church, eh?' 'Mad, quite mad all of them,' I mused as I went into the church. It was bitterly cold inside. I learned that they had the potty idea of bringing hand-warmers, foot-warmers or simply bags of hot bricks to church with them in winter; they reckoned that the cost of central heating was better spent on keeping a few old ladies in coals – or feeding a lot of starving people in Africa or Asia. Mad, quite mad.

The Congregation. There was something odd about the congregation which I couldn't at first put my finger on. Then I realized that it was not composed of old ladies, gentlefolk who attend because gentlefolk are supposed to and ecstatic adolescents. It was mostly just people, as though all the community was there. Young men sharing prayer-books with their girlfriends (even holding hands with a defiant look as if to say 'why not?'), old ladies eyeing them and nudging each other as they sucked their peppermints, married folk, smacking their children and up in the Smoker's Gallery (I thought that the last one had been demolished at

St Brelade's), the old gaffers puffing away happily and greeting each other for the first time that week. All quite extraordinary. Like a parish meeting, you might say.

The Service. Sung Matins, Prayer Book style. The people did not appear highly educated but they seemed to have no difficulty understanding the sonorous, time-hallowed words; they had grown up with them. (One of them, afterwards, told me that he didn't like calling God 'you'. 'Rude, isn't it?' he said. 'I mean, he's Thou, isn't he, eh?')

The Sound. Well, if you like that sort of thing, I suppose it was rather good. Thirty in the choir, having the time of their lives: basses, baritones, tenors, contraltos, sopranos and altos all singing fit to burst. They made a mess of the anthem, chiefly because a boy soprano dropped a pocketful of marbles in the middle of it, but they certainly made a joyful noise unto the Lord. Which is what it's all about, I suppose. The organist was, clearly, a scholar; before the Rector entered he regaled himself – and us – with lovely, treacly Bach and some personal variations, but for the hymns he pulled out most of the stops, and led with the clamorous authority of a Salvation Army Captain. The people seemed to love it, the louder he played the more happily they bellowed. I found myself bellowing too; you could have heard us in the next parish.

The Rector. A big, pink chap with an Oxford degree who looked as though he visited his flock on horseback. He supplied the modern element in the service in no uncertain fashion.

The Sermon. Not much scholarship but no carneying and coaxing either. He fairly roasted the churchful; telling them that going to church of a Sunday did not entitle them to overcharge strangers of a Monday, nor to underpay their workmen on a Friday. He did not seem to have heard of the permissive society: he was hot against adultery – 'Yes,' he roared, 'you may well blush and shuffle your feet, but you'll roast in hell for all that if you don't mend your ways!' It was all very old-fashioned, for even bishops don't believe in hell nowadays, do they, even though Christ went down there himself once.

Then he said that he had a list of old people who were cold and hungry and named several people in the congregation who were to see him that afternoon about firewood and food – and he'd take no excuses. Quite extraordinary.

General Impression. The whole parish is mad. As I went out at least three people shook me by the hand and asked me to share their Sunday dinner. Complete strangers. They're all mad in St Magloire, they seem to think that Christianity is *real*. I mounted my trusty tricycle and, as I started to find my way homewards, I woke up – in bed. The electronically simulated bells of my own parish church were calling me to worship, in a comfy building with electrically warmed kneelers, twenty pounds' worth of hot-house flowers, and a placatory parson who would explain that God was a concept. I didn't go. I wrote this instead.

See also GOD.

Tea

How sharper than a serpent's tooth is an awakening without tea!
– *Don't Point that Thing at Me*, p. 148

Tea was essential in getting Bon across the threshold into the day. However, the following fantasia on teas perfectly prescribed to meet every eventuality of an art dealer's life is a dream beyond the resources of his actual life. No Jock, you see.

Jock, announcing his imminent appearance by a polite cough which almost took the door off its hinges (I have taught him that good servants never knock), brought in a tray for Johanna laden with the sort of coffee which you and I drink after dinner but which Daughters of the Revolution pour into their stomachs at crack of dawn. Small wonder that the American Colonies were the first to win their independence – if that's what they still call it. Before I could doze off again my own tray arrived, just a few eggs, a half-dozen slices of toast and a steaming pot of well-judged tea. Jock, you see, although not bred to service, has a heaven-sent knowledge of what the young master will require in the way of tea. I would pit him against any Wigmore Street physician when it comes to prescribing tea: there are times, as I'm sure you know, when these things *matter*. I mean, an art-dealer who has nothing to face that day but a brisk flurry of bidding at Sotheby's needs naught but the soothing Oolong. A morning at Christie's indicates the Lapsang Souchong. A battle-royal at Bonham's over, say, a Pater which only one other dealer has spotted, calls for the Broken Orange Pekoe Tips – nay, even the Earl Grey itself. For an art-dealer in terror of his life, however, and one who has valiantly embarked on Part Two of his honeymoon in early middle age, only two specifics are in the field: Twining's Queen Mary's Blend or Fortnum's Royal. What I'd call a two-horse race. I forget which it was; I only remember that I slunk out of bed before its fortifying effect made me forget that I am no longer a youngster. (That's all right about the 'size of the dog in the fight and the size of the fight in the dog' but art-dealers in their late forties have *livers* to consider; other organs have to take their place in the queue.)   – *After You with the Pistol*, p. 346

The sticky toffee tea now available for ready money in the tea-merchant's in Stratford would have made him raise a scornful eyebrow, if not go apoplectic with disgust.

That's My Last Duchess   Some time in the early sixties a publisher's reader reported on a novel called *That's My Last Duchess* by Kyril Bonfiglioli:

I think perhaps you should grab Mr Bonfiglioli and sign him up, as good thriller writers who are literate and very funny are hard to find. It is difficult to see how his particular formula can fail. His style is sophisticated and contemporary, his literary name-dropping is impeccable, as is his knowledge of villains' argot; the general violence is well laced with art dealer's expertise, Rabelaisian humour, drinking and gourmandizing, plus a spot of nymphomania – something for everyone, in fact.

This title, taken from one of Browning's dramatic monologues, shows how early the Browning epigraphs were part of the first Mortdecai novel *Don't Point that Thing at Me*. This novel was started when Bon was living at Norham Gardens. He showed me the first few pages with some diffidence and felt pleased and encouraged that I thought them very funny and that he should continue. A novel was a departure from any writing he had done before and from his editing of *Science Fantasy* and *Impulse*.

Tintoretto – *The Resurrection* With one bound he was free! – or was he?

In 1964 the whole family were in need of a financial resurrection. Bon was building castles in Lancashire in hope of an emotional resurrection. The Tintoretto was the culmination of his life as a picture dealer and the beginning of its end. It also burned itself into his imagination in a way that can be recognized in the endings of some of his stories.

In May 1964 the picture was still in his hands; he was editing *Science Fantasy* and needed a story of a precise length to complete the June/July issue. He wrote 'Blast Off' to fill a space. Its word count hardly explains the subject matter. An astronaut, before take-off, expresses his hopes and fears for himself and for humanity. The ordinary pleasures of fishing and breakfasting companionably on the shore by the cooking fire are vivid. He compares his fear and expected suffering with that of his mother in childbirth. Under the veil of science fiction this monologue uses material from the gospels and addresses the conundrum of the Crucifixion. Fear and isolation are the dominant emotions, but the scene derives from Christ's ascension after the Resurrection.

Look carefully at this photograph taken at the time of purchase for authentication. Tintoretto's exceptionally dramatic religious imagination places us between light and dark where eternity and time meet. The stone sarcophagus is uncompromisingly central and strongly foreshortened; its lines of perspective imply a viewer outside the picture slightly off-centre to the right. The projection of its parallels would meet at an infinity beyond the rising Christ's upward-pointing right hand. In the foreground the licentious soldiery are slumped against one another and the sarcophagus's stony sides in a drunken stupor. They have not been able to guard against the resurrection or to perceive it. Three soldiers are awake: one has staggered to his knees and stares outward with a stunned and crazed expression; another peers downwards into an exceptionally clean and empty tomb, his elbows jutting comically sideways; the third behind its great stone lid points his spear towards the rising figure, shielding himself from the dazzling light with his raised buckler. In

the distance – top right – come the three women, jars of ointment
in hand, silhouetted against the dawn sunlight, with a hazy suggestion of Jerusalem behind them. They are coming into the dark
tomb-cave as the first witnesses to the empty tomb. The light of
the resurrection is not yet visible to them. Strikingly no one in the
picture can see the gravity-defying figure in its nimbus of light,
bursting upwards through the rocky-roofed cave. The figure is
isolated in a transcendent experience that only the imagined viewer
may share. There is a sense of a silent explosion.

The ending of Bon's first novel uses the imagery of light and
dark, as well as escape from a cave, in an extended way that seems

to link visually with the painting. Charlie is in an old paint mine, cleaning a Goya and contemplating the beauty of a naked woman. He considers coming out guns blazing.

. . . and what does he see, black against the sunlight, but the shape of a young woman holding a child out to him.

An image from the end of 'The Gombeen Man' triggers a different explosion, an explosion of accumulated sin.

See also FINDS.

Triangles Twice in his life Bon was part of curious triangles. Each time he was the lover of a woman much younger than her husband. On the first occasion he told me with some amazement how the husband's mother had encouraged him, just as Johanna's mother in *Don't Point that Thing at Me* encourages Charlie to satisfy desires Johanna's first husband hasn't cared to satisfy.

The second triangle seems to have involved some complacency on the husband's part. For the husband he was effectively 'a resident tutor' who helped him write letters to the newspapers. Exactly what he and the wife were to each other I do not know, except that I think she was kind and of great practical help to him.

𝖚

Unfinished work When Bon died he had not quite completed *The Great Mortdecai Moustache Mystery*, was accumulating stories for *Ghost Train* and had also amassed a considerable amount of material towards a novel to be called *Lord Mortdecai* or *Cross My Art*, which was to bridge the historical gap between the planned *Silverhand*, sequel to *All the Tea in China*, and the completed, present-day Mortdecai novels.

According to the proposal that Bon sent to Hilary Rubinstein on 24 August 1977, the protagonist of *Cross My Art* (or *Diddling the Nazis*, as Bon and his publisher Tom Rosenthal came to refer to it in their correspondence) was to be 'based on Lord Duveen 1869–

1939, not to be confused with Sir Joseph Joel Duveen (an easy error to fall into because Ld. D. was also once Sir Joseph D. and the D. family very complex)'. It is clear from the proposal that a novel based on Duveen had been in Bon's mind for some time; he refers Hilary to S. N. Behrman's *Duveen* 'to get the flavour of the man' and, after mentioning the tensions between the various 'Houses' of Duveen that any fictional treatment would have to beware of, he shows how he has already taken care to avoid 'any suggestion that the House of Mortdecai was really the house of Duveen':

Before you start hollering for your law department, let me hasten to point out that in my first Mortdecai novel I made Charlie say that his father (first Lord Mortdecai and the protagonist of the projected novel now under advisement) 'poisoned his life trying to over-price Duveen out of the market' and in the Clipper novel [i.e. *All the Tea in China*] Karli Mortdecai Van Cleef meets the famous 'Uncle Henry' Duveen as a stranger. This last was a deliberate anachronism to protect publishers . . .

Before going on to outline the proposed novel's extremely ambitious structure, Bon helpfully provided Hilary with a Mortdecai family tree:

The cobbler Van Cleef m. Annike Mortdecai
Carolus Mortdecai van Cleef (*c.* 1820–1901) (changes name to Karli Mortdecai) m. Blanche Knatchbull
Charles van Cleef Mortdecai (*c.* 1860–1915) (this man I hold in reserve: Army officer? Waster?)
Bernard, first Baron Mortdecai (1885–1945) m. Agnes, daughter of a duke
Robin, second Lord Mortdecai (1915–75) Florence (1920–   ) Charlie Mortdecai (1925–   )

The proposal continues:

Bernard (first Lord Mortdecai) is humourless to the point of mental deformity, vain to the point where he believes himself objective in his appraisal of himself; solemnly relates incidents in which he believes that he has excelled but in which he appears ludicrous. Compare Conan Doyle's Brigadier Gerard.

Robin, second Lord M., is world-weary, malignant, a victim of *Zerris-senheit* and, in fact, dead at the time of this book. Both he and his father have left memoirs which Charlie is now editing – with comments.

The tessitura should be interesting. Charlie quotes large slabs of his father's solemn and often untruthful memoir, counterpointing with appropriate chunks of Robin's, and linking all together with his own incurably flippant remarks. Thus a typical (much compressed) passage might be:

Bernard: 'Most regrettably, and in some fashion which to this day I find mystifying, a clever forgery was substituted for the original picture.'

Robin: 'The kindest construction to put upon this episode is that my father's usually infallible memory is playing tricks on him here. I clearly recall Gottlieb toiling away at the copy in my father's basement. Father paid him £2,000.'

Charlie: 'I can't imagine how I come to be related to such a shocking pair of liars. Robin commissioned the forgery at my father's instructions. Gottlieb was only paid one thousand and he blackmailed the firm for years until the forgery was exposed. I had this from old Gottlieb himself, who still does little jobs of the kind for me. He tried to blackmail me once but I sent Jock to have a little chat with him and he gave up the idea.' [. . .]

The plot, as I see it at present, goes 'something like this':

Hitler, advised by Speer & Himmler, orders all 'decadent' art to be ousted from German galleries and sold to buy truly German art. (Fact.) Most truly German art is truly awful (with obvious exceptions) and Hitler betrays a taste for the stickier sentimental nineteenth-century men – consistent with his taste for little iced fancy cakes. Bernard gets the commission – both to buy the decadent Impressionists and to collect the German replacements. In the latter role he forms a splendid collection of German art and proposes to exhibit it in London (or New York?) prior to shipping it and asks for the loan of some major state-owned treasures to plump out the exhibition.

In all this he is sponsored by the snobbish Ribbentrop, for Bernard is a Lord, has a ducal English wife and does not exactly insist on his Jewish antecedents. Hitler eagerly agrees to the loans and the exhibit, prompted by Goebbels, who sees a great piece of Kultural propaganda in it. The show is to be opened by that illustrious connoisseur, Hermann Goering.

Bernard has been granted an audience of Hitler, who congratulates him, as an Aryan, on having reached the top of the art-trade, normally a Jewish preserve. He goes into his anti-Semitic rant and Bernard (even) is so disgusted that he feels stirrings of racial loyalty and privately vows that he will do Hitler a grievous piece of damage during – or after – this deal. Hence the borrowing for the exhibit of the glorious *Selbstbildnis* of Albrecht Dürer, arguably the crown of German art. The back of the limewood panel is branded and sealed etc. so Bernard has it sawn down the middle like a sandwich and a forgery painted on to the new front of the old back, if you see what I mean, while he sells the original front to a naughty American banker for a huge sum with which he proposes to finance a Russian deal.

By an unhappy chance, the forgery is detected within a year and Himmler sends a team of his nastiest chaps off to USA to retrieve the Dürer and then liquidate Bernard.

Meanwhile, Bernard is off to USSR which, under Lenin's NEP, needs foreign currency badly and will sell a few art treasures. (Fact.) Bernard has audience of Stalin in an office ludicrously identical with Hitler's. While dickering with the curators of the Hermitage, Leningrad, Bernard fortuitously makes contact with the Jewish Underground Movement. (This part will be dealt with soberly and inoffensively.) The underground group is led by a Messiah – at first Bernard assumes this is the latest in a long line of false Messiahs (fascinating history there) but becomes convinced when, after a performance of the ancient *kapparah* ceremony, the Messiah produces the long-lost, great, gold candlestick of the Temple, thought to have been looted in 70 AD but in fact cherished and handed down. How can Bernard help?

Well, they have another secret weapon: they have the Golem itself, made by the great Rabbi Löw in the 17th century [see p. 203]. It is still in Prague, in the loft of a synagogue, in several boxes. It runs off some primitive kind of Leclanché cell (such as is believed to have been known to the Assyrians, in fact) but it is heavily corroded and no one knows how to assemble and reactivate it. But they have a sympathizer in MIT who reckons he can do it. If Bernard will smuggle out the Golem to Mass., they will put him on to the finest Giorgione in the world, lost since the

Tsar's murder, worth millions: he can buy it from them for, compara-
tively, peanuts. It's a deal; it's done. Alas, within a year, Beria finds out
and sends his nastiest OGPU chaps to the USA to retrieve the Giorgione
and then liquidate Bernard. (That strain again, it hath a dying fall . . .)

Meanwhile, as a background, Bernard is continually overspending
madly (like Duveen), driving his comptroller insane with worry, frightful
danger of massive cheques not being met; juggling finances, playing off
one millionaire against another. All will be well if he can hook, as a
customer, the greatest millionaire collector of the lot. But he is Duveen's
customer and will only buy from Bernard if – as he taunts – Bernard can
produce the *Mona Lisa*.

As it happens, Bernard can. He happens to know, through his network,
that the *Mona Lisa* in the Louvre is *indubitably* a replica (replica in art history
means copy *by the original painter*) because a certain Italian nobleman has
the first version with full documentation and provenance. The nobleman
won't sell. Bernard uses all his resources to destroy the nobleman's
investments, then jockeys him into a position where only $5,000,000 can
save him from ruin, disgrace and prison. He sells.

Meanwhile, a leading Chicago gangster with a social-climbing wife
wants to become respectable; has built a mansion; wants top art. Hears of
acquisition of *Mona Lisa*, presses Bernard to sell it to him instead of
millionaire. Finally makes Bernard 'an offer he can't refuse'. One ear-
amputation and a few fingernails later and Bernard sells. But unsavoury
millionaire has already bragged about having bagged the *Mona Lisa* and,
now ridiculed, becomes furious; hires rival mob to destroy gangster, steal
Mona Lisa and liquidate Bernard.

Meanwhile, too, the Treasury is becoming interested in Bernard and
so are the FBI after his Russian trip. [. . .]

The dénouement would be something like this. At the annual Chelsea
Cotillion at the Waldorf, NY, those present are:

The entire Social Register, the *crème de la crème* of the 500 Families.

'Diplomats' from the German Embassy, who are in fact the Gestapo
team mentioned above, a Luger in every tailcoat.

Ditto from the USSR ditto who are in fact the OGPU team mentioned above, a bombski in every ill-fitting tailcoat.

The door-porters, cloakroom girls and lavatory attendant who are

T-Men, G-Men and Secret Service men, all dying to know what it's all about.

The orchestra, composed of musically gifted mobsters, each with a spare instrument-case containing a 'typewriter' and a few 'pineapples'. (This *is* the 1930s, remember?)

The Italian waiters, all of whom are members of the rival mob, a 'gat' or 'heater' on every hip – except for one terrified *chef de rang* who happens to be the hastily disguised Bernard, first Lord Mortdecai.

An irate German 'diplomat' smacks an insolent 'waiter' in the kisser; the 'waiter' pulls out the old equalizer and goes rooty-toot-toot. The shit hits the fan. After a few well-bred squeals, the doyenne of Society shepherds her flock on to the balconies where, ignoring the vulgar hubbub in the ballroom, they continue to dance as genteelly and insouciantly as they can with wetted pants.

Bernard makes good his escape – not, he insists, out of fear but because he can no longer bear the shame of wearing a celluloid, waiter's collar and dickey-front.

CHOICE OF ENDINGS

HAPPY ENDING: This involves a sort of alternate-world scenario. Just as Hitler is preparing to invade Poland in summer 1939, Poland invades Germany. A million Jews from all corners of the earth have gathered in the concrete bunkers of the Warsaw Ghetto, led by the Messiah. They have wonderfully advanced weaponry, computed by the Golem and manufactured in USA. They roll up the German Army. Simultaneous rising in Germany, Russia etc. Armageddon. Millennium. Peace on earth.

UNHAPPY ENDING: Bernard, fleeing from the hotel, finds himself caught up in the fringe of an enormous crowd of Jews who are over-flowing Central Park. The Messiah is being proclaimed. Much emotion. Then the white-robed figure opens the flaps of a great tent to reveal the Golem, twenty feet high, shining like silver, holding aloft the great gold candlestick. Ecstasy. The Golem clanks on to the platform and explodes. *Mushroom-shaped* cloud of smoke. (Clearly, the Rabbi who built the Golem knew about uranium: the MIT man did not.)

Final, very sad and serious, cameo at the Wailing Wall in Jerusalem. Nineteen hundred years of hope and prayer have gone up in smoke.

The day after sending this outline to Hilary, Bon wrote again, clearly enthused with the project:

Length of *Cross My Art* – I forgot to add this: I could do it in 70–80,000 words but there is so much juicy material that I would like to let it spread itself out to perhaps twice that length *if it wants to*. After all, who ever heard of a *short* bestseller? What's that? *Snow Goose? Jonathan Seagull.* What am I, a bleddy ornithologist already? That's for the birds. (Please *send* me a bird: this country is riddled through and through with virginity.)

I would like, too, to interlard the narrative with bogus newspaper-cuttings ad hoc and ad lib, sending up the style and opinions of *Völkischer Beobachter, Pravda, Times, New York Times,* etc. The gun-battle at the Waldorf could best be described by 'quoting' a descriptive column 'by' Damon Runyon – wouldn't that be lovely?

Now, it is well known to one and all that the police in this city do not think kindly of waiters who carry large, coarse Betsys in their pants pockets, especially if these waiters do not happen to be waiters at all but are hoods named Mopsy Fettucci, and they greatly despise such waiters pulling out these Betsys in the Waldorf and going rooty-toot-toot, even if the orchestra is more than somewhat lousy; so I remember that I have duckets for the fight at the Garden, etc., etc.

An internal memo from John Blackwell, Bon's editor at Secker & Warburg, to Tom Rosenthal shows that this outline, which would have been forwarded to Secker by Hilary, was greeted with enthusiasm but also with a certain astute wariness. Interestingly, it also seems to contain an unconscious confounding of Mortdecai the character with Bon the author:

The outline for *Cross My Art* looks appealingly impossible. From any other source it would be pure nonsense, but I haven't the least doubt that Bon can pull it off. I don't much like either proposed ending, but by that stage the synopsis will have been left some miles behind and something aptly sly and mordant will have taken over.

BUT do we not need a contemporary Charlie Mortdecai? I should feel happier if we could alternate between Mortdecai's present and past . . . but this is possibly being overcautious. If, as his letter implies, Mortdecai is blocked . . . there's no point in pressing, but I have an uneasy feeling that this unpredictable author might . . . be going off the rails: *Ghost Train*, for instance, seems to have disappeared up a siding.

In fact, Bon did have trouble pulling off *Cross My Art*. In April 1979 he wrote to Tom Rosenthal enclosing a synopsis for 'another straight Mortdecai romp' to be called, at that point, *The Mortdecai Moustache*:

Am a little stuck on the book about Mortdecai's pa diddling the Nazis – keep on having to do homework on it for which I have not always got resources and finding the framework (Charlie commenting on his brother's comments on his father's guarded account of the matter) a trifle hard to handle. Moreover, it occurs to me that if I did another straight Charlie romp . . . and did it quickly, I might be in a better position to get away with something so unlikely as the Lord Mortdecai one. What do you think? The Charlie one I have in mind has been in said mind for ages – in a dispersed sort of way – and I really think that I could do it in a more or less continuous burst and so much faster than my previous shameful tergiversational tortoise-pace.

Far from writing it in one 'continuous burst', Bon never did quite finish *Moustache* and *Cross My Art* seems also to have defeated him. The quality of the writing he left, however, is extremely high, as the following makes clear.

After a covering page designed, no doubt, to whet his publisher's interest – 'BEGINNING OF CROSS MY ART THE NOVEL ABOUT CHARLIE'S FATHER'S DEALINGS WITH HITLER, STALIN, CHICAGO GANGSTERS AND OTHER ART FANCIERS' – the novel opens with an epigraph:

> Je suis le ténébreux – le veuf – l'inconsolé,
> Le prince d'Aquitaine à la tour abolie . . .

These lines from Gérard de Nerval's poem 'El Desdichado' (literally translated, 'I am the dark one, the widower, the inconsolable / The Prince of Aquitaine in the ruined tower') have the ingredients of a

romantic self-description that appealed to Bon: he and his father
had both been widowers – though in Bon's case he had not been
utterly unconsoled – and in a letter to Michael Powell he refers to
himself as a *desdichado* – an outcast (see FILM). The opening page,
however, recounted in the voice of Charlie Mortdecai, leaves the
melancholy of the epigraph far behind:

'Good morning, me Lord,' said Jock. I raised a sleepy eyelid and gazed at
him. He was bearing my early-morning tea tray, so the time had to be
10.30 a.m. Even Jock could scarcely be drunk at 10.30 a.m., especially
since I had recently had a new and expensive lock fitted on the drinks
cupboard. I felt around in the bed; there were no lords in it; indeed even
my wife Johanna was not present, for I was sleeping in the dressing room.
I closed the eyelid. After a little thought I remembered the dingus on my
bedside table which can do sums, tell you the time, even the date if you
press the appropriate tit. I pressed the said tit with a languid finger. The
date was not the 1st of April, nor was it Hallowe'en.

   'Repeat that greeting, Jock,' I said.

   'I said good morning, me Lord,' he said. 'I received a telephone call
from your late brother's butler at around nine this morning and he
informed me that Lord Mortdecai, as was, passed away peacefully last
midnight after a short but severe illness caused by inserting the barrels of
a shotgun into his moosh and pulling the triggers with his toe. The butler
didn't reckon it worth disturbing you at such an hour so he left it until
'smorning at nine and I told 'im it was more than me job was worth to
disturb you till it was time for your tea.'

   'You wouldn't kid me, Jock? This isn't a cruel practical joke?'

   'No, me Lord, I wooden joke about summink like that, would I?'

   'Then whoopee!' I cried happily. 'I always knew that Robin had a
spark of decency in him somewhere. You are quite sure he has departed
this vale of tears?'

   'Yes, me Lord. The butler says his brains is all over the ceiling and he
has had to walk his late Lordship's dogs himself this morning, although it
not being his work.'

   'Does Mrs Mortdecai know?'

   'I informed Lady Mortdecai half an hour ago, me Lord.'

'Look, Jock, less of this me Lord stuff. Stop it. Cease. The former manner of address will do very well.'

'Awright, Mr Charlie,' he said, but his face fell – or at least . . .

A little later, Charlie makes clear who the other narrators of the story will be:

The diaries of Bernard I have thinned out; my brother's memoirs I have stripped down to those parts which are interesting – and I do not refer to his schooldays when he seems to have had – if one can believe him – coarse adventures with many of the best-known names on the Front Bench today (come back Guy Boothby, the Tourist Board needs you, not to mention the starving families of many a W1 loo attendant); I have salted my father's diaries, I say with those parts of Robin's memoirs which are both fit to print and germane to the thread of the story. Having reached the end I have grown disgusted with the task and have handed the whole thing – along with my charitable pencilled-in comments, to my – let us say friend – KB and given him carte blanche to edit, cut and adorn. I am too nice, you see, to paddle in the sty of publishing whereas Bonfig is not only devoid of such fastidious niceness but is also perennially in need of money (because of his habits you understand) and, best of all, he is possessed of a kind of rancid humour which I am sure Robin would have sourly relished and which might have made even my father sketch a smile on his face. I therefore turn you over to KB – 'nay, I have done, you get no more of me . . .'

KB: Delighted as I am at poor Ch.'s phrase about my rancid humour and hungry for money as any writer must be who has to hire, as I do, a chap to keep count of paternity suits (blood test insert?) and not to mention other, more complicated bits of blackmail, I must still admit that this is perhaps the most unhygienic.

(father's voice)

It has to be understood that when I first encountered the revolting Nazis I had little or no understanding of their absurd political notions. Few people did. Mr Winston Churchill orated, fulminated, sulked – one paid no attention to such men; he was out of fashion, you understand. Cliveden and All Souls were the only stables where the winners were being bred.

True as far as it goes but my father never cantered too far along the race course of veracity – he was not a stayer unless the going was soft and his feelings in those remote thirties were much influenced I fancy by his pique at not having been invited to those magic stables where future winners munched their classic oats.

Yes and whence the finest horse shit emanated. They say that when Queen Mary of blessed memory was laying down her rose garden in Regent's Park, she bespoke every van-load of road apples the racing stables could furnish and bestowed the thoroughbred muck to a depth of ten feet before the first rose was feutred in. I'm sure there's a message there for all of us, could we but see it.

For the first time Bon was planning to give himself a direct voice in his novel. Clearly it would be naive to think that his tale would be privileged as the one reliable narration. How far he would have used it to express some previously hidden layer of feeling we do not know. It is unlikely that the mythical beast in the jungle, 'What-Bon-Really-Thought', would have appeared full face.

Unhappiness Catriona reflecting on her father writes:

It is hard to know how Mortdecai's description of happiness strikes other people but to me it is a poignant reminder of just how well Dad crafted the art of personal unhappiness while being so skilled at making others laugh. Indeed, he told me that the desire to make others laugh was usually a sign of deep unhappiness rather than a symptom of a happy person.

See HAPPINESS for the passage she is referring to.

This poem written for Hilary Rubinstein's daughter is a rare example of Bon expressing unhappiness directly.

> *For Felicity Rubinstein from Thirty Years Away*
> 'Absent thee from Felicity awhile'
> Asked Hamlet as he died; all the prince meant
> Was mourn me for just a day, try not to smile
> For one whole day – a Manly Sentiment.
> But what of portly, middle-aging soaks

Who dine on memories and lunch on liquor;
Who try to earn rich welcomes with poor jokes –
Glad of a civil, half-embarrassed snicker?
What manly sentiment should we express
Who can no longer tell real thought from lies
If you are lucky, you will never guess
What grief for lost youth shifts behind our eyes.
For we've our marching orders; 'Look back never
Absent thee from Felicity forever.'

But Bon's unhappiness was not only personal – it was grounded too in his sense of the violence and lies of recent European history.

Verse The two verses that follow have an autobiographical subtext; they exist only on handwritten pages torn from a small notebook and evidently belong to September 1951, when Bon was married to Elizabeth, in the army and living in Scotland, possibly still in Aberdeen where Aeneas, his first son, was born. Is this the accent of Robert Burns? Bon certainly loved his poetry.

To Aeneas crying on his 1st birthday
Weel, loon, ye've spent ane year on earth;
I see ye're thinking that your birth
Was nae great cause for sangs & mirth
An joy at a';
Nae doot ye think that this life's worth
Is wondrous sma'.

But bide a wee, & judge this world
(Intil the whilk ye're newly hurled)
When the lang scroll has been unfurled
A pickle mair;
At life's door-pin ye've scarcely tirled, –
It is nae fair.

Ye havenae tastit gude kail-brose,
Nor kissed a lass, nor dinged your foes,
Nor happed your shins in tartan hose, –
How can ye've judged
This life, when frae your lang bairns' clo'es
Ye havenae budged?
I ca' these discontentit tears
Impertinence, in one whase years
Are scarce as mony as the hairs
On a gowf ba';
What can ye ken o' worldly cares,
When ye're sae sma'?

I'll no preten' that life's a game:
There's tinin' freens, & leaving hame,
An' muckle dule & grief & shame
An' care; indeed,
Ye'll aften hae to fill your wame
Wi' bitter bread.

But, just the noo, thour't still gey wee, –
Sic clishmaclaver's no' for thee;
Thou still canst bid sobriety
Gang tae the deivil;
For, sure sufficient til the dee
Is the dee's evil!

For Gina's Album

Gina, my ingine isnae muckle,
O' book lear I hae scarce a puckle
My hirplin verse wad draw a chuckle
Frae ony poet;
At Wisdom's fount I didnae suckle,
An' weel I know it.

But here's your daddy speirin me
If I'll scrieve verses twa or three

Tae demonstrate calligraphy
(Losh, what a word!)
And here's the second done, you see;
Now for the third

May you be lucky as white heather
An' bonny as your sonsie mither
An' merry like your reveren faither
(But somewhat leaner)
An' ther's an end tae a' my blather.
'Amen' says Gina.

The next verse belongs to the early seventies when Bon was living in Lancashire. Designed for recitation in the Stanley Holloway manner, at which Bon was adept, it has corrections to the typescript showing him strengthening its Northern accents.

It were Christmas eve in old Ashton,
The butcher's till jingled and clicked
The assistant's pockets were boolging
Wi't brass he had foortively nicked

Then in strode the master butcher
In search of his missing brass:
He said 'Hand over ill-gotten gains, lad
And seetha, here's kick oop t'arse.'

Then oop spoke the butcher's missus
Her voice choaked with bitter tears:
'Yon lad has seventeen children –
What will happen to poor little dears?'

He said 'They may eat bread and dripping
And his wife better go on the Pill,
But he's buying no more Fairy Cycles
Out of money he's filched from my till.'

So all you apprentice delinquents
That fancies your criminal chance:

Wait for gaffer to give Christmas bonus
And don't tek it thasen in advance.

Happy Ending –
After Christmas, assistant coomes creeping
Hands trembling and heart fit to burst;
Says 'I'm offered a job wi yer rival
But I moost have a character first.

Will tha gie me a reference Master?'
Butcher thoughtfully glances at till
Then thinks about deadliest rival
And kindly says 'Ay lad – I will.'

[Yet another happy ending ruined on second thoughts.]

Waistband and waistlines

Blucher ostentatiously flicked on the safety-catch and magicked the pistol away into the waistband of his trousers. That is a very good place to carry a pistol while you still have a waistline; afterwards the bulge becomes a little ambiguous.   – *After You with the Pistol*, p. 196

Bon always had trouble with his waistline and liked this particular ambiguity. For those with an ear for it, there's a bat squeak of a Mae West joke here.

Watercolours

In a corner sat an old brass naval shell-case, crammed with stout sticks and fencing foils of the old butterfly-hilted *fleuret* pattern. Two walls were hung with early English watercolours of the good, drab, bluish kind. Nothing is more tedious, as Sir Karl Parker used to say, than an early English watercolour – unless it be a *faded* early English watercolour. But I cut my business teeth on them and always hold them in respect.

'Know about watercolours?' asked Crouch, following my gaze.

'A bit,' I said, looking him straight in the eye. 'You have a J. M. W.

Turner of the Loire which can't be right because the original is in the Ashmolean; a magnificent Callow of about 1840; a Farington which needs cleaning; a polychrome James Bourne – rare, those; a Peter de Wint hayfield with a repainted sky; an excellent John Sell Cotman; a pair of rather flashy Varleys from his last period; a Payne which was reproduced in *Connoisseur* before the war; a Rowlandson which Sabine had for sale in about 1940; a Francis Nicholson of Scarborough all faded pink – he *would* use indigo; a valuable Cozens and the finest Edridge I have ever seen.

'My word,' he said. 'Full marks, Mortdecai. I see you know about watercolours.'

'Can't resist showing off,' I said sheepishly. 'Just a knack, really.'

'Mind you, the Edridge was sold me as a Girtin.'

'They always are,' I said simply.

'Well, come on, what'll you give me for the lot?'

A dealer has to get used to this sort of thing. I used to take offence once upon a time, before I learned the value of money.

'Two thousand, two hundred and fifty,' I said, still looking him straight in the eye. He was startled.

'*Pounds?*'

'Guineas,' I replied. 'Naturally.'

'God bless my soul. I stopped buying years ago, when the dear old Walker Galleries closed. I knew prices had gone up but . . .'

'The prices of these will be going down unless you get them out of this sunny room. They've taken about as much fading as they'll stand.'

Ten minutes later he took my cheque with trembling fingers. I let him keep the Nicholson in exchange for an Albert Goodwin which had been hanging in the cloakroom.   – *Don't Point that Thing at Me*, pp. 69–70

Ian Lowe, writing to me in 1992, quotes Sir Karl Parker's comment on this passage: 'I will say this about Bonfiglioli's novel, you don't get a chance of putting it down & [I] read it to the end. It is an odd mixture – the last adventure becomes really quite poignant. He evidently has great talent and could make a lot of money if he is able to produce another and another. Strange how many variants there are to my wisecrack about the faded watercolours, this one was new to me.'

In October 1961 Bon hung the first of six Annual Watercolour exhibitions in his gallery at No. 13 The Turl. These involved a tremendous amount of work of different sorts building up to the frenzy of the Private View. By the time the last pictures were being adjusted on the wall a long and animated queue of viewers and customers stretched along the Turl. In the first fifteen minutes a flurry of red spots appeared indicating pictures sold, sometimes amounting to a third of the whole exhibition. Prices were reasonable. Bon would always take something back if doubt was cast on an attribution or a provenance. What he sold people was not only the picture but also what to say about it. Sometimes we went out to dinner to see a newly hung picture from the gallery and to hear that we were looking at 'an unusual early example of X's work. It was before he went to Italy you know . . .' Bon's own words served back to him like discoveries.

See also ART DEALING, DEALING and PICTURES.

Weaponry

Then, on advice, I took a cab to Number 205, Regent Street, where a Mr Beattie sold me a large revolving pistol made expressly for him by J. Lang himself. It was in a mahogany case, complete with moulds for both ball and bullet, a wad cutter, powder-measures and everything else proper to such a weapon. It was very costly, but the best that money could buy. I felt something of a fool as I walked out of the shop, my pockets lighter by so many guineas. It was to be several months before I congratulated myself upon buying so reliable a weapon.   – *All the Tea in China*, p. 86

A folder title WEAPONS contains pictures and cuttings from varied sources covering German armaments, Wild West weapons, a British Army small arms training manual issued by the War Office in 1942, a photographically illustrated account of USA Army methods of knife fighting. These materials were exquisitely interesting to Bon in themselves and also sources of information and accurate reference for use in novels.

On most book jackets Bon included a mention of his having been sabre champion of Scotland in his army days. He was also fascinated by Samurai swords and practices. He read aloud to me from a book translated from the Japanese which suggested that the novice, having perfected the one-stroke slicing of a cabbage from its stalk in the field, should move on to practising upon the necks of peasants before meeting other Samurai in noble combat.

Strangest in this collection is a cheaply produced Californian booklet: *The Militants Formulary* by Don Sisco (third edition), which gives detailed illustrated DIY instructions for making a range of explosive devices for scattering people in supermarket and cinema. Their use is described with unpleasant relish and there is a list of chemical and lab equipment suppliers and advice on acquiring materials without attracting notice. The most sinister aspect of the whole manual is its matey, practical, home-hobbies tone.

Among the photographs he kept from his military service in Sierra Leone are two of Sergeant Gilmore, the weapons training officer.

After the war, after his army career, life was still in the combat zone for him. I think he got rid of his firearms in the last phase of his life in Jersey but kept his sabres to the end.

See also GUNS.

West Africa

I remember little of our journey down the great river, for, at our first noon-tide pause for food, Blanche and I were persuaded to eat some fresh-water mussels, which grievously affected our bowels the whole of the three days. I recall only the all-pervading, sickly smell as of dead marigolds, the eternity of mangroves and the prodigious number of kingfishers of every size and colour which flashed across our bows like streamers of fire. Yes, and a frightful afternoon when we scorched on a naked sand-bank while a monstrous bull-hippopotamus raved and roared in the shallows, daring us to come into the water and fight with him.

The breeze was from the south-west, so it still bore the heavy scent of Africa but I sniffed it with rapture.

These two passages come from *All the Tea in China* (pp. 243–4). Karli is in raptures because he has managed to board ship and is leaving for England at last.

Bon holding a piece from his African exhibition outside No. 13 The Turl, his gallery, in 1963

Bon was in Sierra Leone as a nineteen-year-old conscript with the Royal West African Frontier Force in 1947 and 1948. The voyage by troopship would have taken several weeks. Ever after Bon kept a small collection of photographs of Africans and fellow soldiers. George Turnbull, a Lancashire friend who had also been there, says, 'He enjoyed it enormously. He liked the Africans. The fascinating thing about West Africa is their sense of humour, always laughing, very like the English sense of humour.'

The story goes that Bon's then wife-to-be, Elizabeth, used to knit him thick warm socks of hairy highland wool and that these were so coveted by his bearer that Bon gave them to him. They were proudly worn without shoes and taken off for football to save them from damage. There is indeed a photograph of an African boy standing hands on hips between two barefoot supporters wearing a RWAFF hat and some rather solid socks. Bon used to joke that there were lots of little Bonfigs running round West Africa for all he knew and he kept one photograph of a good-looking African woman. On a Pantheon Books author's questionnaire he claimed among his children 'out of wedlock, Momo, who is now Attorney General of a West African State, and several others'.

My knowledge of his time there is pretty thin. In a reference in his Kipling notes about a kind of Devil's Mass he observes: 'such litanies were still in use in serjeants' messes in 1945 and the Africans of the RWAFF never tired of making up couplets about every European in sight and order of rank'.

His time in Africa left him with an unfulfilled longing to go back.

In 1963, long before the Royal Academy caught up with Africa, he was able to put on a superb exhibition of African art and artefacts in his Turl Street Gallery. A photograph of him taken for the *Oxford Mail & Times* standing outside the gallery shows him holding one particularly female-looking object with a peculiar expression on his face. The photographer wrote on the back: 'If you think I've made you look bloody it's your fault.'

The invitation card for the Private View of this exhibition was hand-printed by Bon with the words 'Ex AFRICA ... ALIQUID'. Oxford customers were to recognize and complete this proverbial quotation from Pliny's *Natural History* and to know that it means that there's always something new to come out of Africa.

He gives a key role as hero's friend and cook to an African, the Doctor in *All the Tea in China*. He is almost a Jock substitute. Karli even compares him to his mother, and his galley is a haven of comfort where he can be found

fisting out great lumps of salt pork from a keg and roughly slicing them into a pan full of frying onions. He was braced against the bulwark of his galley and deftly tilting the pan each time it threatened to spill over, singing a deep throated and barbarous song.

He rolled a kindly yellow eyeball at me.

'Hot roll in the oven, Mr Cleef sah, only jess the one, if you please; rest's fo the captain's table.'

He is definitely the comforter on the ship of fear and physical and mental hardship. Karli calls him the 'moral barometer' of the ship.

– All the Tea in China, p. 99

See also ARMY.

Whiskey   Irish whiskey with the *e* and Scotch without it.

Bon seems to have made sure he is portrayed as a whisky drinker and often emphasizes a class difference in the choice of brand. Jock does not imbibe the same liquid as his master. See WRESTLING. Actually any whisky would do and a better brand was a treat.

Catriona writes about her visits to Ireland, aged fourteen: 'I shall never forget the nasty something dad had in his woodshed there: a whiskey-bottle mountain,' and says, 'He insisted on drinking Scotch whisky just to prove he could get away with doing so in an Irish pub.'

White paling fence   A white paling fence plays a significant part as a weapon in *The Great Mortdecai Moustache Mystery*, which Bon was writing in the 1980s. A curious detail to add to my theory that pictures he had owned sometimes provided a kernel of inspiration for later novels is the discovery that years ago the architectural historian Howard Colvin bought from him a Victorian water-colour, the main subject of which is a white paling fence showing up strongly against dark trees beside a woodland drive.

Woostering

After another invigorating suck at the brandy-tit we parted with many a friendly message to Freddie Widgeon and Honoria Glossop. As he courteously ushered me to the door he paused by what he no doubt knew to be a well-bugged standard lamp and whispered hoarsely, 'Charlie, don't believe a word old Mulliner says.' I gasped but mumbled assent, grinning inaudibly.

– After You with the Pistol, p. 314

Bon was a constant reader and serious collector of P. G. Wodehouse's books. The relationship of Bertie Wooster and Jeeves and Wodehouse's play with language were the main attractions, pleasures to share in reading aloud, in extended reference in his own novels and here becoming a code conveying more crucial messages under a mask of jolly fun.

Wrestling

'Professional wrestling. On the telly. Jock and I never miss it; so many of his friends play. Won't you stay and watch?'

'Good night,' said Martland.

For nearly an hour Jock and I regaled ourselves – and the SPG tape recorders – with the grunts and brays of the catch-weight kings and the astonishingly lucid commentary of Mr Kent Walton, the only man I can think of who is wholly good at his job.

'That man is astonishingly lucid, etc.,' I said to Jock.

'Yeah. For a minute back there I thought he'd have had the other bugger's ear off.'

'No, Jock, not Pallo. Kent Walton.'

'Well, it looks like Pallo to me.'

'Never mind, Jock.'

'OK, Mr Charlie.'

It was a splendid programme: all the baddies cheated shamefully, the referee never quite caught them at it, but the good guys always won by a folding press at the last minute. Except in the Pallo bout, naturally. So satisfactory. It was satisfactory, too, to think of all the clever young career bobbies who would, even then, be checking every Turner in the National Gallery . . .

When the last bout had ended – with a dramatic Boston Crab this time – Jock and I drank some whisky together, as is our custom on wrestling nights. Red Hackle de Luxe for me and Johnny Walker for Jock. He prefers it; also, he knows his station in life . . .

I sank into a happy, dream-free sleep, for there is nothing like your catchweight wrestling for purging the mind with pity and terror; it is the only mental catharsis worth the name. Nor is there any sleep so sweet as that of the unjust.

That was Wednesday night and nobody woke me up.

– Don't Point that Thing at Me, p. 17

Bon loved the wrestling and took his son Aeneas to it occasionally. He urged Michael Powell to watch it on the telly and, had his
film project come to anything, it would have included a wrestling
scene. See his sketch in BROTHERS.

Writing man

*Winner of the John Creasey Memorial Award 1973. This photograph
taken at No. 18 Norham Gardens, Oxford, shows watercolours by John
Newberry in the background and reflections of the second-hand Masonic
check carpet in the glass*

An untitled reflection from Bon's papers opens with a line of Yeats:

All things can tempt me from this craft of verse;
An itching at my bum, the vicar's nose,
A well-filled blouse – even a soaring kite
Which I must watch until it's out of sight . . .
Why can I not, as other writers do,

Work steadily from half past nine till two,
Then take the kids out to the local Zoo;
Play with them later, till it's time to sup
And then with pleasure help my wife wash up?
Can it be really that I am quite odd?
Or am I just an idle, shiftless sod?

Xenophobia Mysogynist yes, xenophobe no.

Yarns

Se non è vero, è ben trovato. – If it is not true, it is cleverly invented.

A proverb to suit Bon's gift for tall tales and verbal finds.

I cultivated, when I could, the companionship of the horniest-handed of the seamen, for those were the great treasure-chests of 'yarns' (this word means lovingly polished lies). They promised me that everything on land had its counterpart in the seas: there was seaweed, of course, a sea-devil, sea-eagles, sea-girdles, sea-dogs (but not they assured me sea-bitches, although I know better), and sea-hogs, sea-lions, sea-jellies, sea-horses and sea-holly, sea-mews and sea-otters, sea-snakes, sea-urchins and, need-less to say, the dreaded sea-serpent itself. Every one of them had talked to a man who had seen the sea-serpent; not one claimed to have seen it himself. This disclaimer, universal among sea-faring men, is an agreed ruse to disarm incredulity, of course.   – *All the Tea in China*, p. 122

Typically Bon had already reminded us of the origin of the word in the seamen's spinning of rope yarns.

As with seamen so with dealers – there is a whole treasury of dealer's yarns. Bon makes good use of a classic when Karli tells us how he made a mistake:

I spent the next few days chiefly in bed, plucking up my strength for the battle before me, whoring a little but also thinking a great deal about how a dealer in Delft should go about becoming rich. Once or twice I sent for a hansom cab and prowled about the area between St James's Palace and Regent Street where, in those days, the serious dealers in old pottery and porcelain held their state. I was shocked – and, of course, pleased – to find how ignorant most of them were. One or two – and they had Jewish names – knew something: not as much as me, but something. The others filled their windows with flashy rubbish. What I did learn from all of them, however, was the prices that could be asked; they amazed me. I, in turn, was amazed that my mama, who had never left her native province, should have given me such good advice in respect of 'walking around and about'.

I did not go into the shops of the dealers with Jewish names; I went into the shops where the goods in the window were laughably over-priced, for I reasoned (and this is still good reasoning) that a man who over-prices foolishly will make mistakes in the other direction, too. I spent a few pounds carefully in such shops. Later in my life I made a great many lamentable mistakes, but in those early days I made only one, for I seemed to bear a charmed life. This was it, and I tell it without shame for it was beautifully done. So was I.

Walking into a nasty little mud-pie of a shop, far from Bond Street, I noticed on the floor an incomparable saucer, polychromed yet from the very earliest part of the Ming Dynasty, when such wares were made with great difficulty and then only for the Emperor himself and his concubines. I kicked the saucer gently as I passed it. It rang true. It was a jewel, a jewel, unflawed. Better, it was dirty and crusted with tide-marks of old milk and a great, horrid, ginger pussy-cat was schlipp-schlopping some sour milk from it.

I walked around the shop, pretending to look at his pitiful stock, then said: 'There is nothing here quite in my line, but I have taken a fancy to your pussy-cat, for my little daughter has begged me again and again to buy her just such a pussy-cat.'

'Aarrgh,' said the shop-keeper, 'aarrgh. My own liddle daughter loves that there pussy-cat better than life itself. I vouldn't sell that pussy-cat for a fi'-pound note, I swear I vouldn't, for I could never look my little girl in the face agin.'

'You are trying to say that this pussy-cat costs six pounds?' I asked.

'Yes, sir.'

I dealt out six good English pounds, scooped the noxious beast into my arms and, as though it were an after-thought, bent over to pick up the saucer.

'The pussy-cat will be accustomed to its own milk-bowl,' I said off-handedly. 'It is dirty but I shall take it with me.'

'Oh no, no, no, sir,' he cried. 'No, not by no means. Vy, that saucer there 'as sold me three pussy-cats in as many months!'

I looked at him without expression.

'Would you care,' I asked, 'to buy this pussy-cat back for one pound? I have just noticed that it is not precisely the colour of pussy-cat my daughter pines for.'

'No, sir, thank you, sir,' he said, 'for to tell you the truth, the moment you discards that cat, were it in John O'Groats or even Hampstead itself, it will be back here by nightfall, shit or bust, for I gives it a little catnip and hopium in its milk each night; it has grown accustomed to it, you see.'

Anyone who has ever fenced knows the feeling of scraping his foil tentatively along the blade of a professor of arms. There is an authority about the resistance, an especial timbre to the ring of the steel which tells the almost-good swordsman that he is paired against a master of the art.

'Good day,' I said.

'Good day, sir. Pray call again.'   – *All the Tea in China*, pp. 44–6

Bon spinning his yarns could hold people spellbound. Many a yarn about him was generated around some kernel of fact. Yes, he found and sold a Tintoretto. But no, he didn't buy it from a country vicar/little old lady beating him/her down from forty pounds to twenty and then sell it on for thousands. I've heard at least five accounts, many revealing rather crude assumptions about dealers. Yes, he did have a boa-constrictor – a very little one – and it escaped, poor little mite. No, it did not return full grown to terrorize North Oxford. See FINDS.

Many a Bon story returns to me sevenfold.

Yewbarrow

Lights were burning up at Yewbarrow and a strain of New Orleans jazz filtered down through the trees – old Bon would be settling down to an all-night poker and whisky session.

– Don't Point that Thing at Me, p. 162

Yewbarrow was Judith Todd's home in Silverdale, Lancashire, where Bon set up house when he left Oxford, yet this reads like nostalgia for a bachelor pad. Harry Harrison, thanking Bon for his hospitality one October, wrote: 'I have nothing but misty fond memories of those days in Silverdale. People ask (Brian, H. Rubinstein, etc.) "What was it like" & I tell them just endless kindness. A bachelor's dream of heaven. We just drank & occasionally ate to our own schedule the whole time.'

The children remember being kindly received by Judith in the school holidays and Bon making a great to-do about cooking for them. They were impressed by the three taps in the kitchen: Hot, Cold and Rainwater.

According to Judith, Bon would put on a lord and master act there, clicking his fingers and saying: 'Judith my glass is empty.' Click. 'Judith my ashtray is full.' She recalls Bon in his worst authoritarian mode telling off the sixteen-year-old Aeneas for some minor offence, as if he were a small child, while she stood behind Bon's back making *Heil Hitler* signs. Even her gift for deflecting Bon's moods with laughter was not enough to sustain their relationship.

Yewbarrow had been Judith's family house and was Bon's hope of a new home after Norham Gardens. The Tintoretto money had almost evaporated before they got there. Bon had headed notepaper printed and intended to continue as a dealer. The bailiff was a kindly man very concerned about Judith's worries that Bon might go to prison for debt. When they parted, Bon took refuge with kind and tolerant neighbours until he moved to Jersey.

He had lost another home.

3

Zamindar A Mogul word for a Gombeen man (q.v.).

Zapata A flowing moustache in Mexican revolutionary style, after Emilio Zapata (1877?–1915).

Bon was on the way to creating an ABC of moustache epithets and famous patrons of face-fungus in his preparatory notes for *The Great Mortdecai Moustache Mystery*. He also experimented with moustaches and goatees himself. See CHARLIE for another one and COWBOY for its effect on his appearance.

Zebra Where Charlie plays the stallion – at least in Johanna's encouraging words – in torrid sex scenes in the Mortdecai novels the element of mockery is part of the reader's enjoyment. For himself Bon chooses to play the zebra, striped pyjamas for the less torrid zone of Jersey, to complete a verse alphabet of sex. Whether this was a true example of occasional verse I do not know. Sorry reader I've lost it.

Zest Listening again to taped interviews with those who remember Bon with affection, I hear the word enthusiasm over and over again. Zest is how he would have put it, enthusiasm being something you had to hide to achieve the proper mask of Britishness.

Though I have told some sad tales of Bon no one should underestimate his zest for life and his capacity for recovering it after the direst blunders and events. An intensity of response to knowledge, the natural world, the highest art, all things curious and strange, sex, an endless list because in the right mood almost anything could trigger his sense of enjoyment. His delight and his longing to share it were the most engaging, and most often remembered, aspect of his character and drew people to him.

Zeus Zeus, king of the gods, a splendid over-life-sized bronze of a man in a vigorous martial position poised to throw his thunderbolt, used to stand just inside the old entrance to the Ashmolean. Bon, a thunderer himself, found it consoling to compare himself with this naked figure.

Though Bon was usually rather anti-Freud, Organ Inferiority was a complex he believed to be common, and he was himself unnecessarily haunted by the need to make comparisons with other men. As he once confessed, he consoled himself by looking at the Ashmolean's Zeus.

Zizz

Then I had a little zizz, a little slumber, a little folding of the hands in sleep. A zizz, you know is a very present help in trouble. With me it takes the place of the kind, wise, tobacco-smelling, tweed-clad English father that other boys had when I was a schoolboy; the sort of father you could talk things over with during long tramps over the hills; who would gruffly tell you that 'a chap can only do his best' and that 'you must play the man' and then teach you to cast a trout fly.

My father wasn't like that.

Sleep has often taken the place of this mythical man for me: often I have woken up comforted and advised, my worries resolved, my duty clear.

But this time I awoke unrefreshed and with no good news teeming in my brain. There was no comfortable feeling that a warm tweedy arm had been about my shoulder, only the old gin ache at the base of the skull and a vague taste of dog dung in the mouth.

– Don't Point that Thing at Me, p. 62

See FATHER.

Zonks

Or working out a fool-proof way of murdering his wife. He offered me a drink but his heart was evidently not in the offer and I, too, was more anxious to do business than to quaff. Frankly, I would rather carry an Irish-made time-bomb around the streets than a package of heroin. If that's what it was.

We walked around the block to a spot chosen by Mr Ree where he was sure that we could not be overseen by stupid, bumbling, British Intelligence blokes. (It will be a sad day for the world when the Oriental gent realizes that Western bumbling is only Eastern guile in a different idiom. Well, a lot of it, anyway.) We sidled into an entry. He opened a capacious briefcase. I slipped a fat envelope into it. He gave me a fraction of a bow and a long, steady look before popping into a large, vulgar, black limousine which had been idling beside a fire-plug under the indulgent eye of a well-paid policeman.

I did not much relish the long, steady look from Mr Ree; it was the sort of look which seems to say, 'Mortdecai, this stuff had better be what it's supposed to be: we have ways of making you scream.' I waved a nonchalant hand, confident that the churning acid in my stomach could not be seen by the naked eye. Then I studied the scrap of paper he had pressed into my hand. It was not, as I hoped, a munificent piece of walking-about money: it was better, much better. It read 'MESSAGE FROM WIFE BEGINS QUARTZ-DECAY IMPLANT JUST A JOKE COMMA FEAR NOT COMMA PLEASE DON'T BE CROSS LOVE HANNA STOP ENDS.'

'Stop ends indeed,' I snarled.

Before the limousine was out of eyeshot another, even more vulgar black limousine swept up to the kerb – just like they do in the story-books. I gave it no more than a brief and haughty glance whilst I made taxi-attracting gestures to passing taxis. The taxi-drivers did not seem to understand my British gestures. Just as my fears were changing into honest British annoyance, I became aware that respectable-looking chaps were issuing from the limousine – the second, longer, more vulgar limousine, you understand. I recked not of them but continued to beckon imperiously at passing taxi-cabs. It was at that point that I was zonked on the back of the head.

Now you who – forgive me – have nothing better to do than read such tales of daring and true love as this which I now relate, must have read many a description of what it feels like to be zonked on the occiput. Stars burst wondrously, blue-birds twitter, fireworks effulge, bells chime and so forth. None of this is true; none has been written by chaps who have actually experienced such a zonk.

Speaking as one who has in his time received not one or two but several such cowardly buffets, I am in a position to record the resultant phenomena in scientific form, such as any serious medical journal would gladly accept for publication.

(A) The subject feels a distinct zonking sensation at the rear of the bonce or cranium. A momentary agony is experienced.

(B) This causes the novice to say '*Aaargh!*' or words to that effect, according to his ethnic group. The seasoned chap, who is no stranger to zonks, subsides quietly, lest he receive just such another.

(C) The subject then sinks into an untroubled sleep, more dreamless than he has known since puberty.

(D) He awakes, reluctantly, to find himself infested with a shattering headache and a great thirst. Moreover, he is surrounded by large, ugly men who view his awakening coldly, for they are engrossed in a game called three-handed pinochle. He goes back to sleep. It is not but a fitful sleep.

(E) He is awakened again, this time by one of the coarse, ugly men and in a fashion so coarse that I cannot describe it in a narrative intended for family reading.

(F) Full, now, of indignation, piss-and-vinegar, etc., he launches a death-dealing karate-chop at his tormentor, not realizing how enervating have been the effects of the professional zonk. The d.-dealing k.-chop misses by several feeble inches. The ugly chap does not even smile: he *smacks* the patient across the chops with a spade-like hand, back and forth and to and fro. In Brooklyn I understand this is tendered as 'whackity-whap, biff, zap'.

(G) Weeping bitterly with shame and rage, the subject collapses onto the carpet. The ugly chap raises him compassionately to his feet by grabbing a handful of hair.

All these things happened to me in the order named and I have a couple of neuroses to prove it. I was taken to a lavatory or toilet – no wait, it's called a bathroom in the USA – and was allowed to be sick, wash my face and, as my grandmother would say, 'straighten my veil'. (In my will I have bequeathed my collection of euphemisms to the National Trust.)

I felt a little better but my indignation was lessened by no whit. I am assured that there is many a chap who accepts a slosh on the brain-pan with equanimity.   – *After You with the Pistol*, p. 315

Not surprisingly this passage segues into one about hangovers and facing death; sex is offered as the sovereign cure – but go back to HANGOVERS if you will.

Magazine Editorials

Bon took over the editorship of *Science Fantasy* magazine with the issue of June/July 1964. He was a committed editor whose editorials testify to the patient and practical encouragement he offered to all who cared about the genre.

In Bon's role of magazine editor, his energy and sense of purpose gained a collaborative spirit that seems to have been remarkably successful. Rereading these editorials now, I am struck by his achievement: he took over a thin, infrequent magazine with a low circulation and a name of limited appeal and steadily, over a couple

Bon with Brian Aldiss and Harry Harrison, who contributed stories and editorial comment to Science Fantasy *and* Impulse

of years, built it up into a fat, renamed monthly with a significantly increased circulation.

The following extracts show not only Bon's customary wit and intelligence but also an unusually wide range of reference for a magazine devoted exclusively to science fiction.

Of course I could just pretend that nothing had happened and that *Science Fantasy* hadn't changed hands, editors and format all in one inter-issue period. But if you are the kind of reader who looks at the Editorial at all you will know that all this *has* happened and will probably expect some sort of comment – perhaps some promise for the future or a manifesto of editorial policy and beliefs. So here is something of the sort.

There is every intention of keeping this magazine going and, indeed, increasing its frequency if this can be done. It largely rests with you: and with the economic cycle which starts with your silver, in your trouser pocket. Every time you miss buying an issue, every time you borrow a number or liberate it from a friend's bookshelf, you strike a half-crown blow at a living organ of s-f in this country. Make no mistake: it is here, in the pulp magazines, that s-f has its essential roots, here that young writers first get a decent crack of the whip. Enthusiasts' clubs and conventions are excellent in their way but what s-f in this country needs above all is circulation. I realize that England hasn't the population of the USA; I'm not thinking of a circulation rise in the tens of thousands. A rise of even three or four thousand an issue would enable us to offer rates comparable with those earned by writers in America: we could then compete at the top of the manuscript market and make it worth while for the rising young writer to look in the s-f direction.

There is far too much talk about s-f and far too little of it being written. Until I took on this magazine and started reading manuscripts I had thought, as no doubt many of you do, that there was a mass of first-class stuff pining away in drawers while the wrong-headed, perverse editors printed reader-losing rubbish. I was wrong. I have just read through a quarter of a million words of MS and half of it was so bad it made me blush. And I don't blush very easily. You loyal, stalwart readers, who go on writing candid, well-reasoned, patient letters explaining exactly what you would like to be reading, are wasting your time. No one over here is writing that stuff, or, if they are, they aren't selling it in England. Except, perhaps, in the form of full-length novels.

So, when next you have the urge to write 'Dear Sir' – write 'Dear Reader' instead and try your own hand at the thankless, unrewarding task of writing s-f. I undertake faithfully to give very special consideration to any first attempts by readers, and, if we print any, to pay the most encouraging rates the kitty will stand. (But write your letter to the editor as well: I shall rely very much on your comments and criticism for the next few issues.)

I know this will make some enemies, but it had better be said. I don't believe that there is any such genre as science fantasy. It is either, at its best, off-beat science fiction with a touch of poetry or, at its worst, degraded science fiction, in which the author wriggles out of his plot difficulties by introducing 'mystic' or 'transcendental' elements (and there's a pair of suspect words!) just as an idle writer of straight s-f gets over the hurdles in his ill-made plot by dragging in another improbable machine. Mind, there's nothing wrong with the improbable machine so long as it is integral to the story: apart from the basic s-f allowance of a post-Einstein physics, the writer is, I feel, allowed one basic stride forward in science or technology around which to construct his story (if it's that kind of story). Thus you can write about what happens when a space-missionary recklessly uses a cybernetic speech-translator to tell the aliens how sinful they are (Katherine MacLean's 'Unhuman Sacrifice', but, when you've got him into a tight corner, you must not let him hop into a handy matter-transmitter: unless the whole secondary point of the story is that he *can*.

What you really cannot do – if you are writing for adults – is have a Venusian princess materialize out of the air, offering to free your hero from the BEM's clutches if he will come to Krzk and kill the wicked High Priest of Zoz with the magic sword of Ugg. Ugh.

My editorial watchword, then, is 'Science Fiction for Grown-Ups!' I hope I shall be able to make it hold good.

From *Science Fantasy*, July/August 1964, no. 66

My first editorial struck a base and mercenary note: I said that what s-f needed most was half-crowns, in the form of circulation. I also said that if more copies were sold we could boost the rate paid for stories and perhaps in the end, check the drain to America of riper writers.

Well, thanks to a handier format, a new distribution network, and Roger Harris's bold cover design, we have broken a little ice. Latest indications suggest that around 15 per cent more copies of the issue found good homes. *New Worlds*, too, shows a similar healthy jump. Hoping that this is only the beginning of a sharp upward trend, I am sticking my neck out and raising the basic rate for this magazine by – to be exact – 19.047 per cent. A start anyway.

My attack on 'fantasy' of the 'sword and sorcery' vintage in last issue produced a startlingly small crop of abusive letters and parcels full of Martian plague culture. Not a single sinister hunchback was detected cloak-enfurled, lurking in my shrubbery. Indeed, rather a lot of readers wrote saying 'good-oh' or words to that effect. Emboldened by this, I shall make another pompous Editorial Pronouncement.

If s-f has a future – and I wouldn't be doing this if I didn't believe that it has – it is not a future exhibiting the signs of a decaying religion, with innumerable sects endlessly subsplitting and high priests howling 'heretic' at each other.

Science fiction's task is to abolish itself. At present it inhabits a sort of quarantine ward where it leads a sheltered but unwholesome existence. We tend to think much s-f fails to be printed *because* it is s-f. Mr Southworth, of Queens' College, Cambridge, in a recent letter, posed the worrying question: 'How much would get printed, purely on its literary merits, if it weren't science fiction?' There's a dusty answer to that one.

In ten years' time, I venture to predict, s-f will have successfully abolished itself as a separate disease and will be in the main ward along with the other of *cacoethes scribendi* or it will be as extinct as the old-style whodunit with the whimsical pipe-sucking 'tec and the corpse with the oriental dagger under the fourth rib. I believe that the first will happen and that our sort of topic will be a normal familiar tool in the rack of every writer. Moreover, I believe that such a freeing of the novel from the bonds of plausibility might well be the saving, not of s-f, but of the novel, which is running down as the dominant literary form: people are beginning to tire of the endless intricacies of other people's adultery. I look forward confidently to the day when a 'mainstream' novelist will not think twice about exposing his characters, like Spartan babes, on the rocks of Alpha Centauri and when his publishers will print the result without the apologetic warning 'Science Fiction' on the dust-jacket.

A word about the preparation of manuscripts. Editors, being more or less humanoid, are inclined to look with a kindlier eye on MSS which are presented with a fair degree of professional turn-out. So may I describe what a MS from a good professional story-writer looks like?

First, it has a covering letter, listing what is enclosed. The MS itself has a preliminary sheet bearing the author's real name and address, the title of the story, the pen-name (where applicable), the number of words to the nearest hundred and the words 'First British Serial Rights', which means that you are selling the first right to print the story, in a magazine, in the UK, once. The next page starts with the title of the story and the name or pen-name of the author. For choice these are not underlined, or the printer may think that they are to appear in italics. Three inches or so above and below this matter are left blank, for editorial purposes. The story itself follows and is, of course, typed on one side of the paper only, double-spaced. A broad margin is left on *both* sides of the line for the subeditor's marks. If there is a division in the story it is unwise just to leave in extra space: put in a row of stars or something.

At the end it is useful to repeat your name and, for safety's sake, your address. Most professionals use quarto paper and this is a great blessing: foolscap is the wrong size for most envelopes and files and is awkward to handle in hotel bars and other places where copy-reading takes place. The whole thing is stapled, clipped or pinned together and a stamped addressed envelope is always enclosed. (One doesn't like to be mean over tenpence but there are only a couple of dozen of them in a pound note.) Post to me at No. 18 Norham Gardens, Oxford, and – if I may say so – the best of luck.

From *Science Fantasy*, January/February 1965, no. 69

C. E. Montague, the 'fiery particle' who turned the *Manchester Guardian* into a great paper, once wrote that all good writers are either 'putters-in' or 'takers-out'. The first sort build a phrase round a 'boss-word', a sentence round a key-phrase, form paragraphs of carefully matched sentences, and inlay them with epithets until their colour and texture is exactly what they envisage. T. B. Swann, whose final serial draws to a close in this number, is surely one of these: one could no more trim down his work without damaging it hopelessly than one could clip a few inches off the side of a good painting. The other sort – the 'takers-out' – tend to work as Kipling did, by pouring out the whole of their narrative as it comes to them, using every epithet that occurs, then putting the whole thing away for a few weeks. Reading the MS again with a clear mind, one finds, if one is honest with oneself, that at least a quarter can be excised. This process can be repeated until there is not an ounce of surplus fat on the story and the result is a crispness and tautness which cannot be acquired otherwise. (Kipling used a camel-hair brush and a pot of Indian ink for his deletions.)

Keith Roberts, I suspect, must work in some such way: his astringent little tale in this issue would have spread, in the hands of many other writers, over three times as many pages, yet every necessary word is there and the background, though only suggested, is as real as though he had lavished description on it. Incidentally, this versatile man is also responsible for our current cover, which heralds his latest story in the Anita series, due next month.

From *Science Fantasy*, March 1965, no. 70

People discussing wit usually end up by pointing out that brevity is its soul. Perhaps that is why the telegram lends itself so well to humour. My favourite example is the interchange between a newspaper editor and a dilatory journalist who had been sent abroad as a special correspondent. After a fortnight without receiving a single news story the editor cabled:

EXPLAIN UNNEWS

The reporter, a man of spirit who disliked 'cablese', replied

UNNEWS GOOD NEWS

The editor, however, had the final word, as editors usually do, with

UNNEWS UNJOB

What I am working around to saying is that there is rather little to say this month, except that I hope readers will agree that our contents continue to show steady improvement.

From *Science Fantasy*, June 1965, no. 73

Reading *SF Horizons* the other day I was intrigued by the apophthegm of Brian Aldiss's: 'The job of a critic consists of knowing when he is being bored, and why.' An executive sentence and one which works very well in its context but I am sure that Mr Aldiss knows, better than most people, how incomplete a truth it contains, especially in the light of a quotation he makes on an earlier page from Simon O. Lesser's *Fiction and the Unconscious*. Mr Lesser, who is a disciple of that ponderously dirty-minded old Austrian gypsy fortune-teller, Sigmund Freud, says, 'Like some universally negotiable currency, the events in a well-told story may be converted effortlessly, immediately, and without discount into the coinage of each reader's emotional life.' It is, as Mr Aldiss points out, a resonant sentence, even though, as Mr Aldiss does *not* point out, its gravamen is negligible and its hyperbole shaky. What is interesting about it is the choice of the phrase 'well-told story' where a more superficial writer would have said 'well-written'.

Nine times out of ten when a reviewer (as distinct from a critic) applies the phrase 'well-written' to a piece of prose he means either that it exhibits bursts of purple mandarin-diction (forgive the chromatic discrepancy) or, more commonly, that he found it abundantly *readable* – in short that he was not bored. I am not here concerned with the former contingency, only with this concept of readability as distinct from literary merit – and its application to the appraisal of science-fiction.

The front page of the *Daily Mirror* is usually full of eminently readable, well-told stories – one would have to be blasé indeed to be actively bored by it – but I am sure that even the editor would not claim that it is well-written, except in a purely technical and commercial sense. We see the Northcliffe method, resulting in typographical athletics, know how this is achieved – a logical extension of the avoidance of polysyllables, pre-digestion of facts, dissection of prose-units into breath-sized gobbets, ambiguous headings and all other easily learned journalistic tricks. We do not equate these simple techniques of applied psychology with literary merit any more than we confuse television 'commercials' with entertainment.

Let us move up a notch. The enormous success of the late Ian Fleming's James Bond series might tempt one to describe them as 'good' or 'well-written' books. They are, of course, nothing of the kind. They describe with implicit approval the base actions of an amoral thug engaged in an unsavoury trade; they are implausible in content, undistinguished in style, palpably deleterious in their effect upon the young and clearly written within the terms of a cynically devised formula intended to appeal to the most despicable elements in our characters. I read them avidly and so (statistically speaking) do you: cruelty, lechery, gluttony and snobbery are a group of indoor sports peculiar to what we laughingly call *homo sapiens*. We are not bored with these stories because, quite apart from the succulence of their content, they are supremely well told and the style is perfectly fitted to the class of material and the kind of reader aimed at. This applies equally to the Hank Janson stories. We are not regaled with descriptions of the changing light on the hills or the iridescence of a bird's wing; we are given crisp details about things we can still take an interest in even when all our critical faculties are switched off: the soft leather shoulder-holster under the tropical-weight suit, the Morland cigarettes in the flat, gun-metal case, the black, knitted-silk tie, the erectile nature of nipples. This is all Lesser has to mean when he talks of effortless conversion of emotional currency: we can enter effortlessly into empathy with Bond because we do not have to wonder, when we are 'being' him, whether we should be smoking Woodbines or Morlands. We can change our money easily: we have been told the rate of exchange. This is a technique which Defoe mastered and Richardson did not, which is why a thousand people read *Robinson Crusoe* for every one who has heard of *Pamela*.

But what happens to Mr Aldiss's definition? If Bond does not bore the critic then his occupation's gone; if *Paradise Lost* does, then his only task is to find the reason, which may lie deep in his own defective faculties . . . no, this definition can only be applicable if we postulate an inhuman super-critic whose values are absolute, who sits shivering with glee over *Paradise Lost*, reads *Martin Chuzzle-wit* with the merest occasional twinge of inattention, stifles yawns throughout *Goldfinger* and falls promptly asleep at the sight of a *News of the World* sex-murder headline. Believe me, there ain't no such animal – and some of my best friends are critics, as the sheriff of Selma might have said.

From *Science Fantasy*, July 1965, no. 74

'Readable' was the word I was worried about in my last editorial and a surprising number of readers seem to have joined me in my preoccupation with this word and its use. It has struck me that during my undergraduate career (a good word, that, with its suggestion of increasing momentum along a downhill slope) I must have written well over a hundred essays about English Literature and Language without ever having cause to mention readability – yet it unquestionably exists and can be isolated and it is the dominant factor when it comes to selling literary [material] to a publisher. As I tried to show last time, it is often quite unconnected with literary merit yet can exist – perhaps *should* exist – alongside it.

'Sapper', Conan Doyle, Edgar Wallace, Agatha Christie, Rider Haggard, Mickey Spillane (to make a rather random selection) all exhibit readability of various kinds to a very high degree, without, in most cases, claiming any particular literary excellence, although time has lent a kind of vintage dignity to some of them.

Defoe, Swift, Jane Austen, Dickens, Kipling, Maugham have both quality and readability, some by God's gift and some by dint of careful craftsmanship. Others – Thackeray, George Eliot, Meredith, Besant – once had both but have lost the latter in the course of time. A very few of the top flight – E. M. Forster's name springs to mind – tower unmistakably although neither gifted with, nor striving for, readability.

What is in all this for us – the s-f devotees? One conclusion is inevitable: our sort of fiction has its roots firmly in the pulp magazines and since these survive by the casual, non-enthusiast readers and not by the relatively few 'fans', readability must be a major consideration. A few years ago it was practically the sole one, until the public became sated by the more repetitious hacks, and the trashier pulps folded up one by one. Even today, when the battle for s-f's respectability is in some measure won, a magazine takes its life in its hands each time it prints a 'difficult' story.

The other conclusion is that, for the habitual reader of science fiction, a special set of readability factors exist, to which any new writer must tug his forelock. Like the detective-novel 'fans' of the last generation, we demand that a story must obey certain rules: we feel cheated if the murderer turns out to be the police inspector. Space-drive must have some kind of *rationale*, robots must obey the laws given us by Dr Azimov, the story generally must be true to itself – must grow out of its own postulates and not be merely a disguised Western. But on top of this we demand – wrongly, I think – that the plot must be new or at least be written around a new notion. This is absurd. A good plot is susceptible to an infinite number of rescensions: Béroul, Thomas, Walther von der Vogelweide, Marie de France, Malory, Tennyson, Arnold, Wagner and dozens of others used the Tristram plot – and so did a lady novelist a couple of years ago. Moreover, insofar as s-f does depend on technological and scientific 'predictions', our generation's crop of imagination has, I suspect, just about run dry and fiction will have to pause while science catches up. If and when we really have a time-machine there may be new parameters in which to imagine; the ones we have are full. The great imaginers of the 1940s pretty well filled them: new writers are either filling up chinks or, like Aldiss, Miller and Ballard, turning their curiosity inwards, away from space, away from what man may next achieve. The two finest novels we have had lately – *A Canticle for Leibowitz* and *Greybeard* – are in a way the very reverse of science fiction: they celebrate defeated mankind.

I hate to say it, but, when I look at the future through the bottom of my ale-glass, I can see about as much hope for science fiction *as we have known it* as there is for the detective novel, unless this insistence on novelty relaxes. It cannot hope to be accepted as part of the mainstream while it is bound by conventions more rigid than the ones it claims to be destroying.

From *Science Fantasy*, September 1965, no. 76

The other day a correspondent wrote to me bewailing the demise of the US pulp magazine, that nursery of many promising writers.

Rising wages and costs and circulations which, instead of increasing, remain at the same level are given as the reasons. There seems to me more in it, however, than economics.

American s-f of the thirties bridged the gulf that many of us could feel was widening between our muddle-minded selves and the science world. We read Sir James Jeans and Sir Arthur Eddington. But this was not enough: we had to feel we were part of the new universe we could feel was being discovered. Cajoled or beaten about the brain by H. G. Wells, we were convinced of the possibility of a rational society. And things in which we still believed were more important than the things we didn't believe.

It is doubtful whether many of us understood the background of the science world. The back-biting, the hunt for kudos, the dogged hard team-work had begun in some scientific disciplines but not in others. In rocketry the sensitive Professor Goddard and the individualistic Wankel seemed to be busily proving at least one s-f point, which was that an experimenter built his apparatus and then, if it worked, found out why it did. For design, a sketch on the back of an envelope would do; more potent still was 'the formula', which was used in s-f stories as a kind of amulet. The implication was, I think, that it was only by chance that *we* had not stumbled on the formula to destroy the world, travel through time or to Mars.

The charm of the thirties – to those s-f fans who were teenagers at the time – was that we knew enough about science to appreciate the new possibilities, and too little to realize what a bore most real scientific research was. Since then the world seems to have grown small, and less full of surprises. We are fairly sure now that there is no lost civilization in the Andes or the Mato Grosso; and Mars, a rolling stone, seems simply to have gathered moss and not to have nurtured a superior race. We shall not be building any spaceships in our back-gardens (with any hope of success, that is). The era of the amateur is over. It is very depressing, though there is a cheerful side.

Modern technology and science, limited to speculation though it is in one direction, opens up new fields in another. Biochemistry, sociology and psychology have become hunting grounds for new s-f themes. Many of these themes are on the borderland between science and ordinary fiction. I disagree with Kingsley Amis, who says that s-f writers are drifting into straight fiction – for me, the border has never been well defined, for we human beings are a queer lot. Just twist the point of view ever so slightly, and you get something extremely bizarre.

But the s-f of the thirties was not an inferior form of the art so much as something different altogether. No one took seriously the cardboard masks of heroes and heroines of the space sagas. They were the masks behind which we became, in imagination, what we thought we should be. We felt our imperfection and we still had the idea that, somehow, perfections could be reached by striving, by will-power, by self-control. Such s-f had something of the qualities of a myth or fairytale and became part of our experience. We participated in it and it changed us a little.

In a curious way, we have all grown up: even teenagers seem much more mature than they were. Perhaps the need for a myth has vanished. Anyhow, we have substituted illusions about ideals for illusions about ourselves being disillusioned, and get the kind of s-f we deserve. Those brilliant images, those characters you can walk around and talk to, are all the result of taking a straight look into a mirror and having cold images of ourselves reflected back, our surfaces at this instant of time.

We may not like what we see, but I doubt whether we are stuck with this view. For one thing, man is a creature of time and environment, among other things, and changes with these, as Bergson pointed out. Man's subjective feelings are part of the total truth he understands. Bergson was thrown out because he introduced unmeasurable qualities into what was intended to be scientific speculation. But this is the very stuff of the best kinds of writing: our continuing selves.

We are, as far as we know, a form of life growing on a mote of dust in a bubble of air, the third nearest of several particles moving around a very ordinary star. But we do not know what life is, and we are very far from understanding stars. In addition, the possibility of there being life on other planets would seem, according to Hoyle, to be pretty strong throughout the universe. Infinite possibilities, infinite interpretations; infinite speculation – and infinite themes for s-f.

From *Impulse, The New Science Fantasy*, May 1966, no. 3

Ever since the Renaissance in England – the reign of Elizabeth I for all practical purposes – fiction has concerned itself almost exclusively with the amatory antics of one particular species of biped – us. From the improbably simple characters of Richardson, Fielding and Jane Austen to the implausibly complex ones of Angus Wilson and Iris Murdoch today, the novel and shorter stories have consisted largely of what, when it takes place over a garden wall, we call gossip. Very occasionally a great novel has been created from 'biped-meets-other-animal' (Melville), 'biped-meets-place' (Defoe) and 'biped-meets-concept', but there has never been a literary 'kind' – in fiction, that is – which has really succeeded in breaking away from *h. sapiens* as the essential pivot. Probably the long and short of it is that most humans who can read are really only interested in other humans, while the kind of humans who are interested in higher things have tended to be the kind of humans who would write fiction. If you see what I mean.

In the 1920s, when compulsory education had really got a grip on the English-speaking world, a number of quasi-literary 'kinds' were developed to exploit the new mass quasi-literate market. The most important of these was the cheap daily paper (it has been said that Lord Northcliffe was the only man to derive any real benefit from the Education Act), but its more frankly fictional contemporaries included such familiar phenomena as the Western, the thriller, the 'romance' and the science story. All these, however, much as we may revere them as the forerunners of fine later work, were – let's face it – trashy imitations of the late-Victorian archetypal bestseller: Zane Grey, Wilkie Collins, Mrs Humphry Ward and H. G. Wells, to name the obvious ones. All of them, of course, were still strongly biped-oriented with the exception of the so-called science stories in which, with their fringe of 'weird', 'strange' and 'supernatural' elements, some thoughtful people, even then, saw the possibility of the growth of a wholly imaginative and speculative fiction with a minimal basis of ordinary real experience.

Here was the chance to shake off the trammels of the Renaissance and to examine imaginatively man's actual and possible environments; to reverse Pope's pompous dictum –

> Know then thyself, presume not God to scan;
> The proper study of mankind is Man.

Here, in fact, was the seed of a literature which might scan God – or his equivalent – in the same searching way that the novel had been interminably scanning Boy in his quest for Girl.

What happened? Well, we got our literature: some of the best writers working today are not ashamed to turn their hands to science fiction, and even the pulp magazines – like this one – print work of a quality which makes their pre-war predecessors look infantile. But has imagination been set free; is science fiction speculating away about the universal context of the scrap of dirt on which we bipeds breed and squabble?

Well, no. Outer space? 'Space opera' – what we want is Inner Space and psychological insights into our fascinating selves. Other possible life forms? 'Bug-eyed Monsters' – all been done before. Religious fantasy? 'Shaggy god stories', out of vogue. Possible scientific innovations? Well, only if they cause us fascinating bipeds to react in an interesting new way. In short, we're back at a highly polished, highly literate, highly sophisticated Square One, on which Theodore Sturgeon – one of the greatest – announces: 'A good science-fiction story is a story about human beings, with a human problem, and a human solution, which would not have happened at all without its science content.'

Oh well, I still prefer it to Westerns.

Short Stories

I want to keep clearly in view that my magazine is supposed to be a collection of *stories*. You know things that people read when they're tired or bored or sad.　　　　　　　　　　　 – from letter to Christopher Priest

Though not a prolific writer of short stories, Bon, as a Kipling fan, certainly intended to master the form and, like Kipling, 'to work by implication' leading the reader to a not fully resolved mystery. 'Blast Off' was the first, written in Oxford in the summer of 1964 when he had just taken over as editor of *Science Fantasy*. An editorial problem had to be solved with some urgency: he needed a text of a specific word count to fill a gap and took overt pride in doing this, while keeping silent about its then unusual theme and religious content. The story was anonymous, purporting to be translated from the Finnish; he modestly slipped it in among pieces solicited from Peter Levi and Brian Aldiss as well as from budding writers. Subsequently he was amazed and delighted when Judith Merril, the science-fiction writer, chose his story for her anthology of modern British science fiction: *England Swings SF* (Doubleday, 1968). The idea of himself as a writer took life and the first pages of his first novel were written.

'Catch Your Death' appeared in Macmillan's *Winter's Crimes* in 1976, a powerful and sinister story concerning a publisher and a writer that gave rise to the Freud letters between Tom Rosenthal and Bon during that period. Powerful in its moral force and historical vividness, 'The Gombeen Man' was soon recognized and appreciated in Ireland when it was published in 1978 in the *Irish Press* under the heading 'New Irish Writing', edited by David Marcus. 'As Simple as That', with its bereaved father and vulnerably haemophiliac children, is also set in Ireland. Published in Poolbeg's collection *Visitors' Book*, it was commended by Benedict Kiely in

Bon appears among new Irish writers with the publication of 'The Gombeen Man' in the Irish Press, *20 May 1978*

his January 1980 review in the *Irish Press*. Each of these stories would have had a place in the projected collection *Ghost Train*, told respectively by an Irishman, a Publisher and (possibly) a Bishop.

Two stories written in Jersey might also have become part of *Ghost Train*: 'Jersey Granite', published in a local magazine, a short and feeble ghost story not included here, and 'How to Frighten Your Wife to Death', written for *The Islander circa* 1983, expressing the destructive effects of alcoholism that were beginning to be felt.

Two stories about exceptionally nasty boys are among his papers: 'Freddie' concerns a character who seems about to be the death of his mother – the twist of the tale is that she dies of *relief* when he is sent off to school; 'A Trout in the Milk' exists only as draft pages in which an angelic-looking boy steals from his kind gran. Both nasty boys, seen from different perspectives, seem to relate to Bon's view of his boyhood self as having a single-minded selfishness essential to a survivor – surviving entails some kind of badness, in his view.

Brief extracts from these stories have been used elsewhere for biographical purposes; they are offered complete in this section for their intrinsic interest. The undersong of his feelings of loss and death can still be heard.

Blast Off

Astronaut's thoughts.
From the Finnish

When I get around this bend I shall be able to see it. There is sure to be a crowd in the enclosure – will they shout or fall silent? Some of them smug, glad to be shot of me, some of them crying big selfish tears, sure that I shan't be coming back, hating the thought, loving the sensation, licking up the tears; most of them not even rubbernecks, just big shots who've fiddled a ticket for the take-off – the people who can fiddle a ticket for anything but they only come to show the other fiddlers that they can, they don't even really want to gawp. There will be a few people who understand what it's all about, just a very few who realize that this is the breakthrough, that it is going to work. That it has to work. That this is the machine that will make Man free of the universe. If it works. And it has to work, like I said. Johnny thinks it will and he's been in on this from the beginning.

Yes, well, there it stands, that's the thing that you have to ride on, next stop the heavens ha ha and don't think you aren't scared don't let anyone think I'm scared I mean I'm don't anyone think I'm not scared oh you know. But anyway there it stands and I suppose like the man says it has a kind of stark beauty and all – long and slim and pointing up to the stars my destination and don't anyone think I'm oh hell. But it certainly does look kind of fine at that: good clean lines and the things like wings on the sides relieving the sweep of the line but not what you'd call a fancy design, more functional really, but then it does have a kind of special kind of mystery and appeal bound up with all that mankind's-hopes-and-fears stuff although this time it's only a one-man star-trip. One-way too, most likely. (Let's not go into that again, do you mind? Thanks.) They even have songs written about it already, like 'The Day He Comes Back What a Day It'll be' yeah that'll be a day but you know it's one man one way and the rest of the race can chase me.

Look I really do advise you not to pursue that train of thought, son. So all right of course I do get to come back, but I don't have to *bank* on it as though I was *stupid* or something, do I? So let's say I'm for sure coming back sure there's plenty of fools in the tank – there goes my unconscious or something making very cheap jokes – but there is plenty and I wish they'd just shut up about it, simply. In a moment I have to climb up there and ride that thing and they don't have to climb anything or ride anything except oh hell call this a take-off more of a kick-off I call it but the benefit to humanity is nevertheless blah blah blah.

Oh all right, so I *like* humanity, but I still wish they'd shut up. And stop assuming that I'm not scared.

All my short life I have wanted to be the first man to go to the stars and was trained up for it most of my life; not a mere man but a Project and all humanity cheers: oh his heroic sacrifice and he'll come back one day and what a welcome we'll give him and boy are we glad it's him and not us, no, what a glorious pioneer, saviour of humanity but why doesn't he hurry up and GO? What a sucker *he* turned out to be and we'll see he gets his name in all the history books is bunk unless he comes back which might be embarrassing and perhaps bad for trade.

Still it is a beautiful machine, no breadboard lash-up this, no prototype with all the bugs still in it but a masterpiece of simple design, clean, erect, ready for business (nearly there now) my old man would have admired the craftsmanship he was a very good artificer I should have stayed with him and learned the trade then I wouldn't be here all famous and terrified SHUT UP!

I can see mother in the crowd all gentle and proud and just quietly crying in a happy sort of way: I wonder whether she has any real idea what this is all about and what sort of a crazy son she had and do you suppose she cares, as long as I don't get hurt and boy are you going to get HURT. There's Johnny with her without whom this project could never etc. and he's smiling too as though it was him and not me and the funny thing is.

Mother will know how I feel and all the mothers here will know because this is like the very end of pregnancy, the long wait is over and now there's nothing for it but HAVE it: too late for hot baths and jumping off the kitchen table and the little Indian doctor that you-know-who went to and you've had it now – now you have to have it and now it's going to come tearing out of you and they say the pain is worth it but CAN'T I CHANGE MY MIND but it's worth it child and they can shove that too anyway mother knows and she's only crying quite happily so perhaps. Look are you getting hysterical? Yes. Are you, though? No, not really, but, do you know, I'd really rather, perhaps, on the whole, taking everything into consideration, by and large, not do this. (Anyway, I'm thirsty.)

I can easily think of about five million things I'd rather be doing this fine afternoon than go riding to the stars on that thing, for instance I'd rather go fishing on the lake with the boys the sails so white they hurt your eyes and the water so cold it hurts your dabbling trailing fingers and you don't care if you don't catch any fish but if you do, oh lake trout fried in an iron pan on a fire of twigs and driftwood on the shore just a shake of salt and some bread and then roll over and look up at the stars and dream of joining their company, or maybe a trip into the mountains and the joy of your pistonning thighs climbing and the heat beating off the rock and all day all alone, you can really come to terms with what you want to do about you know helping the human race and all and going to the stars and first man there and the human race shall never want again. OK you've got it now it all came true and there's your human race – fair samples – in front of you waiting to watch you do it and look at them. The best are sad for all the wrong reasons, their faces all crumpled and slack and uncomprehending, even the ones you thought had grasped the idea. Most of the crowd, however, have bright eyes and parted lips like young girls at a bull-fight or old gluttons before a bowl of tender baby crabs in boiling water. All these I have loved.

(And now you are not so keen. Now the big talk turns into actions which hurt the flesh and deeds which the spirit cannot compass.)

SHUT UP.

And the women now are all around and crying and wailing and carrying on and I didn't bargain for this, no one told me about this in the briefing, no one said anything about women shrieking . . .

'*Filae Ierusalem, nolite flere super me, ied super vos ipsas flete, et super filios vostros. Quoniam ecce venient dies, in quibus dicent: Beatae steriles, et ventres, qui non genuerunt, et ubera quae non lactaverunt.*'

And now I'm at the top of the ramp and the technicians are closing in around me, peeling off my earth-side outfit, checking the apparatus, there's the artificer with his hammer and eight-inch nails, the Public Relations man with a crazy signboard to pin up over my head and they're counting down now and the ground-crew are getting out the dice and the Met-men don't like the look of the cloud-ceiling and now you are not frightened any more for your mother is still just crying happily and she has always known the pain is worth it.

A sexta autem hora tenebrae factae sunt super universam terram usque ad horam nonam.

Et circa horam nonam clamavit voce magna, dicens:

'*Eli, Eli, lamma sabacthani?*' which, being interpreted, is 'My God, my God, why hast thou forsaken me?'

The end and start again.

As Simple as That

Our small twins were little bleeders. That is to say, they were born with haemophilia, a rare condition which prevents the blood from clotting, so that a bruise is a disaster and the least scratch a major calamity. It is inherited only through the female side but girls are hardly ever born with it; if they are, they do not survive puberty, of course. Our children's names were Timothy and Theresa.

It is neither an easy nor a happy task to bring up haemophiliac children but my wife had all the love and strength in the world and we learned to entrench ourselves into a pattern of life adapted to the daily nightmare, the constant terror. It was rather like a war in which all nature was our adversary and in which we had no weapons but constant vigilance, continual fear. We lay down at night with those and they greeted us in the dawn.

Every father's pride at watching his son climb a tree for the very first time must be mixed with a gut-clenching fear that the boy will fall; every mother dies a little death when her child comes home with a leg gashed and bloody from some careless encounter with a barbed-wire fence. Our kids would never, ever, be able to savour the delights of climbing a tree, nor could they approach a barbed-wire fence no matter what adventures lay on the further side. They could not even forage through brambles for fat blackberries.

Children are wonderfully resilient: our Timmy and Terry grew up within the elaborate system of taboos with which we had to surround them and they accepted their difference from other kids just as though it were all part of some grisly Grimm's fairytale. It was something to be taken just as lightly as the stories – but just as seriously, too, as all magic must be taken.

I would not describe myself as a sentimental man – sentiment was not at a premium where I was raised – but I must admit that there were times when I could have wept at hearing our little bleeders pattering out the speech we had drilled into them as soon as they could string the words together: 'How do you do,' they would chant in chorus. 'We're supposed to tell you that we're bleeders and so we mustn't play rough games eckseckera because if we get bruised inside or cut outside we might die of it. It's called hiffomilia.'

Well, we coped. We scraped and saved every penny so that we might one day emigrate to Western Australia and buy a little place near a sandy beach where Timmy and Terry could play without too much danger. No; when I say that *we* coped, I am lying. It was my wife who coped quietly, capably, whilst I dramatized, flung my arms about, cursed heaven and formulated a new and wilder plan every day of the week. Of course I worked; I worked like a madman, boasting incessantly of the money I was stuffing into our 'Australia-or-bust' bank account. I really believed that I was the strong man, the capable man, the man who was going to solve all problems by working just that little longer each day, squeezing out that extra one per cent commission; shouldering my weedy competitors out of the field. 'No friends, can't afford them; never give a sucker an even break' – you know the silly rubbish. The dirty taste still lingers in my mouth. God, how I worked, though. When I came home at night I had just the courage left to play jokes with the kids; just the courage to tell my wife I loved her, the courage to lie that I had already eaten and the courage to clump up to bed with a half a bottle of whisky inside me. Sometimes I took a shower, sometimes I forgot. The worst times were when I ran the shower while I brushed my teeth, splashed a little water on my hair and pretended I had showered. My wife never gave any hint of disbelief or disapproval. I suppose she knew I was doing my best and she was too loyal to face the fact that my best was not good enough. (The only loyalty I can return to her is to continue to call her 'my wife', rather than to use her name. Privacy is almost the last coin a bum has in his pocket.)

It was not until she died that I understood how utterly I had been living off her quiet strength, how shabby and how small had been my money-scrabbling contribution. Indeed, when I say that 'she died' I know that I am piddling with words. Certainly she died. Equally certainly, I killed her. No, there was no coal-hammer, kitchen-knife or hatchet – my worst enemy (well, yes, *me* of course) might charge me with self-pity but hardly with vulgarity – nor was there, of course, any murderous intent.

The 'deodand', or instrument of death, was my two-year-old saloon which was fifteen hundred miles overdue for a service. Inside the saloon was me; inside me was two thirds of a bottle of whisky. Beside me, until I hit the stone-work of the bridge, was my wife.

I had not realized quite how much I loved her until the surgeon came to tell me that she was dead. He was a decent enough man; he would not meet my eyes because he wanted to spare me the contempt which I would have seen in his. (I like to think that he was being compassionate but sometimes at night I think of the animals in the zoo: have you noticed that they never look at us? They have seen a great many of us and have not been impressed.)

Just what does one do in such a situation? For a childless coward there would have been an easy solution of course, but there were the children. They were there. I don't mean that they had been in the car, I just mean that they were there, existing, alive, sure that they belonged to me and that I belonged to them. So, the first dirty job I had to set myself to do was to tell lies to my children. They had not been told lies before. I let myself into the house and heard their grandmother reading *The House at Pooh Corner* to them. I stole into the junk-room which I used to call my study, unlocked the tantalus and poured myself a massive drink. It smelt of blood; I carried it into the lobby and poured it down the sink. In the kitchen I found some cold coffee, black and bitter. I drank it all. Then I went upstairs.

The kids were a little frightened at my damaged face at first but I wiggled my fingers at them and they knew it was me. While they laughed and cried and asked a hundred questions I was able to lock eyes with the grandmother for an instant and give her that fleeting closure of the eyelids, that infinitesimal shake of the head which all old ladies understand. Old ladies know about death, it's the only hobby left to them.

Then I told lies to my children.

I told them that their mother had gone to find a lovely new house for us all and that for a few days I would be putting them to bed myself – how they laughed! – and that my face was all funny and black-and-blue because I had captured a naughty bandit and marched him off to the Police Station. I explained that I was so late because I had walked home: I was tired of our old car and had decided to buy a nice new one. Their grandmother nearly spoiled it all by bursting into tears, but Timothy and Theresa paid little attention: even the littlest children know that grannies are nice but *silly*. Timmy was eager to know what kind of a motor-car the new one would be; Terry, bless her, was much more concerned about the naughty man I had marched to the Police Station: would they give him a proper, hot supper? With cocoa? And a comfy bed? I reassured her on all three counts. Lying, even to children, comes amazingly easy with a little practice. The practice is what hurts. Once you are expert you have nothing to fear but sleepless nights – and you can buy a remedy for those at any public house.

I have to say that the grandmother – she was my wife's mother, not mine – held us all together like a hoop of steel in the ensuing days. Neither by look nor word did she reproach me for killing her daughter and the loving concern she gave to Timmy and Terry was no greater than what she spent on me. Not once did she coax or bully me to eat – but whenever I strayed into the kitchen there always happened to be a dish of bacon and eggs or corned-beef-hash or a nice little pie keeping warm on the hot-plate, with a hot roll wrapped in a napkin and some neat curls of butter in a bowl of cracked ice. We 'passed no remarks' about such things. I forget whether I said that she was an Irishwoman.

Of an evening she would come and sit with me in the study – the drawing room seemed nowadays too large – and would knit quietly while I pretended to read. She never seemed to be watching me but every once in a while, at precisely the right moment, she would say that if I should be fancying a little nip of something she might just take the least little tincture herself. Looking back on those dreadful days now, I seem to recall that the bottle always held a couple of stiff drinks for me as well as the little 'tincture' she would take; never more, never less. I suppose that she was, in a quiet way, rather a wonderful old lady. Certainly, she must have loved her daughter very much to have been so unremittingly patient with me, her daughter's husband. I mean, she can scarcely have liked me. Have I said that she was an Irishwoman? There were many things I did not understand in those days.

I was, of course, at my wits' end; there simply was not enough money for the Australian venture and the senior partner of my firm was beginning to make infinitely tactful noises about how fierce the competition was, how narrow our margin of profitability and so forth. I knew what he meant. He meant that the firm could not afford to carry passengers and that I had become a passenger. We had a chat; he bought out my holding of shares at a more than generous price and the Board of Directors gave me six months' salary and a lump sum based on my commission earned in the previous year. I do not mean to denigrate their generosity when I say that they probably felt that getting rid of what I had become was cheap at the price.

The children's grandmother – somehow I have never thought of her as my mother-in-law – seemed to do no coaxing nor persuading but one day I found myself on the ferry to Ireland, with Timothy and Theresa bouncing and laughing in the back seat of the new car. I remember a pleasant little hotel with a French name in Dun Laoghaire, then an eighty-mile drive to a grand old house in an overgrown park somewhere deep in County Cavan. We were expected: the owner of the house had been at school with the children's grandmother. Timmy and Terry were whisked away by a fat and kindly housekeeper of the sort who loves to feed little children and tell them bedtime stories; I was given a searching glare from two of the bluest eyes I have ever seen, one large glass of Scotch and the most comfortable bed I have ever slept in. There was a dish on the bedside table containing three different kinds of biscuit; I had not realized that there were still houses like that.

I spent most of the next day in bed. People brought me things to eat on trays. The children, I was assured, were occupied with ponies and puppies. I got up in time for the ritual of watching them have their bath, then the grand old lady showed me the library, a library which would have aroused envy in the breast of a saint. There was a pair of leaves from a Codex Aureus of the ninth century, Wynkyn de Worde's 1498 printing of *The Canterbury Tales*, both of the Shakespeare folios – and a thousand other things which no collector today could afford. In the modern section I noticed that all the better things from 1920 onwards were affectionately inscribed to a lady, using her pet name, and I realized with a blush that I should have realized that the owner of the startling blue eyes had been very well known to the world under her maiden name.

She saw my expression change and she laughed happily.

'Yes, I know,' she said, 'you thought I had died long ago. No, don't pretend; come and have some dinner. Then you must get an early night if you are to get to Galway by lunchtime.'

I need scarcely say that dinner was of a robust splendour no longer seen in England except at the High Tables of one or two of the better Oxford colleges.

'*Galway*?' I asked mildly over the *potage printanière*, 'am I going to Galway in the morning?'

'Galway,' she replied firmly in the sort of voice which brooks no contradiction. 'There is a beach there where no one goes; a half-mile semi-circle of soft shell-sand, precisely what your children need. I have spoken today on the telephone with a reliable person there who sells property; he has just the place for you and at a price you can afford.' I opened my mouth, then shut it again. She would know. By way of keeping my end up, so to say, I observed that some of the sixteenth- and seventeenth-century books in the library should be shelved with the fore-edge outward rather than the spine and cited Earle's *Microcosmographie* to support my view. She knew all about Earle and this led us on to Clarendon and the dinner progressed with an added relish of bookish lore

Our coffee was brought to us in the library, where I was allowed to dote on a couple of Grolier bindings, then I was awarded a handsome half-tumbler of Smith's Glenlivet and, in the most tactful way you can imagine, packed off to bed.

'I shall not be up when you leave,' she said, 'but you will be called at the proper hour, your motor will be in front of the house and there will of course be a hamper of necessities in it. Your children are looking forward to their jaunt.' I tried to make a little speech of thanks but was quelled by a daunting glance from those terrifying blue eyes.

'Goodnight,' is what I said in the end, 'and, ah, thank you.' She bowed, but only from the neck of course.

In the morning I had no hangover: hangovers are for people who have not had a proper dinner. On my breakfast tray there was a sketch-map of my route and the name of the reliable person who sold property. The fat and kindly housekeeper had the children waiting for me at the motor-car; they seemed plumper and happier than I had seen them for weeks. I tried to slip a fiver into the housekeeper's hand but she explained, in the gentlest way, that it was not the custom of the house.

At the main gates an old man was pushing a bicycle laden with saggans. Having studied the customs of the country, I lifted an index-finger from the wheel in salute. I couldn't quite catch what he said but it sounded like 'May God be good to youse.' The kids waved to him cheerfully from the back seat: a glance in my rear-view mirror showed me that he was waving his hat at them and that his nut-brown face was split with a friendly grin. I shall never understand the Irish.

We made good speed to our destination but we lost ourselves once or twice so at lunchtime we drew up just outside Ballykeeran on the shore of Lough Ree and explored the luncheon-hamper. There was a nice little chicken, each dissected part neatly put up in waxed paper (it was not the sort of house to have heard of clingfilm), crisp rolls, a crock of buttercup-yellow butter, some hard-boiled eggs, some pâté sandwiches, the hearts of three lettuces – icy-cold in a big thermos – a quart bottle of lemonade *made of lemons* and, bless the grand old lady, a capacious flask of the Glenlivet for me. Out of some well of self-respect I dredged up the courage to have no more than one single sip, washed down with the capital lemonade. The housekeeper, bless her heart, had even remembered to include a damp face-cloth for wiping sticky little fingers.

Much heartened by this repast from times long vanished, I zoomed through Athlone and Ballinasloe and, quite early in the afternoon, made my rendezvous with the 'person who sold property'. I had been a little worried about this because his name, clearly written on my piece of paper, was J. Mac Seosamh and I hadn't the first notion of how to pronounce it. I need not have worried; he was one of those huge, pink extroverts who squeeze your hand until it's numb, pat your children on the head and sell you things before you have time to clear your throat. Well, I knew how to deal with that sort of thing: in my career as a businessman I had sold more people more things that they hadn't known they wanted than this fellow had eaten hot dinners. What vexed me about him was his frantic desire to play the stage-Irishman for the delectation of the British twit. Me. After a few 'begob's' and 'Jasus, Mary and Joseph's', I lost patience, took his arm and drew him a few yards along the pavement.

'At any moment,' I said carefully, 'you are going to say "begorrah". If you do, I shall spit in your eye. OK?' He looked at me blankly, then his great, ham-like face split into an enormous grin. 'I'm sorry, sorr, but the tourists expect it, you see that, don't you?'

'I am not a tourist,' I said. 'And my name is not "sorr", it's John. What's yours?' He looked shy; then defiant.

'Jesse,' he said.

'Bloody good name. Now, just over the street there I see a pub called Hughie somebody's. Does he draw a good glass of stout?'

'He does.'

'Then why are we standing here like a pair of idiots?'

In the pub, the licensee – I already knew enough not to say the word 'landlord' for it's still a dirty word in Ireland – proved to be one of those sour, mistrustful bachelors who pretend to hate everyone but who know how to draw a pint of stout. I bought the kids a bottle each of some awful fizzy stuff – and looked askance at the chipped edges of their glasses.

'Straws, please,' I murmured. The publican glared at me.

'No straws. Dis isn't a Select Bar. Yer not in Dublin now.'

I didn't know how to deal with that. Jesse Mac Seosamh did. He leant over the bar in a friendly way and stared at the publican.

'Straws,' he murmured. The publican met his gaze, wavered, went to a sort of hatchway and screamed down it.

'Ye lazy idle scuts,' he screamed, 'why is there no straws in the house?' Straws arrived, both plain and coloured, before Jesse and I had even penetrated the 'clerical collars' of our pints of porter. I remember thinking this a little strange at the time but almost anything can happen in Ireland and, indeed, usually does.

Refreshed, we drove a few miles to the splendid, curving beach which has all that the heart could desire. On the way I felt confident enough to ask Jesse Mac Seosamh what the 'Seosamh' part of his name meant and how it was to be spoken. 'Just "Joseph",' he said. At the farthest end of the southern arm of the beach there was an old planting of trees sheltering an extraordinary house which looked like a Scottish shooting-box of Balmoral vintage crossed with a Tyrolean hunting-lodge. It was quite enchantingly silly – I wanted it. Before we got out of the car I coaxed the asking-price out of Mac Joseph; it was very low, well within my means, but he warned me that it would need quite that amount again spent on it. I could see that.

A monstrous key squeaked and grated the side door open and I told the kids that they might explore but to take care. They trotted off through the cobwebs and dust-sheets while Jesse and I prodded broom-handles against sagging ceilings, poked pen-knives into suspect woodwork and sniffed knowledgeably for damp-rot. The fabric was not much worse than he had said and he told me that he had a nephew who was the best carpenter in the West.

We were walking towards the main part of the house when Timmy and Terry came pelting out, their faces radiant. I fielded them with my arms and told them to steady up.

'Oh Daddy,' they yelled, 'you never told us it was a surprise! It's the house that Mummy went to find for us, isn't it?' I found myself at a loss for words and Jesse was no help. Tactfully he turned his back and stared out of a window.

'What makes you think that, sillies?' I grunted.

'Oh, Daddy, she's here, you know she is, we saw her, we saw her, she's upstairs, up the big curly stairs, she's standing there, oh do come on, Daddy.'

Jesse came to my aid this time, he must have seen the colour leave my face. He took my arm and said, 'Come along, John' or something like that and the children tugged us into the hall. There was indeed a lovely curly staircase leading up to a sort of mezzanine or gallery but no one stood there.

'We couldn't go up the stairs, Daddy; Mummy wouldn't let us, she sort of waved her hands up and down to say we mustn't go up; she probably wanted to say something secret to you first.'

I looked imploringly at Jesse: he gave me back the look which a sergeant gives a young officer, the look which says that it is *you* have a brass pip on your shoulder-strap. I pounded up the stairs, waving at the kids. I was almost halfway up when the whole thing cracked and crumbled under my feet, my right leg smashed through a rotten tread which ripped my thigh to rashers as I saved myself by a grab at the balustrade. Jesse, good man that he was, coaxed the kids out to the car before extricating my bloody leg from the rotten splinters of woodwork. The femoral artery was intact, of course, or I would not be here to tell the tale, but I bled like a stuck pig. I remember him taking off my shirt and ripping it into bandages before I passed out. On the way to the cottage hospital I came to my senses once or twice and heard him cheering up the children.

As I passed in and out of consciousness I heard snatches of conversation.

'Of course your mam was there,' said Jesse. 'Why wouldn't she be and with that rotten old staircase to keep you from?'

'I think my mother is dead,' said Timothy.

'And what difference does that make?' Even Timmy couldn't answer that one.

★

A few days later we all met in the little town: the children were full of food and fun. They had been staying with lovely ladies.

'The good nuns have been looking after them,' said Jesse.

'They were *not* nuns,' said Theresa, 'they were Carmelites, and Daddy, would you believe it, Saint Theresa is under the special protection of their own patron?'

'Fancy that,' I said in a flat voice.

Jesse accepted a lift home.

'About that house,' I said diffidently. He glanced at me.

'We both of us know that you can never go there again,' he said. 'It did its work.' We drove a little further, towards where I supposed he lived.

'And I don't think,' he said, 'that I have any other properties to offer on the shore of Galilee just now.'

'On the shore of *what?*'

'Galway.' I must have misheard him, obviously. We dropped him at the entrance to an overgrown lane. I knew better than to offer him anything for his time and trouble. Feebly, I said, 'That nephew of yours, the carpenter, is he in the yellow pages?'

'You'll find him all right,' he said.

We drove off.

'Daddy,' said Theresa, 'you never asked me who was the patron, the *real* patron of the Carmelite ladies.'

I pulled myself together.

'Saint Cunegonde?' I asked. 'Saint Paula the Bearded? Surely not Saint Kyril, who cruelly murdered the female mathematician Hypatia?'

'Oh, do stop showing off, Daddy, make a proper guess.' It wasn't a guess at all, of course; I just hadn't wanted to say it.

'Saint Joseph?'

They clapped their hands, proud of me. That was the last time anyone was proud of me. It was almost exactly nine years ago.

I am a childless man now, of course. I'm told that you can survive for years on a diet of self-pity and whisky. I still shave three times a week. That's in good weeks, of course.

Naturally, I cannot believe in God. But as sure as I'm sitting here and as deadly sure as you are scanning these lines, I believe in a big, kindly, pink fellow in County Galway who went by the name of J. Mac Joseph.

He is not in the telephone book.

The Gombeen Man

All five of us had, at one time or another, been sent on these visits of inspection to disaster areas and we were used to tiresome delays, so when the big, Russian-made limousine broke down we delegates were at first only annoyed.

Then boredom set in, exquisite boredom. There was nothing to be seen for miles but snow and the grim ranks of fir and spruce on the slopes. Our bags had gone before us in another car and there was not so much as a newspaper to read.

Soon the cold supervened and we squabbled half-heartedly about this. The 'fug' party beat the 'fresh air' faction by three to two: all windows were closed and soon we were moderately warm except around the feet.

But the real enemy was stealing up on us: hunger. The car had broken down many hours ago; our surly driver, after an hour's ineffectual tinkering with the engine, had set off on foot, cursing, for the nearest town, many miles away, where he might or might not find a mechanic or another vehicle. It was just ten hours since we had eaten – and that had only been stale rolls and something which seemed almost like coffee.

The Trades Union Leader pulled out his watch.

'Six o'clock,' he said wistfully. 'I'm usually sitting down to high tea at six o'clock.' No one answered him.

'In fact,' he went on, 'I swear I could eat a ruddy horse.'

'I am devout Hindu,' said Mr Mukerjee, valiantly merry, 'but I am so jolly starving that I could eat a *cow.*'

To me, squaring my elbows to a 'knife-and-fork' high tea is, in the ordinary way, as unthinkable as eating cow is to a Brahman, but at that time the thought of ham and eggs and chips with lots of bread and butter and strong, sweet tea maddened me like wine.

We all fell silent, gnawed at by thoughts of food, regardless of creed or caste.

'My great-grandfather *died* of hunger,' said the Irish Senator.

We looked at him uncomfortably.

'Oh dear, the poor man,' said the kindly old Anglican priest. 'That will have been in the Great Famine, I suppose?'

'As a matter of fact, no. And he was not a poor man; I don't suppose he ever missed a meal in his life. And his great hunger didn't begin until the Famine was over. But he starved to death, all right. Then again, you could say that my father killed him, I suppose. Or an old woman.'

A great silence fell upon us: even I was at a loss for an apt comment. The old priest sat gently shaking his head, for he, the least worldly of us, had instantly divined that here was some tangled tale of old and unforgiven evil.

'I think,' he said at last, 'that you should tell us about your great-grandfather, my son. It may help us, you see, and will certainly help you.' I, for one, was startled: Anglican canons are not in the habit of saying 'my son', least of all to senior Irish politicians.

The Irishman looked sharply at him with a strange, little sort of a half-smile. You might have been forgiven for thinking that it was a *grateful* half-smile.

'The trouble with you English,' he said to us, 'is that you have no sense of history. The trouble with us Irish is that we have too much of it – and we're inclined to get it wrong. It's been said that you remember nothing and that we forget nothing. I sometimes think that you have the right of it about history: you know that there's nothing to learn from it except that there's nothing to learn from it. Meanwhile, there's children to be fed.'

I started to pay attention: this was, clearly, a most uncommon Irishman.

'You'll maybe remember,' he went on, 'that when we introduced ourselves this morning I told you my name: Fitzgerald. We Geraldines are one of the very oldest of the ancient Anglo-Norman

Irish families; it is a name respected by English and Irish, Catholic and Protestant alike; indeed you'll still find old people in Ireland who'll speak of the name FitzGerald as "the good name", whether the man who owns it is in the castle or the gutter.

'Our branch of the family happens to be Catholic. We were too well placed for Cromwell to tear us down – ah, yes, there's the history again – but the Penal Laws did for us all right. You'll not have heard of the Penal Laws.' He said that last sentence in a flat voice, his eyes glancing around at ours. Three of us made embarrassed, mumbling sounds but when his eyes came to mine I was ready for him.

'Started in the 1690s,' I ventured. 'Not fully abolished until, oh, the 1820s? 1830s? Prohibited Catholics from holding any office or commission or entering any of the professions – that sort of thing?' He gave me a quizzical look.

'You're English?' he asked incredulously.

'Only in spots,' I said.

'Were you at school in England, though?'

'Yes.'

'And they taught you about the Penal Laws?'

'Well, it was a very expensive school.'

While he digested this I awarded myself a cigarette for Historical Knowledge.

'As our friend here has said,' Fitzgerald went on, 'the laws excluded any Catholic from holding a respectable position, but there was more in it than that, and cruelly clever. No Catholic landowner could leave his estate to his eldest son unless the son would "turn" – go Protestant, you understand. If he would not, then the lands must be divided between all the sons.' He paused. We tried to puzzle out why this was the cruelly clever bit. The barrister spotted it instantly, of course.

'God,' he said, 'yes. Yes, I see.'

'There you are, then,' said Fitzgerald. For the benefit of the rest of us he explained.

'When an English landowner died in those days, the Great House and the broad acres would go to the eldest son, would they not?

They'd buy the second son a commission in the army, the third would go to university and take one of the Church livings in the family's gift. Any others would go out to the colonies, or would marry beneath them, into trade, for the money itself.

'Your Catholic in Ireland could do no such thing. Just his portion of the acres – and the roof taken off the Great House to avoid the Cess Tax and Poor Rates.

'As the world knows, we Irish are a fertile race. Now take a Catholic gentleman with six hundred acres and four sons, then each one of them having four sons: you can see that by the third generation you'd have nothing but a generation of petty farmers – and *their* sons going cap-in-hand to some agent for a bit of a conacre lease or even begging to be "tenants-at-will" – if they weren't begging their bread already. There was always the joke when I was a boy that every Irish beggar claimed descent from the High Kings of Ireland: the black joke in it was that most of them would be telling the truth.'

He fell into a morose silence. For my part, I am no lover of 'old, far-off, unhappy things', but the waves of bitter history which exuded from the old gentleman were almost tangible.

'Yes,' murmured the barrister with a sort of reluctant admiration, 'the swine that drafted that law was a bloody genius. No massacres, no confiscations, just obliteration with a slow-burning fuse. "Divide and rule".'

The old Senator gave no sign of having heard him; his teeth were locked into the history of the saddest race the world has ever known. It fell to the clergyman to break the spell.

'Your great-grandfather,' he said, crisply, authoritatively.

'My great-grandfather, by 1840, had sunk lower than any decent tinker or honest thief, for he was the dreaded gombeen man of our little town.' He must have sensed our puzzlement. '"Gombeen" is a word people will still spit at the speaking of; it's the dirtiest word in Ireland, filthier than the very "landlord" itself. A gombeen man was a thing that God himself would hate.' He seemed to have finished.

'I'm sorry,' I said, 'but what exactly was a gombeen man?'

Instead of answering me, he turned to the Hindu delegate and asked him a question.

'You'll have come across the *bunnia* of the Indian country villages? The rapacious, usurious pig who has the whole countryside by the throat with his lendings and his mortgages and his fat, smiling face?'

'Oh, goodness yes,' said Mukerjee hastily, 'I know them well. They are fiends incarnate. They are worse than smallpox, worse than tapeworm.' He nodded vehemently again and again. A little too vehemently, it seemed to me.

'Well, that's your gombeen man. That was my great-grandfather. But he'd lend you money on your crop, that way you could pay your landlord's agent, then he'd sell you yellowmeal by the penny-worth on credit until you owed him a pound note with the interest and all, then he'd send the grippers in to you – the bailiffs – and lift your bits of sticks. Nine thousand people in that parish there were at that time and not a dozen tables did they own between them, let alone anything you'd call a bed. Aye, you can raise your eyebrows, but it's all written in the books. The only furniture in most cabins would be the chest.'

'A chest of drawers?'

'Not at all. Sorrow a chest of drawers for miles around except in the town.' (His diction was becoming more Irish as he warmed to his tale.) 'The chest I'm speaking of would be just a bit of a box to stand by the door – in it there'd likely be your scraps of paper, your wife's good shawl if it wasn't sold already, her wedding ring, maybe a pewter dish and a real china plate and a few coins of money saving up for the emigrant ship to Quebec. The very minute a garsoon ran to your cabin to say the dragoons or the rough-and-readies – manorial police – were out at the evicting and tumbling folk's cottages, or that the gombeen man's javelins were seen in the townland, into the chest would go your potato-pot, your kettle and your bellowes and out of the door with it and into the scalpeen you'd made ready in the ditch below. All that the grippers would find to lift was the wooden water bucket, the rags on your back, the straw under the baby and maybe a bit of a stool that the owld, daft grandmam would be squatting on.'

He was mouthing the words painfully, hatingly, as though history was an abscessed tooth which your tongue cannot resist tormenting.

'Ah, we hated the English landlord of course, but he'd not been seen in the townlands in living memory – he was just a name and a foolish title and likely in Chancery for his gaming debts. The agent was easier to hate for you had to go cap-in-hand to him twice a year on Gale Day to pay your rent and maybe beg a new lease. But the gombeen man you saw every week and you could study his face, that way you could hate him carefully, every night in your cold bed. He was a piece of evil walking on two legs.'

'You speak as though you were there at the time,' I said. He looked at me strangely.

'I am,' he said. 'Did you read *The Canterbury Tales* at that expensive school of yours? You did? Then you remember the Summoner – "He durst not for very filth and shame / Say that he was a summoner, for the name." There you have the man exactly. Indeed, my great-grandfather never durst walk out without a pair of his strong toadies and lick-spittles beside him, nor would he ever fare into a lane with a hedge thick enough or a *sheuch* deep enough to hide a man with a gun. The cottiers on their conacre fields were too cowed to offer him a mischief; it was fishermen he feared, for they were a wild lot and full of badness. He was cruellest of all to them, for they spoke only the Gaelic, which he despised, and they could not be made to take off their knitted caps in his counting-house. They paid for that, all right.

'When the Easterly gales were blowing, you see now, no curragh could put out to sea, for the next nearest haven of refuge was Halifax, Nova Scotia. After ten days of the Easterlies these shiftless folk would be ready to sell their gear – nets, cordage and oars – for a bellyful; and there was none to buy but your gombeen man. Ten shillings silver was his price for the whole gear of a boat, take it or starve. They took it. How wouldn't they? When the fair winds came around again, your man would hire out their gear back to them at tenpence a day – and a penny a week interest. If they made a good catch there was few enough with the pence to buy – nevermind how cheap they cried them – and the stench of piles of rotting fish on the quay would sicken a dog. If they made no catch, well, it was back to your gombeen man for another tenpence of credit.

'It was his grown son – my grandfather – who had to deal with the fisher-folk, for he had picked up a little of the Irish tongue from his mates at the hedge-school. He was a decent enough fellow for the son of a father like that and many a time he could have puked with the shame of it.

'But those were the ordinary years, before the Famine, when out of the nine million people in Ireland only two million or so would be at starvation-point, and that mostly in the summer months before harvest, when there was food to be found in every hedge and decent folk could afford to give any beggar a bite and a sup.

'Then came 1846 and the blight turned lazy-bed gardens of potatoes into dirty brown messes of madder overnight. Do you see now, the tenant farmer grew grain for cash to pay his rent; it was the potato-garden which fed himself and his family. With the potatoes destroyed he now had the choice: thresh and sell the oats so that he could starve under a roof – or eat the oats and be evicted and starve and freeze in a ditch. I'll not elaborate; it's an old tale and you may well have heard the tenth part of it somewhere, which is all an Englishman could hear and believe.

'But my great-grandfather was now in fine feather, for prosperity is no blessing to the gombeen man: desperation is what he thrives upon. He throve. The Quakers and the British Association and the Public Works brought pennies into the countryside after a while and pennies were what he loved, for he knew that twenty times twelve of them made a pound note – and the little fellows rolled into his counting-house as though they had wheels on them.

'The grand harvest of 1847 slowed down his dirty trade but it enabled him to collect a fair lock of capital debts – although he loved the interest better – and, not liking to have his money be idle, he dabbled a bit in the passenger-broking business. He would buy fifty berths in a coffin-ship bound for Quebec for just ninety-five pounds and he would sell them for sixty-five shillings apiece. There was no trouble selling the tickets, for his gaudy circulars promised seven pounds weight of food a day as part of the bargain. The nature of the food was not specified.

'Those who stayed could not believe that God would strike twice at their gardens, so in went the potatoes again – and again the blight destroyed them entirely. It was worse this time, though, for the past year had seen the armed risings under Smith O'Brien, Meagher of the Sword and them, Government in London, had no patience or sympathy left for the Irish at all. They said we were 'whining for charity out of mouths still hoarse from shouting treason'. Ireland was now to muck out her own stable and feed her own poor – 'natural processes' were to follow their own course, which meant that, with luck, enough of us would die to bring the population down to a governable level. They called it *laissez faire*.

'Even the Quakers, the good men, packed up and left, for they had no more resources. A half of the Poor Law Union in the country were bankrupt – and here my great-grandfather made his finest stroke of all. The Guardians of our Union owed him for ten weeks' supply of yellow meal and turnips so your man sends in the grippers to the festering workhouse itself and seizes cots, blankets, benches and the soup-boiler – the whole bill of the races. The blankets he burned in the street outside – they were unsaleable because of the filth and the lice – he had only lifted them for the principle of the thing, do you see?

'By the time I'm speaking of he owned everything eatable or movable for twenty miles around and the proudest men were glad to kiss his arse for a cup of meal to keep the milk in the mothers' breasts. Lord God, but he was the happy man: they say that, on a Sunday, his face fairly shone as he bellowed out the hymns.

'Well now, one day, into his counting-house in the little town comes a young woman in rags of black frieze: she cannot speak a word for starvation and fatigue. She holds out her babby to my great-grandfather, making a mewling noise like a hurt cat. The child itself has a swollen belly and the delicate skin hanging off its sharp little bones like muslin.

'"Has she anything to sell?" asks my great-grandfather. One of his toadies rubs forefinger and thumb together and the woman shakes her head, still whimpering and mewling.

'"Get her to hell out of here," he says.

'"Father," says his son, my grandfather, "the child is dying; could we not – ?"

'"No we bleddy couldn't," he says. "Let the whelp perish with the bitch." The woman stands there for a moment, black against the bright sunshine of the doorway, then, at a coarse gesture from one of the bully-boys, she shuffles away.

'And back goes the man to his ledgers and the smell of the good meat gravy streaming out of the kitchen all the while.

'Two days later the doorway is darkened again with a woman's shape, but this time it's an old crone with streeling hair, you'd think to look at her she was as old as God, and she has a little parcel of rags which she lays on the counter. The man opens it and starts back in disgust, for it's the babe, dead now and with the stench of fever on it. The old woman gabbles something, humbly in the Irish, and he looks at his son for the meaning of it. The young man says that he thinks the old woman has said, "Since your honour killed the child you have the right to bury it, for there is no man left in our clan with the strength to scrape a hole in the earth."

'The gombeen man is enraged: he orders the crone out of his shop. She stands in the doorway, black against the light, the bundle of rags held high in one hand, so light the little thing was, and keens and keens in a voice so unearthly that none dared try to shut her mouth. At the end of it her voice drops to a deep, choking noise and she spews the words up one by one.

'"Get the old hure out!" screams my great-grandfather when she has done. "Out, *out!*" But the old woman has gone already. Back to his ledgers goes your gombeen man, shaking with what might be rage or maybe something else, or worse. That evening, as he sat at his tea, his mouth crammed with the rich mixture of meat and potatoes and buttermilk, he casually asked my grandfather what "the old hure had been scritching". My grandfather's bride, a chaste and well-born girl, flushed at such language and her husband answered his father coldly.

'"I could not follow much of what she said; she spoke in an ancient kind of Erse which only the Claddagh folk use these days."

'His father grunted and pushed away his platter, still a quarter full. My grandmother, anxious to be the good young wife, gathered the platters together and scraped all the leavings on to one.

'"And where d'ye think you're going with that?" he demanded. "Why," said she, "I'm going to put it to the stirabout left from breakfast, and the end of the buttermilk, and make a mixty-maxty for the souls crying in the street." He gave her a black look, full of badness. "Make your mixty-maxty, girl dear," he said, "and bring it here to me." She did, while his own wife poured him a bumper of raw spirits. He took the dish of leavings, sniffed at it and with a flick of his wrist splattered it across the floor, where his two great savage curs had it lapped up in a moment.

'"I feed *them*," he said, jerking his chin at the dogs, "to protect us all from the thieving savages out *there* –" and his chin now jerked towards the street. "If you wish to pamper and coddle lousy beggars you may do so from your own purse, not mine." (This was his dirty jest, do you see, for my grandfather was not then of age and so his bride's decent dowry had passed straight into the old devil's strong-box.) The little bride fled from the room, too proud to be seen in her tears. "Now," says the old man to his son, "you may tell me what the old, crazed biddy was squealing at me this afternoon."

'"I told you, Father, that I could not grasp the whole of it; I only took in what she said at the end – and five minutes ago I would not have told you that, at all."

'"Well, spit it out, you young fool."

'"Well, best I recall, she said, 'Agus mionnaim le fuil na Muice Duibhe a d'fhulaing ag Dún a Rí go mbeidh cuimhne agat-sa ar an leanbh blian on lá innui agus cuirfidh si a mathair i do smaointe agus taispeán faidh mé duitse an bhri atá le gorta.'"

'"Very fine," sneers the old man, "you can gabble and patter as well as any beggar, it does you credit. Does the gibberish mean anything in Christian?"

'"I don't know about Christian, Father, but I can give you the gist of it in the English, if you wish. It was a curse."

' "I could tell you that, ye bostoon."

'The young man flushed at the dirty word and took a deep breath. "She was swearing by the Black Pig which raced across Ireland long before Christ and which bled at Dún a Rí – that's King's Court in County Cavan – and she promised that this day a twelve-month you will be reminded of the babe; the babe will remind you of the mother and, after that, she – the old woman – promises to teach you the meaning of the word *gorta*. It means 'hunger'."

'The old man swilled another measure of the whiskey.

' "Is that all?"

' "That's all, Father."

' "Then get away to your wife's bed and make me a grandson with a pair of mogarees on him, for begob you're as much use to me as a louse in me haffet."

'My grandfather not only went to bed; he went, the very next day, away from that vile house and that crying countryside and took his bride to Liverpool. They were filling the cellars with sand in that city to keep out the starving, fever-rotten Irish, but my grandfather had friends and relatives-in-law who found him a decent post as a bill-of-lading clerk in the Shipping House and he prospered. Meantime he found leisure to beget my father: it may well have been upon a St Patrick's Day for the child was born a few days before Christmas, as many a good Irishman is.

'But to get back to my great-grandfather, the gombeen man. He too prospered while his old dame peered at him through the cataracts on her eyes, saying nothing, for there was nothing in it to say. His toadies bullied and fawned and sniggered and the old woman and servant-girls of his household walked in fear of him and prayed for nothing more than six hours' sleep and a dish of stirabout to give them courage for a day's work. The word of the cursing was all about and around and there was not a soul in the house – aye, or in the town – that didn't tick off the days until the day of the twelve-month that the old Claddagh woman had warned of.

'Well, the day came around sure enough and all the women, in and out of the house, were watching out for something rare to happen to the old gombeen man, but himself gave no sign that he remembered the day except that maybe he called for one more measure of the hard spirits than he was used to take after his supper. As you might expect – for I'm sure you have no patience with superstition – the day passed and the chapel bell knocked midnight and nothing happened at all. Whether the old daft beldam had been puzzled by 1848 being a Leap Year, or whether they keep a different calendar in the Claddagh, I could not say. All I can say is that your man went off to his soft bed soon after midnight, passing no remarks, and it was quite one o'clock before the terrible howl rang out from his bedroom.

'Every living sinner in the house comes pelting in, expecting – likely hoping – to see him stricken dead with a terrible look of fear on his face. But – nothing of the sort. He's striding up and down in his flannel nightshirt, calling down bleddy murder on whoever had put a child in the foot of his bed.

' "There can be no child there," says his old wife timidly, "for there is no child in the house."

' "Do you take me an ejit?" he screams. "Am I not just after feeling its nasty little cold fingers plucking at me toes?"

'None dares look until one of his bully-boys, bobbing-full of ale, swaggers to the bed and rips off the covers. There's not so much as a louse in it, of course, except the fine copper hot-water can at the foot.

' "Ye had a bad dream, yer honour," says the toady, "it was just the owld hot-can ye felt, and it freezin' cold."

' "Cold?" squawks the old wife – and directs a terrible look at the servant girl. "Indeed it cannot be cold," retorts the little maid, "for it isn't an hour since I put it in the master's bed, and it so billing hot I had to carry it with a cloth." But cold it was, as all felt when they touched; cold as the kiss of an unpaid whore. The girl bursts into frightened tears; the old fellow curses the whole lock of them out of the room and goes back to his bed. (It was a known scandal that his wife had long had to sleep apart: she was a flatulent old person whom he had wed only for the farm of land she brought with her and she was a shocking terror for praying aloud every time she heard the chapel bell knock in the night.) Nothing more happened after the man went back to his bed with the hot-can refilled, except that in the small hours he got up and went padding about in the kitchen, stirring up the fire and making himself a dish of something hot to eat, and him having eaten enough for four men at supper.

'In the morning, you may be sure, all eyes were on him but he showed no sign of unease; indeed, he made an uncommonly good breakfast, drinking a quart of strong, sweet tea with his stirabout and calling for a thick rasher of mutton ham to top it off. It's true he told the women to sew up the end of his bedclothes so that no more tricks could be played on him, but that was only what any prudent man would have done. In fact, he might not have given them the trouble, for that part of it was over, had he but known it.

'He had always been a brave man at the table but now he seemed to have grown new courage. Every meal-time he would complain at the stinginess of his fare, although a stone of potatoes would be steaming in the kish and his own plate so heaped with food that you couldn't see the rim of it, and his elbows wet with the grease and gravy dripping over on to the table. The buttermilk now was too thin and sour for him and he would only drink the whole milk, if you please, as though he were a gentleman. You would scarcely see him at his ledgers without the heel of a loaf, a lock of scallions and a great wedge of cheese to help him with the addition and subtraction and compound interest.

'Fat before, he now grew fat as though he was readying himself to send to market. He lost his taste for the good, homely, wholemeal bread and the town baker knocked him up two quartern loaves of the soft, white stuff, morning and night. With fistfuls of this he would rowl and rowl away at the gravy on his plate the way it hardly needed washing after. His great curs would whine for the leftovers they were used to having from him but sorrow a scrap did he leave now. Old Trouncer, his favourite, pawed roughly at his knee one day, desperate for his mouthful. The old man – potato spraying from his mouth – roared to his toady to take both dogs out and shoot them, there and then.

'Only then did the women of the house, silly souls, understand that something was badly amiss and they wrote to Liverpool to my grandfather to come over and reason with him. It was weeks before my grandfather could get leave from his shipping office and meanwhile things mended worse, as they say. The old man fattened so fast that you could watch it and still he whined that the women were starving him. His business suffered, for there was scarce time to cast a column of figures between his great meals, and the townspeople would find excuses to call in and admire the sight and sound of his monstrous eating. I doubt you'll believe me that his last bit of a supper at night was a pound of rashers, a dish of champ made of a quarter-stone of potatoes with half a pound of butter melting in the hole in the midst of it, but it's God's own truth. He grew so gross that the joiner was bidden in to make a chair for him, for his old stool would rise with him when he was helped to his feet, jammed between the great lardy cheeks of his bum.

'He could never be warm in bed now, either, although the weather was warm and the blankets piled upon him. He took to spending the nights on a black, shiny, horse-hair chaise longue in the sitting room, his great carcass muffled in top-coats over his nightshirt and God knows how many pairs of woollen stockings. He swore that his bedroom stank and indeed it did, but it was not the stench of a fat, dirty old man but a strange stink that no one could quite put a name to, although many tried.

'One morning they found him on the floor, having slipped off the couch. None could raise him for he squealed at every touch and he was so soft and fatty that six strong men could not have found a good grip on him. He did not care; he lay on the floor and whined for food and even as his household were pouring it into his great, blubber-lipped gob, he would curse them filthily for starving him to death.

'The priest was called but was met with such a spray of dirty ranting that he gathered up the skirts of his cassock and fled. The very doctor himself was sent for; he drove in his trap from twenty

miles away. He looked and he listened and he put his handkerchief
to his nose and he told the women that it was a matter for a priest,
not a medical man and, no, he would not take tea, nor his fee. He
was out of there as though he had seen the smallpox.

Nothing to Spare.

*Print saved by Bon from a nineteenth-century scrapbook to illustrate 'The
Gombeen Man'*

'As it happened, my grandfather arrived the very next day from
Liverpool with his pretty little wife and baby son – my father to be.
He left them at the inn to rest and came to the house alone to see
how matters lay. There he sees his father spraddled stinking on the
floor, whimpering for food. He did not, as you might think, look
like a great round tub: he was all flabbed out into a soft and
spreading oblong like a foul old feather-bed. His face and bosom
were all beslobbered and caked with gravy and gruel and his tongue
lolled out, looking for all the world like a pig's liver. Still he whined
for food.

'My grandfather was not a clever man and was flushed with the
glory of young fatherhood. It seemed to him that the sight of his
grandchild might gratify – even cure – the old man. Out of the
room he steals and back to the inn. Five minutes later the door
opens: the old man raises his great jowly head and what does he
see, black against the sunlight, but the shape of a young woman

holding a child out to him. The gombeen man makes just the thin thread of a shriek as he dies.

'Well, that's all that's in it. I'm sorry there's no happy ending, but perhaps it will take your minds off missing your tea tonight.'

Catch Your Death

Mr Semphill was a publisher. To be precise, he was a publisher of the better sort, for they are not all of a piece. To be exact, he was the senior surviving partner of the firm of Semphill & Wurtz, which made so many glittering reputations in the 1930s. To be explicit, he was, at the moment of which I write, a furious publisher. He did not tear his hair for, to be frank, there was little of it to tear at except at the back of his head where tearing is painful and a little absurd.

What he did was this: he threw the slab of typescript into the air and so on to the floor, saying — some would call it bellowing — coarse and blasphemous words up to but not including those words at which he had found his secretary drew the line.

He often threw typescripts on to the floor, sometimes out of a truly passionate rage — a well-documented health-hazard in the publishing industry — but more often, during the summer months, because he liked to watch his secretary on her hands and knees gathering up the scattered pages. This was some years ago, you see, when mini-skirts had been invented but those dreary tights had not. The secretary scrabbled and gathered, saying 'Yes, sir' and 'No, sir' at what seemed to her to be suitable intervals, although her mind was more taken up, if the truth must be told, with trying to remember whether or no she was, on that warm summer's day, wearing a full complement of what Mr Semphill still called *lingerie*, for his wife shopped at Swan & Edgar's, you understand.

'Bloody man is clearly out of his mind!' growled Mr Semphill at last, when the floor show had finished.

'Really, sir?' said his secretary, having established, behind her desk, that the small-clothes under advisement were, indeed, under advisement, so to say, and not in the jacket-pocket of the Publicity Manager – for this was after the luncheon break, you see.

'Off his rocker. Demented. Potty,' explained Mr Semphill. 'I mean, curse and blast it, there's his synopsis, two years old, outlining a meditative account of his life as a pacifist during the war. Accepted. Half the advance paid on the strength of a 10,000-word sample. And what have we had?'

'What indeed, sir?' murmured the secretary demurely, for demureness is the best disguise for boredom except in a situation where a girl can turn over and go to sleep.

'What we've got,' bellowed Mr Semphill, 'is a farrago of ill-typed garbage detailing the old bugger's . . .' He stopped, for his secretary had coughed. She had been raised a Methodist: 'bastard' was in the Bible, 'bugger' was not. It was one of the words at which she drew the line.

'. . . detailing the old idiot's passionate imbroglio with some ancient housekeeper of his. It's too much, too much. And, by the same token, he's already passed his length by several thousand words and hasn't mentioned the bloody war yet!'

'Yes, sir,' said the secretary, still demurely. 'The old, er, gentleman does seem to have lost the thread of his story.'

At this point it should perhaps be made clear that the old gentleman of whom the secretary spoke and over whom the publisher raged was none other than Cyril Fitz-Thomas, the great literary panjandrum of the 1930s, whose back list of exquisite novels still brought in an agreeable cash flow to Messrs Semphill and Wurtz and in whom Mr Semphill (his partner Wurtz, who was clever, being dead) had lately invested a decent sum of money, hoping to conjure out one last and greatest work.

Alas, for months his writing had been pouring in, a few thousand words at a time, each instalment more diffuse, less relevant, less comprehensible and further from the synopsis than the packet before. Letters innumerable, modulated from 'My Dear Cyril' through 'Now look here, Cyril' to 'Dear sir' had been sent – some of them Registered at great expense – to Fitz-Thomas's address in the deepest deeps of the West Country. None had been answered, yet still the ever worsening drivel trickled in. Telephone calls had elicited from icy-voiced Telephone Supervisors that the number was, for the moment, disconnected. Further and more pointed inquiries had made it clear that further questions about this disconnection should be addressed to the former subscriber himself. By post. In other words, as anyone who has ever been less than rich will be aware, the old gentleman had not paid his telephone bill.

'Yes, well, what the fffffbrrrrh blazes are we to do about it?' demanded Mr Semphill.

'I don't really see what you *can* do, sir,' said the secretary, wriggling ecstatically because of an intrusive biscuit-crumb. 'I mean, you can hardly go down there in this weather, can you? You'd catch your death.' She wriggled again, although the crumb was no longer causing annoyance.

Mr Semphill gazed at her fixedly. There appeared to be a certain, well, *freedom* imparted to her upper slopes by these wriggles; a freedom not consistent with the dignity of a long-established publishing house.

'Cynthia,' he said, clearing his throat as though with difficulty, 'you know that I believe in giving the staff the utmost latitude in matters of dress but I feel bound to ask you, in the most fatherly way, you appreciate, hrrrumphhh, whether you are, in fact, wearing a bust-bodice?'

'A *what*, sir? What's that?'

'Well, it's a, ah, hrrumphh, a sort of . . . you know . . .' and he sketched in the air the outline of a brassière designed for breasts of a kind no longer fashionable. The secretary kept a straight face.

'I'm sorry, sir, I don't think I understand. Is it some sort of bicycle?'

'Oh, dammit, never mind. What were you saying about catching my death? Eh?'

'Only that you could scarcely go down to see Mr Fitz-Thomas yourself, sir, because you aren't strong, are you? Mrs Semphill has told me so again and again, and trains are such a misery nowadays and you are prone to these summer colds, Mrs Semphill says. Perhaps you could send one of the younger gentlemen . . . ?'

'Oh, bunkum! Between you and me, Cynthia, I fancy Mrs Semphill only says these things to you about colds as a sort of oblique reference, as it were, to the ah quit charming little ah outfits you wear yourself. I'm sure you follow me.'

'Yes, sir,' said the secretary, following him from miles ahead but making a great business of shuffling carbon papers together whilst she secretly searched for her nail-varnish.

'In fact,' boomed Mr Semphill, in a capable, dominant voice, 'you'd better get me a ticket on a train to the nearest station to that obscure place where Mr Fitz-Thomas lives – if there are still stations and trains in those parts. This nonsense has gone on too long, far too long; can't waste time and money in this way, chap needs sorting out, pulling together. I'll put it to him kindly but squarely. He's not a fool, after all.' The last sentence fell loyally but lamely from his lips.

'I'm sure you're right, sir,' she said, hoisting up *Bradshaw's Railway Guide* from the bottom drawer, careful not to display her pleasure at the way things had developed. First, you see, telephoning British Railways ensured at least ten minutes of 'ringing' and 'engaged' tones during which she would be able to attend properly to her nails; second, Mr Semphill's absence for the whole of the following day would give her the freedom of his office couch. The Publicity Manager's office had no couch and the desk there was of chromium and glass, which tended to make her luncheon break as abrasive as it was delicious.

'Will the 8.45 from Waterloo be too early, sir? The next train would involve three changes and you wouldn't be at Little Craving until three in the afternoon and you'd have to stay the night.'

Mr Semphill gave a careful grunt which could be taken as an assent but which, if he changed his mind, could also be construed, retrospectively, as non-committal. He used this grunt often when talking with literary agents.

The next morning, huddled in his first-class-facing-the-engine-window-side-corner-seat, he bitterly regretted his masterful decision of the day before. He vowed, as he had vowed before, that he would never again make decisions immediately after lunching at

Simpson's in the Strand: that saddle of mutton seemed to madden him like wine. To add to his discomfort there was that tight, twitching sensation at the back of his soft palate which told him that he was, indeed, about to succumb to one of his Summer Colds.

The more he thought about the Cyril Fitz-Thomas nonsense the more fretful he became.

'Bloody man,' he muttered again and again, '*bloody* old fool,' – much to the distress of the elderly priest in the opposite seat who was working on *The Times* crossword, trying to think of a four-letter word beginning with 'f'.

The old fool Fitz-Thomas was, to tell the truth, really rather a more serious source of anxiety to Mr Semphill than has perhaps been made clear: certainly more serious than he would have cared to explain to his secretary. He had splashed – in one of his masterful moments – a good deal too much more money in that direction than his late partner would have approved of, hoping to make a great publishing coup out of the *Fitz-Thomas Watched the War* book and so make the right-hand side of the balance-sheet look a little less daunting. But now the hateful little man from the merchant bank was alluding to it each month, pointing at the entry with his exquisitely sharpened pencil and lifting an intolerable eyebrow. Mr Semphill had not seen fit to tell the nasty little man that Cyril Fitz-Thomas had been pouring in, each month, ten thousand words of cryptic crap: he had simply said, in his stuffiest voice, that the author was working well. The little man had made polite noises expressing satisfaction of a kind but in the sort of voice that made it clear that he – and his masters – were by no means truly satisfied and that the sale of Messrs Semphill and Wurtz's back list, in the next financial year, was a pleasanter prospect than that of continuing to finance Mr Semphill's choice of authors.

Mr Semphill could take that sort of thing, for he had been in publishing since boyhood. What he could not take was when, each month, as he left, the little man would look at him narrowly and inquire after his health.

The seats in his first-class compartment are not what they were. Once upon a time one could doze profitably in them but nowadays they are cunningly designed so that only the cheeks of dwarfs can reach the parts against which cheeks are supposed to rest. Mr Semphill soon gave up his attempt at a doze, for it was of no avail. Then he pitted his wits against *The Times* crossword but soon became hopelessly bogged down over Natty Bumppo's sobriquet and decided that it must have been 'La Longue Catamite'. He worked off his spleen for a while by staring at each of his fellow passengers in turn. Then he changed trains. This was years ago but trains were already in the hands of British Rail and their gift for timing was manifest. Since there had been no dining-car on the train, things had been so arranged that there was no time for luncheon during the change: just enough time for boredom and fury but not enough for luncheon. Clearly, some unsung Marxist had won a Stakhanovite medal.

Two stations after having achieved his change Mr Semphill was at Little Craving, his destination. The station was another masterpiece of its kind in every detail: the evil old deaf-mute who snatched his ticket was in a worse temper than Mr Semphill himself and the crone who presided over the tarnished urn, the single, curled-up sandwich under its glass bell, had dirty fingernails. There were – need I say? – no taxis.

Mr Semphill, nursing his wrath to keep it warm, walked, gibbered at by village idiots, quite a mile to a garage-like place where a hairy, filthy youth agreed to drive him to Honeysuckle Cottage – the name was, of course, another of that old fool's jokes. The motor-car, although it probably had some value to a collector of such things, was not *nice*. Mr Semphill spread his *Times* upon the stained upholstery before sitting down.

Honeysuckle did indeed abound at the Fitz-Thomas cottage, there was a positive forest of the nasty stuff through which Mr Semphill had to force a sticky, insect-ridden way to the front door, where he dismissed the youth, telling him to return in precisely two hours so that the last up-train might be caught.

There was, of course, no answer to his knock; it was one of those days. Now long past the stage of caring for the civilities, Mr Semphill tried the door. It was unlocked; he went in. Unlike the garden, the house was kempt and clean, although there was a certain, or rather an uncertain, something which vexed the nose: not quite a smell, more a miasma, a sweetish *presence* so to speak. He did not like it, for he was a fastidious man; he had been known to walk out of the house because his son had been burning joss-sticks, who knows why.

'Hoy!' cried Mr Semphill in the little, furniture-polished hall. 'Hoy!' he cried again on entering the sitting room. The silence closed in upon him. The sweetish presence became more trying: he looked around for some cause, a hyacinth perhaps or some other noxious house plant. There was nothing to account for the smell, for now it had become, to his mind, a smell.

'HOY!' he bellowed once more and now with some petulance.

There was more silence, more sickly sweetness.

Nothing could assuage the mounting rage of Mr Semphill's ulcer except something to eat, for that was his nature. He found the larder, which was stocked with plebeian food at which he sneered but of which he ate. (After all, the old fool Fitz-Thomas was deeply in hock to his firm: the least he could do was to afford something for Mr Semphill's ulcer to gnaw upon.)

Replete with baked beans, margarine, Father's Joy Miracle Loaf (medium sliced) and the sweating heel of some nameless cheese, Mr Semphill repaired to the glum little sitting room to await Fitz-Thomas's return from his afternoon walk – and to rehearse icy phrases with which to greet him. He waited quite half an hour, then threw *The Times* into the horridly tiled fireplace and cast about for something to read. Curiously, there were no books to be seen, only a thin sheaf of typescript beside a typewriter on a sort of tea-table next to a window through which a diseased hydrangea sneered into the room. Had he been less vexed he might have been more puzzled: Fitz-Thomas was not a man, certainly, to keep a Roget's *Thesaurus* on his work-table but anyone conversant with his writings would have expected at least the Loeb *Greek Anthology* and the *Index Librorum Prohibitorum*.

He carried the typewritten pages back to his chair, too well knowing what they were. He was right, of course, as publishers so often are. It was more of the garbage to which he had become used lately: in this latest drab episode Fitz-Thomas seemed to be suggesting that an aged housekeeper, crazed with a lust which he could not match, was putting things into his tea and coffee – love-philtres and such.

'Oh, God!' cried Mr Semphill, rising from his chair so as to give his arms freedom for throwing typescript about. He slumped down again, this time to compose even more bitter reproaches against his author's return. Whilst his belly growled as it worked on the hateful food, so did his mind at the thought of Fitz-Thomas's perfidy. Although he was but a publisher, splendid and almost literate phrases sprang to his mind as he thought of the wasted money. 'We of the thirties, indeed!' was one of the bitterest of them.

When the latch at last clicked, he arranged on his face the most baleful look of which it was capable, focusing it upon the spot where the old fool's visage would appear. This was wasted, for the person who entered was a decent-looking, elderly woman with a huge shopping-bag and a pink nose. He scrambled to his feet, for he had been properly brought-up, and mumbled explanations and apologies.

'Thass awright, my duck,' said the old lady placidly, 'jess yew set yourself down again while I make yew a nice cup of strong tea, jess like Mr Fitz likes it.'

Mr Semphill sat down, collected himself.

'Will he be long?' he asked at last.

'Longer than yew'd care to wait, I *dare* say,' she tittered in an old-fashioned way, 'ah, a sight longer, a *sight* longer.'

Mr Semphill fidgeted, for he was not a man who loved to bandy words with yokels.

'Where do you suppose he is, then?' he asked.

'Well, upstairs, in course,' she said, looking at him wonderingly. 'Where else would 'e be, d'yew reckon?'

Mr Semphill didn't reckon anything, he mumbled something adequately polite and trotted upstairs. The first door he opened was that of some sort of linen-cupboard; the next was a bathroom. Opening the next door made him reel back in disgust: the rich, rotten sweetness was here overpowering and a quick scurrying of little animals encouraged him to play the coward. Clapping his Brut-scented hanky to his nose, however, he entered. Mr Fitz-Thomas was in bed. He had been there a long time. His eyes, nostrils and mouth were unnaturally large and black but moved and writhed in a lively fashion.

'Cyril?' said Mr Semphill.

The flies scarcely stirred, they were languid, heavy with food. Mr Semphill remembered where the bathroom was. He managed to get there. When he emerged, a few minutes later, he did not go back to the bedroom: he had seen enough to know that there was nothing he could do. People who have been at Rugby, you see, are capable, unrufflable, *resourceful* – everyone knows that.

Downstairs, the decent, elderly woman was sipping her tea. An American, Mr Semphill reflected, would have called her 'a little old granny lady' – she even had a strip of black velvet ribbon around her scraggy neck, secured by a minuscule diamanté clip. She seemed to be a very *nice* old lady for her class (as a child, Mr Semphill had learned from his mummy that class was easy: just call all ladies women and all women ladies) but Mr Semphill had often admitted, sometimes even in public, that he was not always right about people. Moreover, this nice old lady had omitted to report a death – the death of a Semphill & Wurtz author, and one to whom a great deal of money had been paid. His mind was already rehearsing phrases suitable for the little man from the merchant bank.

A nice cup of tea was before him but he had no time for such trivia; he excused himself courteously.

'I dessay yew'd like summink a liddle stronger?' said the old lady. 'Praps a glass of rich brown sherry, my duck?'

Something of that sort was, indeed, just what Mr Semphill had in mind, he usually took a little something at about that time of day. The old person foraged about in the sideboard, wiped the neck of a dusty bottle and set it before him, along with a fine baluster glass of the early eighteenth century. Mr Semphill drank thirstily: the wine was past its best but strong and good, it seemed to rinse away the nastier sweetness of the memory of upstairs.

'Tell me,' he said carefully, when the sherry had somewhat soothed his jumping nerves, 'how long has Mr Fitz-Thomas been, er, as he is now?'

'Oh, I reckon he'll have passed across quite ten or twelve munce now,' she said cosily, pouring a fresh cup. 'Yew know what these writers are like, I'm sure, never know what they're up to from one moment to the next, do yew?'

'No, you don't,' he said heavily. 'Do yew,' he added without meaning to.

'Popped off sweet as a nut like, in his sleep,' she volunteered as Mr Semphill poured himself a little more of the sherry. 'Can't of felt a moment's pain – yew should of seen his expredgion when I found him: a smile on his face like a baby's. Yew could tell he was the better for giving up them cigarettes.'

'Splendid,' he said. 'Capital. So glad. But I must say that what's occupying my mind just at this moment is, who's been sending in work purporting to be his for the last, ah, ten or twelve months? Eh?'

'Ah, well, I bin posting it, in course, dearie, sticking them labels of yourn on the packets, but he's bin writing it, for it's more than my pore wits are up to, innit?'

'He has been *writing* it? I don't quite see . . . I mean, how could he do that?'

The old lady fidgeted uneasily.

'Well, in course he han't bin aggshurly using that type-machine his own self; I mean, yew seen he in't in no sort of shape to come downstairs and do that, is he? He sort of uses me for that, yew see.'

Mr Semphill didn't see. The long, exasperating day and the rich sherry were fuddling his brains.

'Well, no,' he said, 'I must confess that I don't really quite see at all. Could you . . . ?'

'I dunno, I reelly don't. It's jest that every day when I've done the dishes he sort of tells me to sit down at that liddle table and tap away at that machine until I can't tap no more and when there's a big fat old bunch of paper I jess naturally give it to the postie, don't I?'

'Of course, of course. But the material he's been writing is, well, it's rather, er, autobiographical, isn't it?'

'Well I never. I dunno nothink of that, sir. Mr Fitz is a lovely gemmun, he wouldn't write nothink of that, never said a low word in front of me all the years I bin working for him.'

'No no no, you mistake me, Mrs er . . . ?'

'Miss.'

'I'm so sorry, I should have said . . . what I mean is that some of the material is, well, pretty personal – like the references to yourself, for instance . . . what do you feel about them, eh?'

'Put me in his book, has he?' she cried happily. 'Well I never, what next!'

Mr Semphill swallowed his third glass of sherry in an ungenteel fashion.

'But madam . . .'

'Miss,' she said.

'Miss, er, hrrumph, you must be aware of what you wrote – or rather, as you say, what Mr Fitz-Thomas dictated to you . . . I mean, there are some very strange statements . . .'

'Bless you, dearie, I wooden know about all that, I was raised to gentlefolk's service from a liddle girl, never could quite get the hang of that reading and writing. No, nor never missed it, neither.'

For a moment Mr Semphill felt that he understood it all, then a strange feeling stole over him: a sort of vagueness and a friendly, familiar pang from his ulcer. A motor-horn sounded outside; it hurt his head and the kindly old lady popped out of the door for a moment and sent the noise away.

'Now then, my duck,' she crooned, 'yew look right poorly; drink yew up that sherry-wine, tes the very same that Mr Fitz was supping the night he got taken across, poor gemmun. Then jess jew come upstairs and I'll pop yew in a warm bed before yew catch your death.'

She was surprisingly strong for such a frail old creature; this was a good thing for he could never have managed the stairs by himself.

'Now, jess you lie there,' she said, when he was in bed, 'while I go and wash my feet.'

The bed was wonderfully warm and cosy. He pulled the counterpane over his head. It was nice in there with Cyril Fitz-Thomas.

How to Frighten Your Wife to Death

If you had asked Harry what his politics were, he would have thought for a while, scratching the deep dimple in his chin as he always did when thinking or pretending to think, and would finally have said that he supposed he was a Conservative, really. There would have been little conviction in his voice, he wasn't that kind of man, really. He would have said it in much the same way as an army conscript might say 'Church of England' to the Orderly Room Sergeant when asked for his religious denomination, even though he had never been inside a church since he had squealed as the vicar splashed font-water on to his fontanelle, while his god-parents wept or looked at their watches, according to sex.

Harry's politics, though, such as they were, are of no importance; what he really cared about was not Conservatism but Conservationism, which burned in his breast like a blue flame. When he spoke of The Ecology and The Environment you could hear the capital letters clearly. He would hardly have recognized a Lesser Spotted Sedge Warbler if it bit him in the leg, but if he heard that one of its haunts was threatened by a property-developer he would be the first to write a furious letter to the *Guardian*. (As a matter of fact, his choice of newspaper tells us something about him, too, doesn't it?)

His conservationist-kit consisted of several small, inaccurate books, a pair of Audubon binoculars, some stout, weather-proof clothing, a shooting-stick, a pocket-flask and a starter's pistol. Do not be misled by the last item: Harry had no interest in starting the Hundred Yards Dash, nor the Under-Sixteens Hurdles: the pistol was simply for scaring magpies away from the goldfinches' nestlings on his two-acre estate. At the time that he bought the pistol he was a sensible, methodical man who could take a problem apart, rearrange the pieces and arrive at a cost-effective solution. Like the pistol.

It was not until he married and went to live in South London that he started to fall apart himself. His wife put the wildlife books, the shooting-stick, the stout, weather-proof clothing and the binoculars into the attic. He kept the pocket flash handy; indeed, he started gradually to find it handier every day. The starter's pistol ('horrid thing,' said his bride) found a furtive home in the drawer where he kept his dress-shirts and other rarely used mockeries. It was in the guise of a small automatic and was made by Perfecta, who operate in the DDR, which is one of the halves of Germany. It took a clip or magazine of 6mm Platz-patronen, zugefaltet (that's crimped blank cartridges) made by those kindly benefactors Dynamil Nobel Aktien-Gesellschaft who, as all the world knows, give away a morsel of their profits each year in the form of peace-prizes to people like Mr Begin.

It was, as I have said, exactly like a small automatic – a lady's handbag-gun or a 'Saturday Night Special' and made a noise convincingly like one of those nasty little .25s.

I have also already said that Harry started to go to pieces when his new wife insisted that she did not like mud or any other kind of wildlife except wild mink and wished to live in one of the newly fashionable bits of South London. Perhaps I mean one of those streets off Lavender Hill. Harry did not like it. He did not, of course, start to crumble immediately: there was the usual sequence of married bliss, commencing with the mindless fury of honey-moon-heat, followed by the 'whose little tiggy-winkle is this?' stage; then the 'guess what I've got on under this frock' bit; then 'I expect you've had a hard day at the office'; then 'Dearest, I've such an awful headache' and, finally, – 'Darling, *must* you?'

Harry soon found the pocket-flask too small; London too large; his wife too loud. Each evening he took a little longer to get home from the office – approximately one large gin longer. He came to know barmen by their Christian names and one or two of them, unrebuked, stopped calling him 'sir'. Then he took to bringing home a flat half-bottle of an evening – and of gin – with which he would cunningly replenish the decanter in order to allay his wife's suspicions. (The fact that he hadn't noticed that the uppity classes never put gin in a decanter tells us yet a little more about him, doesn't it?) His wife's suspicions were, of course, unallayed, for she was all woman. But also, being only a woman, it did not occur to her that all could have been set right by unearthing his conservationist's kit and packing him off each weekend with a packet of sandwiches to Dartford or Dungeness or some other bird-infested spot, there to adjust his addictive personality by watching warblers, tending terns and making Citizen's Arrests on those he could catch scorning the Voles (Violation) Act 1983. She could, I repeat, have done this at a trifling expense of time and trouble but (I repeat again) she was only a woman.

Soon the flat half-bottle, pocketable in his top-coat, became a full-bottle bulge in his briefcase. Harry was now, to put it bluntly, on the sauce. Most wives claim, quite accurately, to be aware of everything that takes place in their marital abodes and Harry's wife (I forget her name, it's of no importance) was one of those. She knew; she knew. Since priests are dying out (probably through interbreeding) and all bad psychiatrists have priced themselves out of the market, she took her doc-like devotion to *Surgery Hours 5 p.m. to 8 p.m. Except by Appointment* and Told All to her physician who, in exchange for £7, gave her seven minutes of his time, a free brochure from Alcoholics Anonymous and a glossier one from a drying-out clinic in which he happened to have a half-share. She gazed at this literature aghast.

'But Harry would . . . would *strike* me if I . . .'

'I'm afraid, dear lady, that you will have to learn to live with that sort of thing from now on,' murmured the physician, easing her to the door with a hand under her elbow as he tapped the button for 'Next Patient Please, Nurse.' There was no extra charge for the courteous ushering-out; his bank-side manner was impeccable.

She dropped the brochures in a litter-bin at the bus-stop, for she was a tidy soul, and Harry did not strike her that night. He did so a few days later, of course – 'Doctor knows best, dear' – but she was not the kind of wife who could learn to live with that sort of thing. She was a slow learner, you see, and the Evening Classes in Transcendental Meditation had not yet opened their bowels to the hungry.

How it happened was like this: he arrived home at an hour which even the most tolerant wife would have described as 'late'. He had with him the proprietor of a nightclub, a tastefully clad 'hostess' and two splendid chaps whose names he couldn't quite remember. They could all stand up, more or less, and one of them actually took his hat off.

When Harry's wife reminded him, in a tight-lipped sort of way, that he had missed her Very Important Cocktail Party and that she had given his burnt pork-chops to a passing dog, he punched her in a playful and husbandly way on the upper left *maxilla*. Harry's guests flew out of the double-glazed sun-porch and Love, I need hardly say, flew out of the window. Well, let's be reasonable; no wife much likes to have her teeth strewn over the valuable carpet, especially in front of people to whom she has not been properly introduced, does she? I mean, let's try and see her side of it, shall we?

Her side of it, after they'd taken the wires out of her face bones, was to make a couple of telephone calls: one to the reputable Company who insured their mutual lives and didn't yet know about Harry's little weaknesses (she had shrewdly made no claim in the matter of her *maxilla* or dentistry) and another to a naughty friend from her past; the sort of friend who doesn't much care to talk on the telephone but who can get you almost anything you care to name so long as you pay in used fivers. He didn't ask why she wanted it.

A few evenings later, Harry signed the new insurance proposal forms in a blurred sort of way. That week a parcel from the naughty friend arrived in an even more blurred – you might almost say *clandestine* way. It was a smallish, heavy parcel.

After that, Harry's wife waited, patiently gritting what was left of her teeth, for twelve months. (Dash it, I've given the pay-off away to anyone who has read the fine print on a life-insurance policy!) Harry was contrite for a while but this merely made him drunker and drunker. He was not the belligerent sort of drunk – although he did absent-mindedly slap his wife around a little from time to time – nor was he the passing-out-cold/sick-on-the-carpet kind. He was more the no-one-has-ever-understood-me and you-drove-me-to-it and I'll-kill-myself-and-then-you'll-be-sorry sort. His wife watched; waited. She liked that. She liked it very much.

All the same, it must have seemed a very long twelve months but time passes, as I dare say you've noticed, and at last it became ripe. Harry, too, was at his ripest on the selected evening; after missing her face with two open-handed slaps he sank on to a passing sofa and sobbed bitterly, going into his 'I'll kill myself' routine. This time she did not give him the final nightcap as she helped him up to bed; she helped him up to bed drinkless, taunting him sweetly about his throat-cutting mumblings.

'Harry, sweety,' she said sweetly as she propped him against the wall beside the tallboy, 'you're becoming a bore about this never-never suicide; in fact you've been a bore on the subject for ages. You know perfectly well that you wouldn't do anything so dreadful in front of me, it would frighten me to death, you know it would.' His eyes flickered with the crafty flicker of a man whose brains were good before he addled them.

'In any case,' she went on, taunting in earnest now, a saw-edge in her voice, 'you simply just haven't the guts any more, have you, sweety?'

That did it. A rumpled, sniggery smile wobbled over his slack mouth as he formed the thought of a splendid, drunken joke. He flopped to his knees in front of the tallboy, fumbled in the dress-shirt drawer for the starter's pistol and clapped it to his temple. He had a fleeting notion that it was a little larger, a little heavier than he remembered but by then he was pulling the trigger.

His wife gazed, entranced, her lips wet and parted. Her first thought was that she had never liked that wallpaper anyway.

Her second thought was that it was too late to telephone the Insurance Company, but that could wait: it was quite a fortnight past the twelve-months suicide clause. As she dialled 999 she began to arrange her face into a grief-stricken state. Women can do that, you know.

Correspondence

Family Letters

Bringing together these letters has been a moving, disconcerting and informative experience.

Rereading Bon's first letters to me now, I can see how his fear of being 'horrid' already shadows his hopes for our new love; strange, then, how I didn't notice this in the excitement and magnetism of our first encounters. Then the charm of seeing him with two little children – his way of lifting them from rock to rock across the gaps too big for them to jump on a Cornish beach – tapped into my as yet unconscious maternal drive.

The selection of letters to me belongs to three phases: wooing, marriage – one when he went on a much needed holiday in Majorca – and post-separation and divorce when we gradually developed a genuine but guarded friendship.

Reading his letters to the children upset my long-held belief that he hardly ever wrote to them, forgot all birthdays (except when resentfully reminded by me) and did not acknowledge their sometimes laborious letters to him, while complaining to friends of *his* birthdays being forgotten. His daughters Catriona and Amanda have kept all the letters they received from Bon.

[*Bon and I met for the first time on 26 June 1958, at a supper given by Bon and his flatmate Anthony; we met again many times over the days immediately following, and then on the 13th I went for a two-week holiday to a remote cottage halfway down a cliff in Cornwall. The next day Bon wrote to me for the first time.*]

[Monday, 14 July 1958]

Dear Margaret,

All yesterday I thought very glumly of you chugging W. and S. in a succession of stopping trains, each one grimmer than the last and at last I got so depressed I decided to stop thinking about you till midnight but of course that didn't work. I hope you survived the journey and that your friends showed up and your bed had been aired and so forth.

I'm not very good at writing to you, by the way, I've been practising since yesterday but I don't seem to make any progress.

Balliol has eleven firsts so far, Lesley Anne Crawley has glandular fever, Helen Wade has job as a chambermaid in Newquay and I have, since this afternoon, an authorized overdraft. Iraq is revolting, as I've always maintained, so perhaps I'll be called up before my viva but I wouldn't really like that much.

I think you are very beautiful indeed, if you want to know.

Last night I dined with Norton Smith on the lovely bloody cold beef and fried peppers and acidulous conversation: I'll never understand how a man who can cook like that should hate so many people so much of the time. On Friday he has his viva with Wrenn and Coghill, God help him, for his BLitt. He is a badly scared man, partly because he scares very easily and partly because his thesis is rather lousy here and there. E.g., all his references are rubbishy Cxvii editions in his own library instead of up to date ones or ed. princs.; this is silly and impolite and they may rather hate it, he thinks.

Anthony's mother is giving us a refrigerator if that's how you spell it and a washing machine, both from the house they are selling up in Beaconsfield. Today I got two more shells and some big honey-coloured beads which you probably won't like. I also started work; I have the keys to the Department of Western Art now and feel quite pompous. Spent the morning in the Ashmolean Library identifying orphans' slides at a great rate of knots, much to the amazement of Wind's she-secretary who had given them up (heh, heh!). Nice things like Roubiliac waxes and Fuseli drawings and Bellini's medals for Mohammed II, if you'll believe it.

I finished *The Catcher in the Rye* and last night I read Yeats's *Rosa Alchemica* and I suppose next I should do something about my viva but the very thought fills me with fatigue. When in a letter you start telling people what you've been reading it's time to stop I suppose. I feel so diffident telling you that everything has changed for me in the last few days because of you, because it sounds about as convincing as 'your obedient servant' but I really do love you terribly, and all sorts of hopes and things that I thought were wrapped up and put away for good seem possible again, if you know what I mean. I have a very strong feeling that I have been given another chance and that if I'm very good everything may be all right after all. Everything has been wrong for a very long time now, but I expect you'd worked that out for yourself.

Is Veor on the telephone? Shall I bring a rug for me to sleep under or is there a blanket? What can I bring in the way of eating food? Do you want anything brought from your house? Do you want any dragons slain?

I'm sorry I forgot to give you anything to read on Saturday, shall I bring you something? Here is a chap-book to be getting on with. I hope it's much too fine to read and that you are having a splendid time, and I wish I was there or you were here or something. Anyway goodnight now because this is a rotten letter and getting worse.

     Yours literally ever
     Bon

[*Letter written on Balliol College paper. On the first sheet Bon drew a pin-man feeding a carrot to the lion on the Balliol shield; the second sheet has the pin-man offering to box the Balliol Lion.*]

66 Cranham Street, Wednesday

Darling,

I've been sitting gawping at this for a quarter of an hour so if I don't start it I never shall. Thank you for your letter, it made me feel drunk or something, it was like Traherne writing . . . James Joyce. No it wasn't, you're not in the least like anyone or anything in the world, you're Margaret and I'd lie down and die if it would amuse you. I hate mingy little footling scripts like this, they are like people who write RUBBISH in the margins of library books. The boys are just finishing a monstrous tea/supper of beans . . . sausages and gooseberry compote and they are making a noise like wapiti in a Zambesi wallow. I haven't even spanked them since I saw you yet – you're having a most disquieting effect on me. (That's a sort of stuffy, shy way of saying I'm desperately in love with you.) If you can't get this letter open try tearing the edges off. LATER (boys are in bed.) I'm going to take this all the way to the GPO because I've surely missed the post. I rang your mother up to apologize for not having been in lately and suddenly realized she sounded rather like you and listened entranced but missed most of what she said – she must have thought I was crazy.

That's right of course, there isn't nearly enough room left to explain how much I love you but do get it into your head that I do, honestly, utterly irrevocably Bon.

PS Your spelling is rotten isn't it. I do love you. B

[26 October 1958]
66 Cranham Street, Sunday
Wiggy's telephone is 55871 – he will always take a message.

Darling,

I was so cheered up by speaking to you just now and of course I forgot everything I had to say to you, but while I think of it: I do love you very much. I didn't actually forget to tell you that; I suddenly got rather shy or something.

This last week has been so rotten with one thing and another and a high temperature most of the time and then two days of imprisonment with the boys. I was rather foolishly banking on your coming yesterday and got so glum when you didn't that Anthony got positively alarmed and led me out to the pub and tried, rather touchingly, to get me slewed; but of course all the beer that ever flowed under Burton Bridge wouldn't have made me forget you so I went home and listened lugubriously to Mozart and then took Boswell's *Johnson* to bed and read till it was light. (Crikey what a sentence.)

I've got an option on a decent copy of Fuller's *Church-History of Britain* with the *Hist. of Cambridge* and *Hist. of Waltham Abbey* bound in: if you would like this please let me know immejitly [*sic*] and you can have it for your last birthday.

John Bryson is having one of those Ricci paintings for £25, the architectural capriccio. This is a low price by London standards but [will] show me an ample profit and pleases him. I can now hold on to the other as long as I please until someone insists on giving me £30 for it!

I'm glad that you seem to be back in your stride as regards work, I hope you find something rare and apposite in the Cambridge Library. I suppose you have already thought of the Pepysian collections at Magdalene College?

I expect I should really have written before but have felt rather diffident about posting anything, especially since in one of your Cornish letters [you say] that you set small store by correspondence. In any case, I have been expecting to get in touch with you by telephone at any moment.

I really am sorry that I remained snoring brutishly while you rose and left on Thursday (Wednesday?) last . . . Please don't be upset any more, you know I am always chronically short of sleep and this makes me hard to awaken. I knew all that day that you were feeling sore about it and I was most ashamed.

PLEASE don't let anything happen to stop you coming on Thursday, I miss you very much and four more days and nights without you are as many as I can manage, I think.

I love you more and more all the time and want to be with you always.

Yours Bon

PS

Anthony and Alison send their regards and apologies – they went through Cambridge in a hurry and a day late so they were unable to call on you.

The boys send you their love and all sorts of sticky messages and say when are you coming to see them.

Darling I do love you terribly, please try to love me. I feel very lonely today and full of good intentions never to be beastly to you again.

Bon

[25 November?]
Shop, Tuesday

Darling,

Thank you for your letter reassuring me that you are feeling cheerful; I have been so worried, being sure you had gone away sickened and depressed. I was well aware that I was being bloody much of the time but quite powerless to stop it. I really must try harder next time, it's so stupid to be horrid to someone I love so much. I am very glad to know that you will be coming again this Friday.

Now it's Wednesday night and I have honestly been too busy to finish this. I'll go to the General Post Office to ensure that it goes tonight. The writing is like this because it's Anthony's pen and will not work. Business is really quite goodish – bought two almost good pictures yesterday and taken about £10 since Monday. Bought for us a hubbly bubbly pair of candlesticks; you'll shriek when you see them.

The Mobeys bought a pair of chairs for £40 against my recommendation; Audley Miller and Victor Jones have both seen them now & both definitely say they are spurious. Oh well.

How did you manage to pay the excess fare via London with only 2/-?

Alan said you had caught your train.

I have put your flannel away. Must stop – this writing offends my sight. Looking forward very much to seeing you 9.40 Friday.

    All my very best love

    Bon

WRITTEN IN MOVING CAR   [Bon on holiday, 1965]
                                        Cala D'Or
                                        Mallorca
                                        Spain

Darling,

Hope you have received some of my p.c.s – have not telephoned because too difficult and complicated.

Writing this in Alan's car driving through almond groves – peasants beating them with sticks – and fields of capers (like convolvulus) and cactus figs to Palma (40 miles).

Sun blazing unremittingly. We have just passed tiny hooded cart drawn by one-eared mule and containing tiny, aged drunk nun.

Living on beans, lettuce, fish (fried sardines, bonitos, mullet) aubergines (6d per kilo!), gazpacho, wine. Reading, zizzing, eating, arguing with Alan.

Fellow guest returning London tonight will post this along with note for Olive Bevan.

    Very much love to Amanda, Catriona, Christopher, Rod, Aeneas & your own patient tolerant nice *self*

    Bon X

                                  [Bon on holiday, 1965]

Leaving here tomorrow to look at the family shack in Bologna then straight on to Venice. In emergency: c/o Lennox Boyd, Hotel Cipriani, Venice. Am having a lovely lazy greedy time and truly wish you were here. Hope Amanda and all the other small fry are well.

Love Bon

[*After leaving, Bon wrote fitfully to me and the children. The first of the letters reproduced below probably dates from 1972; in its mixture of rueful self-pity, affection, common sense, amused point-scoring and veiled threat, it well represents the mixed emotions he must have been experiencing at this time.*]

[1972]

Dear Margaret,

Thank you for your nice and friendly letter. I am ashamed to say that I was briefly in Southmoor and Oxford this last weekend and didn't come to see you and the children: I don't think it does the children much good and it certainly upsets me. I had my punishment, though, for while chez the Mobeys they were visited not only by Sandy but also Philip, which didn't add much to the gaiety of nations.

I am sorry that you can't afford the sumptuous writing paper I indulge myself with but then I economize in little things like journeys to Syria, Monte Carlo, etc., heh heh.

I assure you that when money starts to roll in I shall do my best for you but please remember that if anyone uses legal weapons against me at the moment I have to go bankrupt and the baddies will get a damn sight more than the goodies; while I can keep the juggling balls in the air things may yet be well and the man will get his mare again, etc. etc. St John's have a Queen's Bench order against me for £6,090 which they could enforce at any moment; by the end of this summer I shall have nowhere to live – and so on.

We must both hope that the book does very well indeed; it just might, you know. The advances, when they come, are very good for a first novel but they won't keep you and me and St John's in idle luxury for long, as you will appreciate. If I can pay St J's £2,000 in the foreseeable future they will write the rest off; if not, they will lower the boom and pick my bones. You can check that, if you wish, with Mr Torrance, Bill Herbert's partner, but I'd rather you didn't because I'm a bit of a nuisance to them and they're not getting any money for advising me. Between ourselves, they're holding St John's off by virtue of a letter from David Goldberg saying that I'm pretty well round the twist and liable to blow my brains out if anyone [gets] at me – which is approximately true.

To be precise, I've had £250 so far from the book which is the half English hardback advance payable on signing contract. I drew £100 on account from my kindly agent and paid some *desperate* tradesmen's bills and bought a new, not very grand typewriter because the old one was leaking nuts and bolts and I had to move the ribbon by hand – literally. The balance of £150, when it came, paid a small summons and bought my ancient Jaguar: I had no wheels at all which is a nuisance in Oxford but quite intolerable in Silverdale, where the metropolis of Carnforth is five miles away and the Holy City of Lancaster twelve.

Please drink up to half of the bourbon. Please ask Roderick how much I owe him. Please tell Christopher to pinch some catnip out of someone's garden and wipe it on the box where he wants the cat to litter. Much love to all of you and let's keep all our fingers crossed.

    Yours v. affectionately

    Bon X

[*Bon's letters to his two elder sons, Roderick and Aeneas, were few and are not to be found; the following letters to his three younger children – Christopher, Catriona and Amanda – run from 1972 to 1981.*

    His efforts to be a different sort of father from his own – keeping in contact with his children with advice and encouragement, trying to find common ground with them and assuring them of his love – shine through. Heart-felt and well intentioned, some of the letters make painful reading to anyone aware of their context; the contrasts between his life and his advice, the unrealistic offers of money – even, on one occasion, of a sports car – when court-awarded maintenance was not being paid, are poignant. Reading them at this distance in time, however, it is his love for the children and his efforts to meet them in letters that come through most strongly.

Bon may not have realized how his repeated wish for Chris to go to Balliol worked to their mutual discomfort and discouragement. Yet the letter he wrote after Chris had failed his end-of-first-year exams at Swansea rises clear of his own preoccupations and shows Bon at his best as a sensitive mentor and encourager who is full of good sense.

Bon's pet name for Chris – Gig or Giggs Wig – conflates a couple of literary sources in Kipling and Browning with two more immediate derivations: from Chris's younger sister's pronunciation of his name as 'Gigga' and from the children's book Stig of the Dump; *Bon had been amused and pleased when Chris recommended the book to him, hence Gig of the Dump – i.e. of Norham Gardens.*]

Silverdale, Lancashire – 3rd July 1972

Dear Gig,

Thank you very much for your interesting letter (although spelling and writing are not very perfect!) and for the shell set in plastic which I think is excellent and a pleasure to own.

Purple certainly seems an unusual colour for a room but if you really like it that's all that matters, isn't it? You can always paint it over when you get tired of it. Personally, I very much like a rich yellow, like the yolk of an egg, which makes a room look sunny on the darkest and gloomiest day, but many people dislike it.

Do please work as hard as you can at your lessons and stuff: a bit of hard work now can save you ages of harder work – and disappointment – later on.

I would so much like you to go up to Balliol when you are old enough if you can get enough suitable levels, in fact hereby promise you £100 if you do. Incidentally, your godfather, Christopher Fildes, bought you a few dozen bottles of vintage port (now kept at Harveys in Bristol) which you get when you go up to Balliol or when you are 21 whichever is the sooner, did you know that?

Perhaps you think I am boring on the subject of spelling and handwriting but taking pleasure in doing these things well is the mark of a man who likes *words* and words are *language* and it is language which makes us civilized people – not brutes. My only objection to hippies is that they have thrown away the language they inherit and seem only to speak in grunts – 'uh, well, like man, uh, you know?' None of which means anything. They may be very nice people but, if they are, why can't they tell us what they believe, instead of grunting and honking at us?

Please be kind to your little sisters, I know they are a pest but they can't help it. The worse they are, the more credit to you for being patient with them.

Please brush your teeth at least twice a day, especially before you go to bed. Most people now have false teeth before they are 25. Imagine the horror of having to take your teeth out and put them in a glass of Steradent every night. Ugh.

Tell Mum that I have just had the American contract to sign and that I should have some money for her very soon. And give her my love – and Catriona and Amanda.

And play it cool, man – whatever that means!

Love from your very affectionate Dad

[1970s]
The Stables
La Malzarderie
St John
Jersey,
C.I.

My Dear Old Gig,

I am very ashamed not to have written to you before now: I have been labouring understand under a very heavy cold and bronchitis and haven't felt like doing anything much. In any case, I am a very lazy letter-writer, as you know.

Thank you very much indeed for your most generous and imaginative Christmas present: I ate the caviar with great pleasure and am still working on the Stilton, which is in splendid condition.

The pot the cheese came in will be most useful for making savoury butter and things.

I enclosed a few matchbox tops and things which may be useful. If you tell me what sort of stamps you want I'll look out for them for you. I have quite a lot of old Indian ones if they are within your interests. My own collection of Indian ones is quite impressive now, but I haven't been buying lately. I'll show them to you when you come over, which I hope you will. Please explain to your sisters that I can only put up one person at a time, so they will have to take their turns if they want to come.

I do hope you are starting to think seriously about O and A levels etc.; I would very much like you to go up to Balliol and, if your qualifications are OK you shouldn't have too much trouble because they give a little consideration to sons of Balliol people and the Master is very friendly to me. So do try; it's worth it. A bit of effort for the next two or three years will make all the difference to what happens to you for the next seventy years, as I am sure you realize. Listening to music is fine but you should find the time to read as much as you can, as well – it's a good investment.

Sorry about the lecture but I am a bit worried about Aeneas and Roderick having to cope with the world without any qualifications to help them and I don't want it to happen to you. (This is in confidence, of course.)

Well, anyway, I hope you and the little girls are well – give them my love – and to you of course. Write if you can find the time

Your affectionate Dad X

[Jersey, 1970s]

My Dear Gig,

Thank you for your letter. I am very glad you are making an effort at acquiring a good handwriting: you will be glad of it in later life and, although you will probably not want to keep copper-plate as your standard 'fist', it is nevertheless a good basis on which to mould your final choice. You'll find you get a better effect more easily by writing smaller: large letters show up all the imperfections. Try hard for evenness and regularity, too.

Here are some stamps and things I have been saving up for you. The postmark on the Russian card is Leningrad (in case you don't read Russian very well) and I suggest you keep the postmark intact rather than soak off the stamps.

I'm afraid I cannot at this moment say whether I can put you up Aug. 13–26; for one thing, the Martlands have a whole family staying with them at that time and will be a bit frantic; for another, I am in the last stage of the 2nd draft of this novel and am expecting to be told that if I can deliver a final version by the end of August, it will be published in the spring list or even – I hope – at Christmas. In that case I would be writing frantically and cursing and shouting and not fit to cope. Last, James junior has filled the bakehouse with all sorts of building materials & at present it is quite uninhabitable: he hopes to be in a position to move most of it into his new house (which is coming along very well, by the way) but it depends on the workmen, etc. Oh, another thing we are having a false ceiling put into the stables sometime, which would mean I would have to move out for a week or so: we don't know when they can start.

Moreover, I may well have to go to London to argue with publishers, and Florence just couldn't cope with another person along with the five already there. Sorry about all these excuses: you know I would love to see you. All may yet be well but don't rely on it: I'll let you know as soon as I can.

I hope you and your mother and sisters are well. Pompey sends his regards. I've actually got two different publishers competing for this book – no question of having to offer it around. I'll let whoever will publish earliest have it, because I'm very low on cash just now.

Much love to you and all the others
Your affectionate Dad X

PS we've had a lousy wet summer so far but the barometer is climbing now and today is a beautiful day. D

PPS did I tell you I was given a canary for my birthday? It's a wonderful singer. D

[1975]
Belle Vue
Mont de la Roque
St Aubin
Jersey
Channel Islands
Sunday

Dear Mr G.-W.,

Thank you for your card. Yes, I do like Magritte, with reservations. He is a wonderfully witty (and sad) artist who has a lot of thoughtful things to say to people of our time who understand him better than they did back in the thirties. He can and did sometimes slide into mere jokiness and also a striving for the startling effect for its own sake. I expect you have seen Paul Klee's work: well he was a great artist of splendid wit. An American (I think) called Steinberg drew uncannily like Klee but was a great wit with much artistic talent. I'm sure you appreciate the difference. Rolf Harris (ugh) can produce plausible instant landscapes on telly but they are mere wallpaper – no more art than those awful whimsical prints they sell in Boots of little kiddywinks with huge, tearful eyes. (By the way, I once solemnly lectured on the surrealists and assured my audience, with my tongue in cheek, that the Time Transfixed painting on your postcard was entitled 'Shortening odd' because the clock, having been offering twenty to one, was now only giving seventeens . . .) An interesting thing about the pictures is that the steam from the locomotive is not going up the chimney (if there is one); it seems to be feeding itself into the underside of the old-fashioned clock (19th century) which is flanked by 18th century candlesticks. I'm not sure what he's trying to say: probably he wants you to use the picture as a do-it-yourself-thinking kit.

Yes, of course you can come here in April: let me have a firm date and place of arrival in good time, please. I can't actually afford your fare but I'll scrape it up; with any luck I should have the

Spanish translation rights money by then and be able to send Mum a bit too. By the way, have you looked into the student rates for air-travel? They are really meant for people travelling from school to home but perhaps if your headmaster gave you a letter saying that you were visiting your father, the airline might take pity on the pathetic victim of a broken home . . .

Glad you're working on the guitar: everyone should at least try to master a musical instrument because even if they get nowhere it at least teaches them something about themselves, like their actual musical ability, power or perseverance, etc. If you find you are getting nowhere don't be disappointed or stubborn about it, just write it off to experience and list it as one of the things you're not good at. Only idiots expect to be good at everything; realizing as soon as you can, without wasting a lot of time, what things you have no talent for is a great help towards channelling your energies into the things you are able to excel at. That sounds a bit negative, it's not meant to be. What I mean is, for instance, Anthony Harris can solve mathematical puzzles as easily as a bird sings; he cannot comprehend why other people don't instantly recognize musical keys; the mumbo jumbo of higher economics is like the ABC to him. On the other hand, his ability to write lucidly is hard won; whole areas of literature are a closed book to him, and his love of the visual arts has been painfully learned, and, I suspect, gives him little real pleasure. (In short, he and I are as different as we can be, which is probably why we get on so well.)

Hope you are thrashing away hard at schoolwork; it's got to be done *now*, I'm sure you realize that. If you can get entrance to Balliol I'll buy you a sports car; that's a promise which reminds me that I had a friendly not from the Master the other day in which he mentions that he sees you from time to time.

Do you know the trick with little electronic calculators? '142 Israelis fought 154 Arabs over 69 oilfields for 5 years – who won?' You punch out 142, 154, 69 and then multiply X by 5, then punch the = key and turn the calculator upside down.

Love to Mum and the girls from your affectionate Dad X

[On contribution form for the Jersey *Pilot*. Undated]

Dear Gig,

Just a hasty note with a few common Jersey stamps enclosed I'm afraid (but there is a new issue soon & I'll try and remember to get a 1st day cover also hoping to find you a copy of a pamphlet recently produced about Jersey rarities of some sort I forget what).

The reason I'm writing is to enclose this cutting: do you remember we were talking at Norham Gardens about the discipline in your school, sanctuary groups, etc., and someone (Mum?) said, when I suggested teachers should strike, 'no chance'? Well this appeared in *The Times* just a few days later. Show it to Mum after you've read it.

Love to her and to Amanda and Catriona. Thank Mum for giving me such a lovely Christmas – she knows I'm a hopeless letter-writer – and try to be kind to your sisters. You'll be pleased with them when you are a bit older, you really will. And always remember that the age you are at is a hell of a time for a boy; we've all been through it. Try to come out of the other side undamaged. Eat good food: eggs, cheese, milk, meat, liver – don't stuff with bread – because you've only two more years to make your growth. Read all you can. Try to qualify for Balliol – I'd like that very much – but don't let it worry you. 'Many are called but few are chosen' as my old tutor said.

Anyway Balliol is full of weirdies and Maoists now, I understand. But read anyway.

I look forward to seeing you at Easter.

Your very affectionate (believe it or not) father

Bon X

[Undated]
Daly's Kilmacaran
Shercock
Co. Cavan
Éire

Dear Old Gig,

How are things? Have just written to Mum and she now has a Christmas present for you. Why I didn't write about Oxford entry thing was because I was a bit despondent about the certainty that you would have to have a language. I went into it very carefully and was assured (also by seeing some of last year's exam papers) of even getting enough Spanish into you in time unless you are gifted in languages – and if you were you would already have one, if you see what I mean. In any case, I have been frantic during the last three months at: organizing my great move to Ireland, house hunting, trying to get books finished to keep me frantically afloat – all that sort of thing. I'm so sorry if you feel I've let you down but I think you have made the right decision; if engineering is what you want to do, then Oxford is not the place. My engineering friends assure me that a BA (Eng) is not nearly as useful in the field as, say, a good grade from Imperial College. The name 'Oxford' has no magic there and precious little anywhere else nowadays.

It's a pity poor old Rod couldn't get into the Imp. Coll. For his geology, but he just hasn't got the gift for organizing himself, bless him, bless him. You *have* got that gift; for God's sake use it . . . It's a bloody cruel world, if you aren't qualified you'll end up driving buses – as many language and sociology graduates are now doing; every hour that you spend at your books now will decide if you are a rich and happy man in a few years' time. Or not. You know that.

I do hope you are not wasting too much time doing odd jobs for spending money; at this stage I'd much rather send you a few quid for something you have need of rather than think you were exhausting yourself earning it when you could be at your studies.

So ask if you need a bit of cash and devote the time saved to getting proper sleep, organizing your work and having some fun. Anyone facing a serious exam is just like a boxer getting in training for the big fight: if he's f—d.

Mum tells me that you are potting very well just now: I'm sure it must be a most satisfying hobby and very relaxing. When I get settled and organized I must get a printing press again: also very satisfying and useful. But heavy!

If you'd like to come over for a while in the New Year (any time after that) and have some peace and quiet without distractions you know you'd be very welcome indeed. Nothing to do, I'm afraid: no TV, no cinema, no girls. Just walking, bird-watching, reading, writing. But peaceful. I'd scrape your fare.

Now, don't forget if you need a few bob just write and ask. I don't need to know what it's for as long as I know it will help you to get – or stay – organized.

Please give my love to your sisters and tell them that I'll be writing to each of them very soon.

Sorry about all the heavy father advice. The truth is that I'll have to have someone to support me in my old age, heh heh! 'Yes, yes,' I shall quaver, 'my son the engineer sends me a new Rolls-Royce every year, I don't know how I'd get about without his help.'

It's wickedly cold here just now and I'm feeding turves of peat into the fire as fast as it consumes them which is fast.

I'm munching a roast beef sandwich which is good I hope you make sure and feed yourself properly and don't dodge meals. You have only next year left in which to do your growing. You realize that I'm sure.

Much love from your Dad X

[Undated]
Shercock
Co. Cavan
Éire

Dear Old Gig,

As you say, I owe you a letter. It was really good to see you [Chris and Aeneas had recently visited their father] and to see you looking so well and organized. You made a great impression on my mad Irish friends: people keep on stopping me in the street and complimenting me on 'dem lovely gossoons of yours' and especially on the lovely manners on them. I dare say you know by now that pleasant manners are quite as valuable as A levels in their own way. So of course is a clear and intelligible speaking voice, nudge, nudge.

They were also filled with wonder that two such young men could take beer with their elders and know when to stop – a talent rare in this country. Keep it like that. I understand that at the bank manager's party you and Aeneas were the only ones who went away sober. The sort of amused and bewildered respect that I enjoy here derives largely from the fact that I am the only drinker in town who never allows himself to get drunk; it would have been a feather in their caps if they had sent you home drunk, I'm sure you understand.

I wish you the very best of luck and success at Swansea. Have fun but remember that you are there to Work. A good degree will enable you to have much better fun later. I don't need to tell you to keep away from the drug idiots. If you screw, use a contraceptive. If the girl tells you it's OK she's on the pill, use a contraceptive just the same: a girl on the pill is obviously a bit promiscuous and there is a terrible lot of VD about, particularly the non-specific sort which antibiotics have no effect upon. If you have any sort of VD scare do get to a doctor, on rollerskates. Above all don't get conned into marrying anyone till you're really ready to settle down. Oh, yes, and for christ's sake don't get involved in studentspolitics [*sic*]: they are just a waste of your precious time. Keep money in reserve for rent and rail fare. Write to me if you get into trouble, in fact write to me anyway.

That's all the heavy father advice I can think of just now – and now that you're an undergraduate, this is probably the last time I can say Love to my dear Mr Giggy-wig.

Dad

[Undated]
St John
Jersey
C.I.
but soon at Kilmacaran
Shercock
Co. Cavan
Éire

Dear Old Gig,

A hasty note to ask how you are and to express a hope that you are coping with life in Swansea and not succumbing to the natural wish – at this stage – to drop out and become a road-sweeper or a pop-singer. I really do hate to play the role of heavy father and advice-giver, especially since I have handled my own life in such a lackadaisical and self-destructive way, but I really must urge you to stick by the dreaded books and get the bloody qualifications: then you can drop out if you want to, secure in the knowledge that you can always drop in again.

A lot of awful fathers urge their sons at university to 'make friends who will be useful to them in later life'. Don't do anything of the kind. Just avoid boring friends and tedious enemies (which are worse). Consider the next 28 months as an investment which will keep you for the next 50 years following. And for God's sake don't get married for a few years; marrying a girl before you are established is like swimming the Channel with a concrete block tied to your left testicle.

Did I tell you about my [stitch-up] friends in the police force? Who said the fuzz relies on the 'paddy factor'? [What] makes Irish criminals pretty well arrest themselves? Like the two micks who demanded money from a post office and when they were told to naff off said they would be back with guns? And came back with guns an hour later, to a post office full of fuzz? Well, it happened again last week in Manchester. No, really it did. A sergeant wouldn't take him seriously; xx said, he wished to complain about the casualness of the police. He was put through to the inspector in charge of complaints, who asked him his name and address. The Irishman told him. This is true. Well, it was in the *Daily Telegraph*.

Do you remember Dick Miskin? Well, before I went to Ireland I sold him my Indian stamps and he has now gone stamp-mad. If you want to part with your Jersey or other collections, he would, I know, give you a generous price.

Just when my publishers had freed me from small cash worries by giving me £250 a month against contract, I find myself in a ghastly tax mess which means my agent will have to withhold all monies until £994 is paid off, which means no revenue till July. Unless I can wiggle out of it . . . Don't worry I'll survive, I always have.

Not sure when I return to Ireland. Publication day for *All the Tea in China* is pencilled in for April 10th now, but might be earlier. The auguries are good; my new publishers are enthusiastic and believe in spending money on publicity; also, it really is rather a good book, if you want to know.

I have heard from Hughie (pub), Gertie, Rory &c and they all say 'remember us to the boys and tell them to come again'. Say what you like about the Irish, they're a warm-hearted lot. You two made a great impression with your behaviour and appearance and my image benefited mightily from having two large, 'dacent' sons coming to see me.

Much love as always from
Dad

15 November [1977?]
Kilmacaran
Shercock
Co. Cavan
Éire

Dear Old Gig,

Thank you for the Cash tapes faithfully returned and for the Derek & Clive one – I thought the last was only going to be a copy – do you want this original edition returned after copying or shall I send you the money for it? It is of course absolutely hilarious; the only pity is that there are so few people here to whom I'd dare play it; a lot of them seem broad-minded but suddenly you come up against a wall of disapproval in the most unexpected areas. I would not risk the Jayne Mansfield one here, for instance in Irish folklore women just do not have such orifices.

Glad to hear that you are getting on well at Swansea. Good that there is a pottery club – what is the other one you have joined? Can't decipher. Looks like 'Canihy Club'????

Your digs don't sound too cheap at £9 a week but I suppose it's the going rate. It's pretty well half your grant. But if you don't have to pay in the vacs it's not so bad. At least you could go home in the vacs, which is more than I could do when I was at Oxford. On £240 a year . . . Sorry to hear that you were hit in the jaw: glad you had the sense to walk away. My generation believed that this was unthinkable: a pompous and destructive belief. It takes more courage to walk away than to follow a mindless code. Also, getting involved in a squalid brawl where you might get your skull kicked in or your face mangled with a broken bottle; or get in trouble with the police, university authorities &c just doesn't make sense. You don't have to prove anything to someone who just punches people in the jaw for no good reason.

Please keep me posted about your next address; but please note I shall be at La Malzarderie, St John, JERSEY, for about the next three months. I am not going to South Africa, I found that services were expected of me (not by the Martlands) which made the trip undesirable. The old person who was subsidizing me did not just want a body-guard/escort. I'm sure you follow me.

Take care; eat properly; stick to beer; be considerate to your landlady; do your work conscientiously and if there's anything you don't understand run to someone who does. (I say that because when I was doing Germanic Philology I got into an awful mess because I was too proud (= stupid) to admit that I had got lost and wasted a whole term. My tutor was a cross old man who believed in the 'throw them in at the deep end sort the men from the boys'

[*rest of letter missing*]

[Summer 1978]

Dear Old Gig,

Just heard from Mum that you got ploughed in your prelims and are expiating by shovelling shit at the paper mill. I am truly sorry at your disappointment but I would urge you not to consider it the end of the world. OK, you failed an exam. That doesn't make you a failure. No one is a failure at 19 – or, indeed, at 90. So shovel a little shit while you consider things; but shovel it well and go on shovelling till the job's over. I shan't give you a lot of crap about how your failing the exam wasn't your fault. Career-masters, teachers, tutors and the undersigned must have to accept some fifty per cent of the blame: you have to shoulder the rest. You know that. I wasn't perfect at your age; indeed I'm not quite perfect now.

A couple of suggestions. Find a job where they have to give you time off to go to polytechnic; cop another A level and keep the others up to date; try for another university place in a year. Or; write to the army/navy/air force recruiting people who are always advertising for people with a brace of A levels and will put them through university with a handsome allowance if they will serve as officers for three years afterwards. You must have seen the advertisements. It seems jam to me. By the age of 25 you would be a graduate ex-officer. Marketable.

Whatever you do don't just throw up your hands and drop out

and buy an earring and grow an Afro hair-cut and peddle dope.
I'm sorry I know you are too smart for that, but you know what I
mean. Don't join them, beat them. They believe they have found
the answer but they have forgotten that one day they will be thirty;
then even sooner forty and then – AAARRRGHHH – fifty –
and with nothing going for them.

Keep in touch. Come over whenever you like. Ask me for travel
money; don't be stupid proud about that.

I don't want to seem sentimental but I'd like you to bear in mind
that there is someone who is proud of you.

Dad

[Summer 1976]

Dearest Catkin [Catriona],

Thank you for your lovely postcard: it is a far better watercolour
than I ever succeeded in making; I know a good deal about
watercolours but I never could do them! If you want a criticism or
two, here we go. (A) The washes are very good and liquid and the
distance values are excellent. The chief fault is that you have added
some dry, brushy strokes or acid (viridian?) green which clash with
the nice liquidity of the rest of the work. If you start with good,
wet washes – stay in that style, don't pick at it with fussy, dry
'tickles'. (B) The slope of the hill on the left is too flat and straight:
even if it was seen like that, the artist has the right to give a bit of a
wiggle to ease the eye. (C) The effect is spoiled by the big brown
'CB' in the corner. Always sign unobtrusively and in one of the
colours which are dominant in your picture. In this case, you could
have signed in green, in the bottom left-hand corner, and in much
smaller letters. I am returning the watercolour so you can see what
I'm talking about, but I want it back please because I'd like to keep
it. It is really promising, otherwise I would not be bothering to
criticize it, would I? . . .

Your very affectionate
Daddy
xxxxxxx

PS My dear old tutor, John Bryson, died last week at a ripe old age (80). I was very fond of him. When you were born I told him, with great pride, that I had a baby daughter. 'What are you calling her?' he asked. 'Robert Louis Stevenson,' I said. 'Ah,' he replied, 'I've always thought Catriona a charming name. See that people pronounce it properly.'

D xxx

[Mid 1970s]

Dearest Cat and all the others,

Thank you for my beautiful and cleverly designed Easter Card. I'm afraid I did nothing this Easter – didn't know it was here until I found the shops closed.

I enclose for Chris a block of 4 Barbados stamps which are from Mrs C. N. Martland

Bedford House

St Brelade's Bay

Jersey, C.I.

who you will remember to thank *promptly*, please, also a few others which you could *share with each other*.

I am a bit hard up just now because my publishers are in a muddle and are 3 months overdue with some money they owe me. Here is a pound to share or perhaps you might like to buy a little present for Mum.

I have been quite ill with pneumonitis and pleurisy which was nasty while it lasted because the Martlands were in Barbados but the Evanses came in every day with grub and made the place a bit warmer with a paraffin stove – they are really v. kind people – so it wasn't bad. I'm having my chest X-rayed this week to make sure that it's all gone away. I have to leave here on May 1st because they want to pull the Stables apart and enlarge it, which is just as well because my new doctor says I mustn't live in this cold and damp; he wanted me to go to a nursing home but it costs £20 a *day*! and anyway I had to look after the hens and doves and their poodle. I don't yet know where I'll be going but Nick Evans says I can camp on his boat for a couple of weeks and Paul Ostromoff has a nice warm dry loft which he would convert to living quarters (and then I should be near Pompey!)

I'm writing my third book, it's about the Opium Clippers in 1840–50 and I think it might be really exciting. It will probably be done by Macmillan's. They have wanted me for some time now and they're a very sound firm.

My love to your patient Mum and tell her that I'll send a contribution just as soon as I have any to send. (By the way, I have a chance of a regular monthly appearance on the local TV; also the Jersey paper has started a colour magazine and they have asked me if I'll write for it.)

And love to all of you from
Dad XXXX

30 August [1980]
[Dundalk, Éire]

Dearest Cat

A short letter to wish you the best of luck in your interview at Christ's on the 11th: I'll be thinking about you with love and confidence. I don't really understand about O and A and S levels but I take it you have enough for entrance? A pity about the Maths; none of us has much talent there and you don't seem to have inherited your grandfather Slater's genius in that direction. I don't know what value Latin has as an entry qualification but it would have been a very useful tool if you're going to read French or English. For one thing, it shows us how a fully inflected language worked so that we can recognize the remains of such a structure when we tackle almost any European modern language. For another, it's by no means dead; we use a Latin word in every line of English, or French, not to mention the Romance languages. Even the daft Celtic languages have to borrow: 'Post Office' and 'School Bus' are four Latin words: in Irish Gaelic they are 'Oifig na Poiste' and 'Bus Scoile'. (I may have misspelt those a little, I'm certainly not going to waste my time learning Irish!) Last, the best of the vast Literature in Latin exhibits a wonderful compression or concision which appeals to me; I try to chew a couple of lines of Horace or Catullus every night and always come across a neat little nugget; like Catullus, in an attack on Julius Caesar, saying *unice imperator*. A computer would probably translate this as 'unique emperor' but what Catullus is saying is what the snide politicians used to say about Macmillan: 'Well, he is the best Prime Minister we've got.' (Literally: 'only general'; understood: 'our, er, *only* Commander . . . *now* . . .') But I digress, as Charlie Mortdecai says.

I'm annoyed that they only gave you a D in art; I think wise old Aeneas may well have got it right when he said that your work might have looked too saleable; nowadays you're not *supposed* to make art that people might want to buy, you're supposed to get an Arts Council grant to walk through Ipswich with a 20-foot plastic sausage on your head and then set it on fire in the children's playground. Go on doing what *you* and other people like.

Sorry to use both sides of this paper; it's hard to come by over here.

At your interview, I don't think I need to suggest you dress well but not too dashingly; there's a chance that one of the board is anti-woman-admission and another chance that a woman don may be queer. Watch out for them making gentle jokes; smile happily but don't fall about. Be ready to answer questions like 'Why do you want to read French', 'Why do you want to come to Cambridge', 'Why did you apply for Christ's College'. Tell the truth – don't get trapped with a fib; if they ask you whether you've read much Montaigne, tell them 'No, but I'm looking forward to reading him.' If they ask you what you like doing in your spare time, tell them 'punting, arguing, eating, carpentry' . . . something a bit out of the way. (You must have heard potential beauty-queens burbling their standard answers. 'Ow, I love horse-riding and classical mewzic an' Art an' all that . . .')

I'm sorry I forgot the date of your birthday; I'm not a diary-keeping person. Here's a book: you might like the bit about Péguy; he was a lovely stylist with an inimitable way of repeating words and playing variations on them but a little marred by a potty veneration for Joan of Arc – who was a bit potty herself: my theory is that she had puberty and menopause simultaneously . . . ! Ask Mum what she thinks of *that* off-the-cuff value-judgement.

    Very much love & success in all you do

    Dad xxx

PS I hate the new English 12p stamp: I'm sure Jane Eyre didn't really write *Charlotte Brontë* – it was another fellow of the same name.

[Undated]

Dearest Catriona,

    I'm very glad to learn that you are still brushing your teeth. Another boring bit of health advice: never read in an inadequate light. False teeth are a horror but false eyes are unobtainable.

[Early/mid 1981]

Dearest Cat,

    Thank you for your amusing letter: I have a number of unpleasant letters to write today so I shall limber up by first writing a pleasant one to you. I'm glad to hear that you have found a compatible boyfriend and I think that a week in France together is a good idea; if you can still stand the sight of each other after that, then you'll know the compatibility is real and not the old star-dust.

    You are lucky to have found someone to exchange with you in Italy this September; you'll want to have some cash-reserve for Norwich. I don't suppose I need to warn you about watching the pennies when you get your grant – you doubtless remember how poor old Christopher blew his. You have every right to buy yourself presents with money you've earned but the grant is for rent, food and books and it comes from the poor sods who pay taxes. Try and get a really good degree; it's something you can always fall back on and, and after all, it only means, basically, eighty weeks hard work spread over three years. I may have said this before but it's worth repeating: don't join too many extra-mural things at first and don't get yourself lumbered with a lot of friends who may turn out to be bores and nuisances by your second term. Spend your first few weeks getting orientated towards your work and the general set-up. Pay the whole term's rent and other fixed things in advance. Join one of the banks which offers a no-charge service to undergraduates and keep your account in credit: a good record at your bank will be a great help in future years whereas a lousy one will stick to you all your life and damage your chances of getting an overdraft, mortgage or whatever when you really need it. End of paternal sermon.

My plans are a bit fluid at present so don't make any firm plans about coming either to Jersey or Ireland yet; I will let you know where and why I am as soon as the situation jells.

I've been languishing in hospital lately; have had a little cancer cut out of my temple because it was sitting right beside the temporal artery and a few other jobs done. Blood tests showed I'd got an alarming liver condition (no, not cirrhosis nor hepatitis) and, unless something was done about it, I had, at that time, about two years to live. One of the blood-functions (AST, whatever that means) which is normally 25–40 was reading 900! the highest they'd ever seen. However, within a month they'd got it down to an acceptable 52 and the other functions are also now at a steady level and the Senior Lecturer (teaching hosp., you see) says that I should easily make my century if I take care. I've got to eat a lot of protein, take lots of vitamins & minerals and not tease my liver with curries. Worst of all, no alcohol for six months and then only if my blood-checks have stayed steady. I don't especially miss the alcohol, although I would like the occasional refreshing pint when I visit the village and a night-cap on going to bed, but it's easy to resist the mild temptation when I remind myself that a couple of convivial shots could, at this point, literally be the death of me. I'm too *nice* to die.

Just before I was due to be discharged, David Goldberg took me out for the weekend for a bracing climb up the Cloud (Peak District) and on the way back we had a rather awful car accident (not David's fault, in fact his presence of mind saved all our lives) and I was the only one hurt except for the idiot motor-cyclist who was dreadfully mangled. I was concussed, cracked a few bones unimportantly and sustained a deep kneecap wound which still hurts, so had to endure another dose of the hospital.

Did I tell you that I went to Florida (all expenses paid) earlier this year? Here is a comic picture of me at the Palm Beach Chamber of Commerce meeting (champagne and strawberries breakfasts for 500!) I seem to be giving an impersonation of Robert Morley.

I'm very pleased at your handwriting; it's an inexpensive hobby and a valuable skill. So many people write so foully that when one receives a handsome letter it is with a pleasant shock. Two points: take a little more care over capital letters (e.g., the middle of the M should go right down to the line) and leave larger margins all round. Am also very pleased at your news of Amanda; as you suggest, her problem has long been the disparity between her inner and outer maturities and, when they finally get into step, she should be something quite special. Oh, all right, you're pretty special yourself, as you well know.

Love to all, with an extra helping for you.
Your Daddy xxx

[16 December 1981]

Dearest Cat,

I remember Norwich – just – as a rather engaging little city but, as you say, draughty. There are some *superb* roof-bosses in the Cathedral nave & particularly in the Cloisters, where my favourite is *Herod's Feast*. If you go to see them, take a pair of binoculars and lie on your back. Roof-bosses are tremendously important in medieval art history because they were too high up for the 17th century iconoclasts to smash and for the equally savage Victorian 'restorers' to scrub and tart up.

Your loving
Dad

[Undated]

Dear Amanda,

I am returning your drawings because you may want them for your portfolio. What follows is a fatherly sermon on art. If it's too boring, put it aside and try it again next year. If you doubt its validity, show it to your art-teacher and see if he/she agrees.

My friend David Niven, of whom you probably have never heard, tells a story of playing a three-minute scene in front of the cinema cameras; after each shot the Very Famous Director (whose name I forget) simply said, 'Do it again.' After seventeen or so repeats and 'do it again', David stalked up to the Director and said, 'Look, how the hell do you *want* me to play this scene?' The Director fixed him with a weary stare and simply said, '*Better.*' Why I think this anecdote is relevant is because I have just been thinking of a friend who was at a v. g. art college – Heatherley's (?) or the Byam Shaw – one of those places; and had a brilliant teacher in her first term. He told the group: 'Each of you draw a zebra.' They drew. He took the pile of drawings and, without looking at them, tore them up and dumped them in the waste-paper basket. Next day he said, 'Each of you draw a zebra – *better.*' Naturally, they drew like mad things, for all they were worth. The Teacher said, 'These will be much worse and, in any case, this is what happens to most art' – and again, without looking, he tore them all up and dumped them. Sure enough, on the third day, he said, 'Each of you draw a zebra. Wake me up in forty minutes.'

Well, some of the po-faced ones drew even more zoologically accurate zebras, some drew zebras idly, sure that the waste-paper basket would not care; and some simply doodled or drew joke-zebras – even *rude* zebras! Ah, but *this* time the teacher spread the drawings out on the floor, gathered the group around the exhibit and analysed each effort with merciless expertise.

He was either a very good teacher or a very bad one. Probably the former. I'll write more of this later but I enclose 3 scribbles with notes & return your sketches. I'll see you in a fortnight or so,

I hope. Lots of love (I'm *glad* you signed yourself 'Your very happy daughter.')
   Dad xxx

[*Note commenting on a picture sent by Amanda.*]

[Undated]

Good, careful work. *Too* careful. Get to know *bones under the face* – lips, eyes, eyelashes, etc. are easy – just art-school tricks. Never mind about the 'shading' – go for the line – the clean, *certain* line. Chinese artists muse over their piece of paper for hours, then, with one sweep of the ink-brush, make the wonderful line. If it's not right, they don't erase or shade, they chuck it away and start again.
   D

[Undated]

Dearest Amandissima,
   A brief scribble to say, first, the little book enclosed is slightly special; not only is it signed by the author but he has also stuck a little 'origami' inside the front cover himself. So don't let anyone 'rip it off' you.
   Second, here is the most basically useful thing I know about drawing: *fill the paper.* Look at the area of paper available, then decide how to use it all. Here are a few hasty scrawls: No. 1 is how heraldic artists 200 years ago used to draw a 'Lion Rampant' on a coat of arms. No. 2 is how they did it 100 years ago. No. 3 is how the good herald would draw it today. (I don't mean that I've drawn it *well*; I'm just talking about using the space available.) I bet your art-master will explain better than I can.
   In great haste and love,
   See you very soon
   Your loving Daddy
   who is glad that you are happy! xxx

[Undated]
Shercock
Co. Cavan
Éire

My Dear Daughters,

I have every intention of living for another naughty forty years. However, if some malicious bus-driver should mow me down tomorrow, I would like you both to remember your daft Daddy as he appears in the enclosed photograph: happy, silly (I never said I wasn't) and, if you look at the lower left-hand corner, not *very* far away from a pretty girl's shoulder . . . *SHOULDER*!!?

We shall all foregather soon but, as I say, in case of accidents, I'd like you to remember me as the happy idiot in the photograph . . . But an idiot who fought to get an education, who did his best, which probably wasn't good enough, and who loves you both very much.

    Take care.
    Your boring but
    affectionate
    Daddy

[Undated]

Dearest Amanda,

You must very soon decide what you *want* to do, what you *can* do and what you *need* to do so that you can do what you want to do. You see, Roderick could have been a fine geologist but he couldn't cope with the necessary Maths. Christopher could have gone up to Balliol if they hadn't let him, at school, drop the necessary language qualification. As a matter of fact – don't laugh – I once wanted to be a vet (!) but only got a pass in Biology. Thank goodness. Do bear in mind (I may have said this before) that the attractive careers such as acting, dress-designing, art, are all terribly overcrowded: there's plenty of room at the top but you have to be a very good climber to get up there before you die of starvation.

From what I can see, most art colleges today are self-perpetuating hives of mindless, buzzing idiots, concerned only with turning out more buzzing idiots with diplomas to teach yet more b.i.s. The young Gainsborough, today, wouldn't have a hope of getting into the Slade; a young Laurence Olivier would be laughed out of Junior RADA and if young Shakespeare applied to read drama at Bristol he'd get a kick up the bum.

If you really want to do art, for instance, I'd say get an undemanding job to keep you in food and clothes and work at your *own* art in your spare time. If possible, find a good, real, working artist who'll teach you the techniques which matter in exchange for washing his brushes and his socks. That was the way most of the best started. Bratby, arguably the most vital English painter in his prime today, walked out of his art college (Goldsmith's?) in disgust and when he became famous and they offered him an honorary Diploma he told them where to stuff it. Bad manners but good criticism.

If you want to act, you'll find that a RADA diploma is not worth one pinch of flea-dirt. Get a job as dogsbody or property-girl in rep; if you can take it you'll learn.

If you want to dress-design, apprentice yourself to someone who's made it.

Most vocational courses usually only mean that you start in the rat-race three years later than the other kids.

Here endeth the sermon. I hope that what I've said is true; certainly it's as true as I know about. Anyway, whatever you do or try, just remember that, although he doesn't write as often as he should, you have a very

loving

Dad xxx

Writers at Work: Letters to Christopher Priest

This correspondence ran from January 1966 to November 1978. It obviously gave both writers an opportunity to exchange ideas about their craft, which they very much valued; each kept the other's letters. (For Bon, this was one of two particularly sustaining and long-running correspondences with fellow writers; the other was conducted with the science-fiction writer Harry Harrison, whose letters to Bon were typically warm, helpful and encouraging.)

As the correspondence opens, Bon is fifteen years older than Priest and has just included the latter's first published story in the magazine *Science Fantasy*, which Bon was editing at the time. Priest's first letter is missing. Bon's reply is amused: 'You are clearly not serious when you kindly assure me that you believe me to be "a very hip person": it is a friendly and tolerant pat on the shoulder but it is quite untrue – I glory in the name of rectangle – in sixties terms, an old square.' He comments on various science-fiction matters and continues:

There is one more point I'd like to make about this literary-literate business and it's a rather hard one to express. I know you will not think I am swollen-headed if I say that I am highly literate, very well read and the victim of an extremely good education. The point is that I and many people like me do not like literary recreational reading. *Analog*'s engineers and nuclear physicists and sociologists – usually profoundly illiterate people – do like it. They are desperately uneasy about this CULTURE thing they know they haven't got. Every time I go to a party here in Oxford I'm buttonholed by science dons all bursting to talk about art to prove – presumably to themselves – that they are not outside the in-group of people who Know about Things Like That. It's pathetic. The art

historians, philosophers, critics and literary historians are at the other end
of the room telling dirty stories and pinching girls' bottoms. So, in spirit,
am I. Last Wednesday I delivered a lecture on Paolo Uccello; tomorrow,
if I had to (God forbid), I could deliver a competent lecture on Kafka.
But what I am going to read in bed is P. G. Wodehouse or Ed McBain
or even C. S. Forester. In short, I believe that stories are for recreation,
not a painless way of acquiring culture. I am determined not to delude
myself that I am editor of *Horizon* or *Encounter* or the *Review of English
Studies*: I want to keep clearly in view that my magazine is supposed to
be a collection of stories. You know, things that people read when they're
tired or bored or sad . . .

A brief exchange of letters in November and December 1976
concerned a proposal from Priest to make an anthology of the best
science fiction from *Impulse*. Difficulties and personality clashes in
editorial relationships and production after Bon's departure are
described. Priest ended a letter 'If you want to go on hearing from
me make me reply!!'

Then in June 1978 Priest wrote again, having picked up Bon's
books in Amsterdam and read them on the boat going home: 'The
peace and quiet of the afterdeck was shattered at frequent intervals
by my roaring with laughter. What fun! I can't remember how
long it is since I read a book that made me laugh aloud. For that
alone I loved your books. But there is so much more to them. Your
sense of high and low for instance . . . Your author's asides to the
reader are perfectly timed, I think, and there is a wonderful sense
of what I can only describe as *knowledge*. You write of this and
everything else with marvellous relish. I found the climaxes to both
books quite gruesome, and perhaps the more so for the sustained
levity.'

Bon replied to this in early July and on the 6th Priest sent him a
copy of *The Space Machine* and offered more 'if you're truly interested in the rest of my stuff'. This opened a phase of the most
intense and detailed discussion. The following are extracts from
this correspondence.

[Early July 1978]
Shercock (*Not* shercook)
Co. Cavan
Éire

Dear Chris,

Thank you very much indeed for your heartening letter about read-ing the two Bonfig Penguins (bought in *Amsterdam*!) – praise from a pro is praise indeed. Laughing out loud is praise one could not buy.

In return I can only say that I guzzled *Indoctrinaire* at one sitting and agreed with *TLS* that it was – what did they say – 'remarkably well controlled'? Something like that. None of the self-indulgent fireworks of the usual first novel. It had something of the gently developing grue of Le Fanu's *Uncle Silas* without the flash trickery of Kafka. I bought it, in hardback. Someone stole it. Naturally. You sent me *Fugue for a Darkening Island*, and I've read it twice. When I open the right box (paucity of shelf-space here) I shall read it again. I vividly remember the two opening paragraphs: the first where Whit-man says he's 5'11" and is really rather a decent chap and the second where he says he is 5'11" and smells badly. I loved it. Lateef's character develops beautifully. If you want a spot of crit., here it is. John Betje-man wrote to me about my first novel: 'steady with the adverbs'. I pass that on to you. Second: both titles a bit counter-productive, whatever that means. I think one must imagine a stupid, menopausal woman going into a bookshop and asking for ' "Fugg-you for a dark-ling Ireland". It's by a priest.' They get sent to the Catholic Reposi-tory. The third bit is about the sex-passages but I think I've perhaps vexed you enough and too much mitigated my praise for the books.

I'm ashamed to say that I've read nothing of yours since; I see no English papers here, have dropped out of SF generally and am 75 miles from anything you would call a bookshop. Tell me a couple of your titles that I would enjoy and I'll order them from Blackwell's. I truly will.

There's always a room for you here.

As ever

Bon

[Early August 1978]
[Kilmacaran, Éire]

Dear Chris,

I have been reading *The Space Machine* along with other books, as is my wont; your bedfellows, if you want to know, were Q. Horatius Flaccus, Graham Greene's new *The Human Factor* and Glendon Swarthout's *The Shootist*. I am sorry to have to say that Greene's novel trailed the field embarrassingly. I have often noticed that old men's books (G.G. is 74 by my reckoning) read uncannily like rather good *first* novels. See, for instance, A. E. W. Mason's *Musk and Amber*: you would say 'a very promising start' if you didn't know that he was 77 when he wrote it.

Your *Space Machine*, on the other hand, came happily to hand and I enjoyed it immensely; it romped along in a most convincing way. You were to tackle a pastiche of *fin de siècle* style and you sustained it uncommonly well. Lovely reading. You were also brave to write a tale of which everyone who knew their Wells would know – more or less – how it had to end, but you carried it off with great élan.

Frankly, I think you were ill served by your editor. There are numerous small discrepancies and anachronisms which it was *his* job to pick up. If you want a note of some of them for the next edition, I have scribbled some memoranda which I'd be happy to type out for you. Nothing important, but I know you like to get things right. My only major disappointment was the way you threw away the promising 'Amelia's handbag' motif. I mean, at first one had the delightful suspicion that she could not be parted from her sip of brandy – a charming and bizarre failing in a young Victorian lady. This would have been a delicate thread of amusement to run throughout the book. If, on the other hand, the whole point was that she could not be parted from her store of sanitary towels, then you could have pointed that up (p. 268) with a bit more of a crunch. Like:

'Never *mind* what they are for, Edward.' Sorry, sorry, if I didn't like the book so much I wouldn't be bothering my ass to dissect it, would I?

Write when you have time.

Yours admiringly

Bon

2nd August 1978

Dear Bon,

I was just beginning to think you would never write, and then you did, bringing an inordinate amount of happiness on a grey and somewhat gloomy day.

Modern publishing being what it is, there's very little likelihood of a second edition of *Space Machine* . . . but you never know. (A revised edition of *Indoctrinaire* is coming out soon.) So if you have the time and inclination, I'd welcome your notes on my anachronisms. I'm tapping my fingers suspiciously, as I'm sure you know. The danger of anachronism stood out like a boil on the forehead all the way through, and several people went through the typescript looking for them. So if some slipped through I'll be (a) mortified and (b) delighted to hear of them. Is *kopje* one of them? Because it's the one people are always challenging me on. It comes from p. 143 of the first edition of *War of the Worlds*; a fact that surprises many.

On Amelia's handbag. Throughout the book I was concerned not only to *set* the book in period, but also to *write* it in period. Edward is the writer of the book, not me . . . and so I felt that I could not allow him to tell us things about him and Amelia that would have been offensive to him to report. Yes, Amelia was definitely one for the nip o' brandy; Edward reports it, and I had to leave it to the modern reader to fill in the rest. Which is exactly what you have done; you know what she's doing with the flask, and so does Edward . . . but he would not set it down. (The same is true of the sex stuff in the book: the modern reader twigs what Edward does not tell.) The sanitary towels were my buried joke . . . and a bit of a joke . . . and a bit of a joke on myself. Being basically a shy young lad, I'd never actually *asked* elderly ladies what they did once a month before modern technology gave us tampons and sanitary towels. So I launched into a week's adventure of research, trying to find out. No success, until I realized that the answer was staring me in the face, so to speak, in the Harrods 1895 catalogue on the medical requisites page. Top entry was something called 'absorbent towelettes', which I'd glanced over several times without twigging. From there it was but a short step to finding the rest. So my little joke was that Edward sort of finds out about them quite late in the day . . . and *still* doesn't realize what they are. But you, like many people, got the point.

You never talk about your writing in your letters. Are you working at the moment?

I remember a review I read, a few years ago, in *The Times*. It was by Philip French, and it was of a Hammond Innes novel. The review said, in short, that he, French, had never read – far less reviewed – an Innes novel, so he thought he would have a go. After a few words of excited praise he concluded with the following sentence (and I quote loosely): 'It is my fervent hope that Mr Innes has enjoyed a good night's sleep, has partaken of a wholesome breakfast, and is looking forward to a good day's work on his new novel.' Which, if I may say so, was very much the sentiment I felt after reading your books.

I am still on the wagon, except last week I had a glass of wine. I practically keeled over. Quite extraordinary. One also notices booze on people's breath far more . . . also erratic driving.

Oh, I meant to tell you. (Getting back to *Space Machine*.) My research included buying a bottle of smelling-salts from the chemist down the road. I had no idea what they even smelled like . . . and felt I should at least find that out. So when I got home, I unscrewed the cap, placed the top in my nostril and inhaled in the way one inhales one of those Benzedrine nasal de-blockers. Three days later, when I had recovered my eyesight, and could breathe again, I knew *exactly* what Edward would do to poor Amelia when she passed out. You see, it's all autobiography . . .

However, onwards!

Cheers

Chris

[August 1978]

Dear Chris,

Thanks for your letter; entertaining, stimulating and gratifying as ever.

No, I had not thought of *kopje* as an anachronism because I distinctly remember seeing it used (and explained) in a volume of the *Illustrated London News* of about 1880, dealing with some minor campaign whose name escapes me just now. One of the early Zulu Wars. I think the one in which the Prince Imperial was killed.

Your preoccupation with and shyness about inquiring as to menstrual millinery fills me with amusement; your admission (exaggerated, one hopes) that it took you a *week*'s research to get the answer shocks me. I mean, even Sussex University ought to teach people how to use reference books. I have just spent a revolting ten *minutes* foraging in my own modest library in this primitive cottage and I now know far more about the subject than I care to. The tampon (otherwise tampion, tompion, etc.) as a surgical plug is centuries old; its commonest version was the 'tent' (late Middle English) – 'a roll or pledget, usu. of soft, absorbent material . . . formerly much used to . . . & . . . or *natural orifice*'. (*S.O.D.*) You may recall Shakespeare's naughty joke 'Modest Doubt is called the tent which searches to the bottom of the worst'. (Incidentally, one of my favourite words is cognate with 'tampon': 'tappen', which means the fibrous plug which seals a bear's arsehole during hibernation. How *about* that?) (The mammoth had a built-in flap of skin which protected his anus from the Siberian frosts; his cousin the elephant has a similar arrangement which keeps out ticks, winged insects and others pests. No public-schoolboy should be without one.)

I note that Sears Roebuck were using the words 'sanitary towel' at the turn of the century but of course Edward would not have known that expression or, indeed, towelette or any other. Your point was well taken and the joke good. What I mean in my last letter – and perhaps I expressed myself clumsily – was that one rather lost sight of – and regretted – the handbag motif during the last third of the book and that one was left in some doubt as to which part of its contents was essential: the indispensable booze or the disposable towelettes. (When we meet I shall bore you to sobs with a lecture on the semantics of toile/toilette/towelette/toilet: I am in the Olympic class as a bore on words.)

In your place I should have drawn on my resourcefulness: I'd have asked a youngish chap with a suitably aged sister to ask her to ask her mother to ask *her* mother. Did I live in Harrow I'd have taken a taxi to the British Museum Library. A week's research . . . pshaw.

You made me feel very ancient with your account of having to buy a bottle of smelling-salts; they were a commonplace when I was a child. (Say, forty years ago.) (Here à propos of the word 'forty' is a handy piece of knowledge: a criminal who used to work for me once told me that I should never write a cheque for eight pounds. It took me ages to realize that 'eight' is the only number which can be decupled by squeezing in the one letter 'y'.)

Have just been to nearest hospital (Drogheda, forty miles away) for a protracted session with radiographers and nasty interview with surgeon. Have got to be 'admitted' next week so that the latter can perform an endoscopy and biopsy. Terrifying and fiendishly expensive. The hospital's name – I'm sorry, you have to believe this – 'Our Lady of Lourdes's Hospital of the Medical Missionaries of Mary' and the cable-address is 'Caritas' but there's little *caritas* when they make out the bill. The price of a private ward is roughly the same as a suite in Claridge's and the surgeon's and anaesthetist's fees would raise a few eyebrows in Harley Street.

My ravishing sixteen-and-a-half-year-old daughter Catriona is staying with me for a few days and having great fun. Local youths are trudging two miles to drop in for a 'cop o tay' and in one case rowing three miles across the lough (honestly) to ask if he could borrow a trout-fly and then casually mention that there is a dance on in Carrikmacross and 'wad yer darter ever like to go wid me sister'. No sweat; Catriona is as capable as she is lovely and the Irish, as I'm sure you know, don't fuck.

Do come over yourself one day; it would be an experience for you. Try not to be on the wagon. There's little else to do. (Bring your own lady and typewriter.) I think that every SF writer I know has had to go on the wagon at one time or another – occupational hazard? I have often thought of doing so myself but the bloody thing is always moving too fast. Giving up cigarettes is easier – I do it most mornings – but I think I can give up giving them up now: the surgeon at Drogheda *did not suggest it* and this was the nastiest thing about our interview. I'm sure you follow me. (That information is classified, by the way. Please.)

Warmest regards to yourself and love to the doubtlessly *edible* Pauline. Pray write an angry letter proving that everything I have written on the attached sheets of niggles is wrong, pedantic, tedious, nit-picking, crapulous roly-moly and tumble-cum-trivy.

Yours aye
Bonfig

[*In his reply Priest confesses that he didn't even have a proper* Oxford English Dictionary *at the time of writing* Space Machine *and marvels that they are now discussing sanitary towels: 'Stepping back from all this for a moment, I am interested to witness the sight of two (apparently) grown men discussing this subject with such pedantic interest.' He is looking forward to receiving a copy of* All the Tea in China *and goes on: 'By the way, the scene where Mortdecai kicks Jock's head has a peculiar intensity to it. I dunno . . . I found it very affecting. I also like the* chutzpah *in the second book, where so many unanswered questions about the ending of the first book are left . . . unanswered.'*

His letter ends with a crossword clue: 'Listen! A sexual perversion. (5,2,4,4).' Priest writes again on 31 August and Bon replies.]

[Late August 1978]

Dear Chris,

The worst of getting one of your wonderfully stimulating letters is that it means I shall find myself replying at such length that I shall be unable to write any cash-type nonsense that day so I shall make this short: I shall, I *shall*.

I did not really think that you had spent a week researching ladies' vulva-blotters. By the way, I find William Whitely's catalogue of 1912 offering both towelettes and 'Ladies' Turkish Diapers'. I join in your amusement at two (chronologically) grown-up men discussing such things with all the pedantry of two grammarians bickering over 'the doctrine of the enclitic "de", dead from the waist down'.

Certainly I am a pedant; it is a cheap and wholesome blood-sport. (Which reminds me to raise an eyebrow at your statement that you did not own a 'proper Oxford Dictionary' – is there another sort? – that such a book is 'square one for a writer' and that not owning it constitutes 'an imbalance'. Oh, fie! As you say, the complexity and dangers of the English language are 'one of the great daunting excitements of life'; it is hard for you and me to realize that most people neither know nor care tuppence for their language, they are like sluts using silk shirts for dish-clouts . . .

Thank you for your concern about my jaunt to horsepiddle. It turns out that my oesophagus and stations onwards are riddled and pitted with ulcers and that I have a hernia of the diaphragm but that 'none of these conditions appear malignant' which means that instead of a neat little cancer which would be whipped out in a twinkling I have a gallimaufry of nastiness which must look like a publisher's conscience and which will kill me unless I take to white fish poached in milk.

'Instantly give up smoking, all alcohol, all seasoned foods,' said the merry surgeon.

'Couldn't I do something easy like holding my breath for ten minutes?'

'Ha ha,' he said. 'Very well. I'll see you in ten or twelve months. With a massive haemorrhage. Might save you if they get you here fast enough. How far away do you live?'

'Fifty miles.'

'Ah.'

Those boys really work at frightening you, don't they . . .

Do write when you can unstick yourself from the molten embraces of Pauline.

> Yours
> Bon

I open this and waste a good envelope to say 'Oh *NO!*' The 5,2,4,4 can't be *Prick Up Your Ears*, surely. I mean, even the *Guardian* wouldn't . . .

?

    B.

[September 1978]

Dear Priest – I feel I should write 'father forgive me' –

I *do* now enclose a copy of *ATTIC* which I said I would send on Monday but the postman hasn't been since Saturday and, absurdly, on top of all my other miseries I am now afflicted with THE GOUT! Laugh! Enjoy! Gout is like mothers-in-law, tooth-ache, lumbago, gonorrhoea and piles: exquisitely painful but non-lethal and therefore fair game for the laughers. What it means to me, apart from a nasty reminder that I've had my fun and must now start to pay for it, is that I can't get my fucking shoe on, nor drive my loving motor-car. (Was it you that wrote in a 'fanzine' (ugh) years ago that my editorials had an 'old colonelish' smack to them? You were jumping the gun.)

At that point I sent myself to bed, as is my wont in times of stress. Tonight I am revivified by the arrival of my succulent new typewriter, all worked by phlogiston or Gaussian waves or twisted elastic or something and I hasten to write to you upon it. I had a monstrous one when I was in business (yes, electric typewriter) but never dared dared approach it myself because my secretary used to GRRRRR at me and the machine itself used to run off a gross of yesterday's letters if I even looked at it. This thing seems much more amenable and has an exxxxxx sorry

sorr

sor

so

s I daresay I shall soon get the hang of it hang of it hang of it hang of it hang of it hang of it; it's just a matter of practice you know. Let the beast know that you're its master, d'you see . . .

Your commiserations about my enforced diet and regimen would be welcome if I wrrr (come UP you bitch) if I were in fact keeping to the surgeon's orders. I am not. I have promised myself to make no curry for a few weeks, to cut my 60 a day cig-intake by a half or better and to drink my whisky with more water – indeed, with milk if late at night. That's all. At your age I might take it all more seriously but at fifty my reaction is 'sod 'em'. Who wants to live for ever? . . .

Have just skimmed through *Padre in Colditz* which is the edited diaries of a *Methodist* padre in Colditz. Truly fascinating because so real, because the pretentious, gullible little bugger is only aware of 10% of what goes on around him but describes that with all the meticulous silliness of a Parson Woodforde. Most of all, this padre (J. Ellison Platt) is an absolute model for your Edward in diction and attitudes. I'll send you the book if you'd care to see it.

Well, I think I've got the hang of this machine now with a few exxxxxxfuckitxxxx exceptions so I'll sign off with many a good wish and compliment. Might be in London next month – see you perhaps?

> Yours aye
> Bonfig

PS I have just *made up* a crossword clue in a revengeful spirit. Here it is (and it's not a joke):
'But old Priest' (three and nine letters)

[November, 1978]

My *Dear* Christopher,

Thank you for your letter and your munificent present: it will stand proudly alongside Lubbock's *Last of the Windjammers* and *The China Clippers* – but Masefield's own copy!!! I am indeed a rich man today. You are wasted as a mere brilliant author: you would make a fortune as a professional consultant prezzy-chooser.

About letters: I had it in the back of my mind that *you* owed *me* a letter; this almost certainly means that somewhere, under the detritus of bills, half-eaten sandwiches and tattered girlie magazines which pollutes what I like to call my desk, there lies an almost-finished letter to you which I did not post. Sorry. Sorry. For the last few weeks I have been thrashing about agonizedly in the throes of getting a typescript into some sort of shape that even a printer could read: I'm sure you know the state of mind. Anyway, the book is off and away and I have emerged. Tomorrow I might even pluck up courage to clear my alleged desk. Tomorrow ... well, *you* know.

Although I have never been lucky enough to meet the surely esculent Pauline, I grieve to learn that she has been laid low by a sinister wog bug. I hope that by the time you read this she will be bouncing about again and bulging with health. If by any chance the effect of the malaise is of a gynaecological nature, I'd be happy to give you a letter to a dear old mate who is perhaps the best consultant in that field in GB and spent years in West Africa so knows about tropical wotsits. He navigates between Lancaster and Kendal and, introduced by me, you would not be charged a penny.

I am sorry that you have had a head-cold but delighted that you call it that; I am quite pissed-off with the way everyone today calls a cold the 'flu'.

Really glad that you got some fun out of *ATTIC* and grasped the fact that it was 'a strong, meaty yarn' but nothing more. I had a lot of fun writing it and allowed myself a lot of shameless self-indulgence. I loved your bit about my 'inimitable streak of pure nastiness'. Curiously, since taking up fiction-mongering, I have become a compulsive truth-teller in private life and the same goes for abstaining from nastiness. Catharsis? For real nast, wait until I send you the new Mortdecai romp next spring. I relished your praise first because you are a professional of longer standing than me and second because I value your opinions, if you want to know.

Glad you said that you felt you learned things from it; one of my very oldest friends said the same thing. I used perhaps 10% of my notebooks-ful of research and then, tearfully, cut out about a quarter of that. Lusting to impart all the lovely stuff I had accumulated but terrified of 'showing off'. Long ago, in the army, I had a spell of teaching instructors how to instruct and one of my great pearls of wisdom was that a teacher should know more than he teaches – or teach less than he knows. I'm sure you see the analogy. It's really strange how, if you spend hours mastering every sail on a clipper, for instance, but only, in the end, mention the 'main topgallant', that mention seems to come through with so much more authority. When I say it's strange, I really mean it's *strange*. Like your quite sparse allusions in *The Space Machine* – one has an unquestioning conviction that you know your HGW inside out. I wish I knew how it works. It's like the mysterious 'readability' – some of the lousiest authors have it, some of the best don't.

Glad you liked the recurring 'Jane' Austen joke: my second ex-wife, a humourless, feminist prig (but lovely with it) thought it was neither amusing nor in any kind of good taste. Marghanita Laski liked it though . . .

Animadverting to the craft of writing; you may perhaps be amused to know the four things about 'the life so short, the craft so long to learn' which I often chew over. 1/ Sheridan: 'Your easy reading, sir, is damned hard writing' 2/ Stevenson: 'war on the adjective and death to the optic nerve'. 3/ C. W. Montague: 'all writers are putters-in or takers-out' and 4/ Harry Harrison: 'get the narrative hook in, right at the beginning' . . .

It is hell here; ice *inside* the windows despite turf fire; car immobile; an infestation of rats in the loft who galumph up and down the false ceiling, happily munching the Endorats I have carpeted it with and, apparently, thriving on it. Bastards. Mice I can live with; they clean up crumbs which would otherwise nourish the black-beetle population. Spiders eat flies. Mosquitoes, after one sip from my bloodstream, stagger away hiccupping and singing dirty songs. But I do bar cattle-ticks and rats.

Since I cannot get into the village I have broached a bottle of Italian *Stock* brandy and I feel the old nostalgic headache beginning – it takes me back to happy days in Sirmione.

Yours aye

Bon

Write soon – I prize your letters.

'I Carried a Biro for Ronnie Kray': Letters to Michael Powell

I Carried a Biro for Ronnie Kray was one of Bon's working titles for a film that he hoped to write for, or with, Michael Powell. This possibility seems to have arisen from somebody having sent Powell a copy of *Don't Point that Thing at Me* (in its American edition, for which the book had been retitled *Mortdecai's Endgame*), possibly with a view to a screen adaptation. At one point in the correspondence, Powell refers to David Niven having called from France (on 22 May 1973) to say he 'loved the book', but it is unclear whether at this stage the planned collaboration was for an adaptation of *Don't Point,* or whether the project had already mutated into an original film to be based upon the gangland exploits of the Kray brothers. What is clear from the following correspondence is that the collaboration with Powell (for whom he obviously had great respect), and the possibility of writing for the mass audience of cinema, gave great stimulus to Bon's creative imagination, and the two men quickly developed a warm friendship that could well have borne fruit.

The first of these letters – of which I have, alas, only the first two pages – is from Bon, written from Jersey in early June 1973; he is replying to a letter from Powell of 30 May.

[June 1973]
Jersey

Dear Mick,

Sorry I haven't written before: I've not been well.

They now insist I stay here until the first week in July and I can see no real reason why I shouldn't – unless, by any happy chance you should want to confer with me, vis-à-vis. With the sun shining on the unjust, whisky at £1.23, cigarettes at 70p per hundred and food more or less free, it seems madness to return to the grime and expense of London before I have to. Moreover, Pompey is as happy as a hedgehog here, whereas in London he is a continual worry and reproach.

Do try to find time to come over for a few days and promote yourself a little sun and sea: this place is in the deep country, far from the horrid hubbub of St Helier.

I loved *The Brotherhood* [book on the Krays by a former associate, Leslie Payne]; I almost laughed myself into a decline. My favourite bit is when Ronnie collects his mistress from the cupboard and laconically says, 'She's fucking mad; she's always standing in cupboards.' There's a wonderful Thurber/Runyon flavour about the way he writes: superbly bland the way he writes of his own frauds as though they were just another profession; po-faced and finger-waggling when he is deploring roughness and mere villainy. The Krays emerge as dullards compared with the Richardsons, don't they, rising up, bewildered, on the thermal of their random brutality, then crashing overloaded by their silly greed: 'when you cut the Krays in on a job you didn't end up with 65%, you ended up with a paper hat'.

If you asked me to do a script inspired by this book I would certainly jump at the offer and could, I believe, do it well. (I have two friends who would give invaluable help: one is an antiques stall-holder in Bermondsey Market who used to be a fence and who owes me a favour and one who is a court official and used to be a bent policeman in the Vice Squad and for some reason thinks the world of me – he used to come and ask humbly if he could wash and polish my Bentley and would never accept anything but a cigar and a Scotch in the kitchen.)

Would it be necessary to use the books as such: it seems to me that the libel law might be a bit of a worry and I'm not sure that one would want to annoy the Krays: their arm is still long (they got G. H. Ince off all right, didn't they?) and they will be out of nick one of these days. They perhaps wouldn't mind being shown as right villains (Capone used to watch the Edward G. films every night with relish) but they might resent being shown as ridiculous. (Don't sneer, please. I'm an experienced coward, as I've said elsewhere; I've been mildly 'hurt' ['hurt': thieves' cant for beaten-up costs £10+ – 'badly' or 'really' – ditto: as above but hospital-quality costs £50+]. Did you know? and I detested it and I have no intention of having it again. My fence friend went straight because he was 'badly hurt' and he says you're never the same again, you lose all your bottle – and I remember him when he would have punched a tiger on the hooter just for fun.)

(Gentle reader, have you ever been kicked up the arse *really hard*? I am told that it is a terrible thing; one would almost prefer the frontal equivalent.)

It seems to me that one could do a libel-free script about just such a *consigliere* as Payne rising from guttersnipe to bogus city gent on the stepping stones of some Kray/Richardson-type gangster brothers and give oneself freedom of invention without stepping on any toes, legal or criminal.

13 June
4 Albemarle St, W1

Dear Bon,

What a brilliant fellow you are. You seem to be able to do anything and you could charm a mole out of its hill. But is not your address more Dryden than Milton? Your handwriting most certainly is.

I am of course f— that you have found *The Brotherhood* so funny and so fertile. Mind you! I love your Wimsey Wodehouse thriller. But it's not the one to start our collaboration with.

Yes. I like Au près de ma blonde shape. Very much. I look forward very much to our few days together. In answer to your inquiry: when I work with a writer it is a complete collaboration and you are in it to the bitter end. You are also in on the producer's share of the net. I have a feeling that you will take the complexities of film making in your stride: it is the simplicities that fool writers.

A film has a musical, not a literary shape. So you have made a great start.

Bless you & thank you. Be seeing you.

Micky

[14 June 1973]
Thursday

Dear Micky,

Thank you for your wonderfully cheering letter: I must say you do know how to cheer me up. My nature craves approval; I'd rather be called 'clever dog' than be given a marrow-bone.

As usual, you're right; the Address was certainly meant to be *c.* 1700 – I wrote 'Miltonic' in a moment of left-handedness, just as I wrote Kay Kendall for Celia Johnson in my novel.

Did I tell you we had an *adventure* on Sunday? Trapped by fog miles out at sea with a heavy swell and chop. I was not drowned. Pompey *hated* it but behaved very well. I have recommended him for a decoration.

I am reading *The Moon's a Balloon* [by David Niven] and falling about laughing – one bit so convulsed me that I had to run out and read it to the gardener, I couldn't take so much pleasure unshared. Mind you, it's infuriating; it's so bloody *unfair* that a man should be tall, dark, handsome, a top actor, a nice guy, philoprogenitive, happily married *and* a brilliant writer, too. Oh, well.

I've sketched out what I think is a fairly funny scene for when the Krays go to NY to meet the top Mafia brass. I'll post it tomorrow. If we do the film, do you think it would be a good idea to have a 'book-of-the-film' ready to come out just before the film does? As the Jewish old lady said when she offered chicken soup to the man with a bullet in his brain, 'Well, it couldn't *hoit*, could it?' Or could it? I am a child in these matters.

Thank you very much for what you wrote about your attitude to collaboration.

Yours ever
Bon

[*Sometime between that letter and the next Powell must have accepted Bon's invitation to come and stay at the home of James and Florence Martland, with whom Bon was living on Jersey. The visit was obviously a success.*]

[Undated]
The Stables
Jersey
Tuesday/Thursday

My Dear Michael,

Thank you for both your letters. James & Flo quite *ravished* with theirs: you are now their favourite man. Thank you, too, for putting up with my rough hospitality and for being nice to J & F with such a sure hand. Pompey is repining; sends you his reproachful love. James says to tell you that he awoke at 4.30 remembering that the place you were both trying to remember was Villefranche. Whenever I see Ray he says nice things about you which I will not retail 'lest having that or this you might grow proud the while'. After you left, the security search man and woman were gazing after you saying 'Ee, what a lovely feller' so I couldn't resist telling them who you were and they let me play with their search-gadget, very impressed about you. There is, of course, a lovely little cameo shot or do I mean scene there for us, isn't there. You may now cross all the foregoing out for the remainder of this letter is business.

1. I *return to London on July 9th*. Definite. Ticket bought. (Unless, of course, you should by any chance need my presence in London before that.)

2. If you wanted to build the '*book-of-the-film*' into the Company

deal, you would have to clear it with my publishers who have some sort of claim on my next book. I am keen.

3. *Am I a fast worker?* Yes, very, if given stimulus, encouragement, occasional praise and freedom from small immediate worries.

4. *How would I like to work?* I'm not sure what that means. If you mean in daily communion with you, the answer is yes; (a) because of cross-pollination and (b) because it would save time and waste of effort if I could check with you daily or oftener. If, on the other hand, you want the physical details, then I like to work in the country and hate to have to break off for meals at times set by other people. I particularly like the country because I'm worried about Pompey in London, he hates it and can't understand. My basic needs are anywhere at all to sleep, however rough, I can sleep anywhere; freedom to make myself a sandwich whenever I feel like it without disturbing other people (I have a *dread* of disturbing other people), *The Times* every day, Scotch whisky, cigarettes and a quiet pub within walking distance. Non-essential luxuries: a TV set, a hand of poker once in a while, an Indian restaurant once a week.

5. *Time.* I shall have a rough draft treatment finished before I leave Jersey. Unless there are massive alterations I should have a fair copy, agreed by you, ready by July 20th at the latest-latest. I don't know how long it takes to hammer out a shooting script but I can't see how, with intensive effort, we couldn't have something ready to work with in the remaining forty days before the 1st September. I have nothing in train that can't be dropped. My only commitment is to get my gear at Canonbury packed up and cleared out by September sometime. Florence has promised to come over and help me with this: she is a little ball of fire in such matters.

6. *Copyright.* It seems to me that no action for plagiarism can lie so long as I stick to what Payne reports as *facts*. Most of it, in any case, will have come out in court or will be in police files.

7. *Niven.* My fingers are crossed. I enclose a letter to.

8. Can you get a copy of John Pearson: *The Profession of Violence* (pub. 72) sent to me here if in time or ready when I return?

9. *Cyril* is a lovely name. Percy is too comic. I am tentatively

using Barney Fitzgerald: it has a touch of Irish blarney, a faint suggestion of gentle birth and a 'barney' also means a street fight or squabble. Like it?

10. *Opening sequence* in which Barney is established as informer. See sketch treatment enclosed.

11. *Dates*. I can't do that research from here. I'm not sure that they're as critical as you suspect. Need a year be mentioned? Would it not impair comprehension by *polloi*?

12. *We recount Barney's early life.* Check.

13. *He meets the twins.* See sketch enclosed.

14. *Wrestling aspect.* See sketch enclosed.

15. *Should twins' life & times be integrated etc.* I think no; there are too many threads already. I have established their childhood (see sketch with policeman); we see their personae as wrestlers (see etc.) and we see also how they work (see etc.) and I'd write a scene where they quite unwarrantedly bash someone and explain to a puzzled Barney that this is the secret: 'Never let 'em know who's goin' to be "obliged" next – it keeps 'em all bloody terrified.' (As in Payne's book). The rest of their life-story is squalid and uninteresting.

16. *Establish Vallance Rd*, Mum & Dad etc. See sketch – wrestling-match scene + television bits.

17. *The twins <u>share</u> a bedroom.* Yes, better. And the police, when they burst in, move to the outside edges of the two beds and upturn the whole lot into one struggling, snarling mass of bare bums and tits, then dive on to the mass and apply handcuffs to everything in sight. Lovely.

18. *The twins meet the Syndicate.* A sober version of my farcical one: they are intimidated by the Wall St level Mafia; Barney has miscalculated; they are directed to Las Vegas.

19. *Las Vegas.* Right. Easy.

20. *The twins 'protect' the Syndicate in Mayfair.* Right. And from the beginning the twins realize they are outclassed and that they have mounted the tiger.

21. *Barney sees the crash coming and shops them all.* Yes. He sees his occupation gone because the Yanks are taking everything and the

Londoners are mere pensioners themselves now. Moreover, he is horrified that the Greens see their salvation in springing Ted the Dread, the Mad Axeman (Frank Mitchell in real life) from prison and thus establishing a fresh reign of terror. Barney knows this is no use, he knows, unlike the twins, just what they're up against. He tries passionately to make them see what the form is: that they are in the shit. They take this as a sign of disloyalty and decide to abolish Barney. As part of their attempt on his life, he sees the writing on the wall, goes to the police and makes a deal.

2. *What happens then* is, roughly, that Barney's testimony makes everyone realize that the Gaming Act was madness and we see the Yanks being courteously escorted to their planes. The Greens, besides hating Barney (now well hidden), realize that the jig is up unless they can get their ascendancy back: some of their best men have faded away now that the Mafia has been given the bum's rush. They no longer have Barney's stabilizing influence, his educated sense of what will *work*. Now is the time, they say, to spring Ted the Axeman, their prime tool of terror, their ace in the hole, their Caliban in the cave. (Whenever they have been in trouble they have mooted this, and we have had little cameos of Ted in the nick, each time, educating his muscles, learning *karate* (true!) & mobbing-up warders.) (They do not understand that ascendancy, as in a poker game, is only powerful until it flickers, then the shite-hawks close in.) Get out while you're ahead. But they know no other modus vivendi, they have to try and get it back, like a stupid poker-player – we sense they're going to lose it all.

There is one last flash of illusory glory: Napoleon has dragged out all the old uniforms; the Old Guard will charge once more and all will be well. But it will not be, in fact, 'La Garde meurt, mais ne se rend pas' – it will be the *real* mot de Cambronne: merde. But we do get the last burst of splendour: the long black cars go purring off, full of men who really believe they control the earth. There is one of those self-propelled lifts which chaps who mend lamp-posts use. We see early-morning exercise in the prison-yard; the rope over the wall, Ted swarming up it with horrid simian power, the lift-thing is in position, it collects him and dumps him in an open car which screeches off. A lovely operation. (True, oddly enough, although it was another villain who was being sprung.) Consternation of underworld at Ted loose.

Then bits and bobs of the Greens riding high again – or seeming to; swaggering in the clubs, murmuring 'D'yer wanna see Ted then?' in recalcitrant ears; a flash of some dummy being carried off, screaming and blubbering, to 'see' the dreaded Ted; Ted getting sulkier and ever more discontented in his flashy flat with the flashy whore; things not going right, the Greens wishing they had 'ole Barney' back again to advise them; then the whore pumping Ted full of small-calibre bullets and him dying on top of her. Black, nasty, final, doomish.

The Greens trying to telephone people, nobody is at home. Then the dawn scene of the plain clothes men raiding Vallance Road. Then Barney's face telling us that they got a total of ninety-eight years between them; he raises his *Financial Times*, the camera backs away, we see he is in prison himself. He lowers his paper a moment and says, still full of panache: 'I'm only doing five – I can do it standing on my head.'

(Although nowadays – vide Mr Newman – they say 'standing on my prick'. I don't know how much obscenity you will allow in the interests of verisimilitude?)

I think that answers – satisfactorily or not – all the points in your letter. Here are a few odd extra ones.

A. Please let me reiterate: do not, I beg you, be vexed if I seem to poach on preserves not my own, or pre-empty or presume or merely jump the gun. I am a child in these matters and it seems to me that, at this stage, it is most productive if I simply pour at your feet any fruit which my brain-tree grows, sweet or sour. There is an advantage to my innocence: hitherto I have been a mere audience-unit and I write what *I* would like to see. Venice and Cannes may deplore the corny but the lumpen-proletariat doesn't. Do tell me, if you think fit, – is this a film to make money alone, or is it to be a work of art and to hell with the box-office or are we aiming high at the double crown? If you decide that I am more useful not knowing just what is in your mind in this respect, don't hesitate to say so: I respect your judgement absolutely. As far as I am concerned, you are the Maestro; I will sit at your feet, I want to learn; this is the first time for years that I have had something I want to do and I will go to all lengths to get it *right*. Naturally, I reserve the right to argue!

B. *Comprehensibility and Trendiness*. Being a *desdichado* and, in England, classless, I can truly say that I mix happily and freely with everyone – I like it. Judith always twits me that if I meet an amusing lavatory attendant I ask him to stay. (These are my credentials as an audience-researcher.) What I want to say is that I believe huge slabs of the audience have very little idea of what is going on in present-day films. I will cite you chapter and verse one cinemato-graphically; it's all *words*. That's why I think we need Ted the Dread: when disaster strikes, the twins at last decide to spring him, the elemental struggle with other gangs begins, the shit hits the fan (sorry). I see it as a sort of escarpment: the long, pleasant rise towards hubris, the stout Cortés surprise at the top when the Mafia are given the boot, the leap into space when they spring the axeman – then the long, sickening plunge to earth. Only Barney lands more or less soft: the rest never knew what hit them; indeed, they never really knew where they were *going*.

C. Here are three title suggestions to brood on, none very good. *The Filth*, which is what London criminals call the CID. *The Slag*, which is a word meaning a wretched and unpopular citizen in the same argot. *Porridge for Two*.

Have you stayed awake throughout this long rambling burble? I'm sorry. Sorry to inflict it on you, I mean.

    Yours, cher maître,

    Bon

PS I designed this paper but the printers hadn't got quite the right type.

[*The last letter I have is from Powell, responding to a completed outline from Bon and offering at the same time further insights into his own practices and tastes as a film-maker.*]

[Undated]
Sunday

Dear BON – Welcome back to you and Pompey. Welcome to your Rough Treatment. The sooner we can agree it, the sooner I can get you money and a commission from a distributor. I have the finance for the film held in escrow by my backers. The finance for the script and original story can only be raised on a Treatment, plus a suggested Cast. This, because it is an original story.

Meanwhile nothing prevents your agent submitting the same Treatment to your publisher as a book. If you don't like your present publisher, let's hope they refuse it. You can then take it straight to another one, hopefully better.

To have *The Green Gang* commissioned both as a film and a book seems to me a very happy situation and one we should try to bring about.

I share this cottage with Pamela Brown and, after hearing bits of your letters, she wants you to bring Pompey down here for a day. I am working on a script of *The Right Honourable Gentleman* which will take me most of the summer and I am only coming up to town for meetings over *The Tempest*. I shall be in town this week on Tuesday and Thursday and shall ring you. If you go away could you leave your message at the Club? Tel. 629-5462.

My black spaniel Johnson loves Labradors. I should have ordered John Pearson's book from Hatchard's. I will do it tomorrow. I have had a lot of visitors the last few days, re Egypt.

Neutral about 'Barney Fitzgerald'. It doesn't seem quite Niven. We will consult him. He should be here soon.

YOUR OUTLINE

Only two times in a splendid flow of invention, of which I am not sure (1) think your sequence of the Inspector handing out arms to his squad and the raid on Bethnal Green should come as part of the fore – little sequences. It's all action, built up to by your butch (good name) – Barney sequence, and it is necessary, without of course a word of explanation, for your audience. We will find together a way back 30 years. You realize of course that the Terrible Twins should be in their prams dressed identically, fighting each other? (2) The solo importance of Ted the Dread: to make him carry the whole weight of the new reign of terror, as if he were King Kong, is very funny, but I am not sure that it will not seem too close to farce. Ted is certainly the instrument of terror and I think he should be terrible, otherwise his execution with 22 bullets will not be terrible either – it would be as long as a bull-fight – but we must resist the temptation to make him comic; and it is the new Reign of Terror, which the Twins start, which is terrible and brings about their fall.

Not too keen about *Isle of Dogs* as a box-office title. The Yanks would like it. *The Green Gang* is no more than a good working title, I think.

Obscenity only permissible if it is normal domestic obscenity.

Back to your rough sequences: they are splendid! You are so right in your conception of the Twins. You are so right that Peter Sellers could never play these animals. I think your wrestling-match sequence is great, really great. The showmanship, the insight into the minds and actions of these thugs, the hilarious and horrifying mixture of human and animal quite lifted me off my feet. And if David Niven doesn't see the chance he is getting, then he doesn't deserve it. It seems to me that all the special gifts which made your book such a unique triumph have been deployed by you in this story with even greater effect.

I adore the corny and I hate the obscure and the – pretentious.

The only living director whom I consider my superior is Buñuel. But then he had a head-start on me in 1925.

Films are for a mass-audience and should be spelt out. We intend to make money because it is dishonest to make a film for any other reason. But if we make it as well as we can, it will be art, too.

We are entertainers. We entertain by being the storytellers. We are therefore one jump ahead of our audience. But only one. And sometimes we should let them overtake us – and fool them.

I have already started inquiries through criminal barristers and solicitors for our technical help.

See you soon.

Your fan

Mick

[*After this there is only a note from Peter Sellers to 'Dear Mickey', in which he says 'the idea sounds marvellous' and which was forwarded to Bon by Powell with the scribbled addition, 'I am keeping Peter as a talking-horse even if we decide he can't play TWINS. He and David [Niven, presumably] are chums.' What happened next, and why the project foundered, is a mystery.*]

The Secker & Warburg Correspondence

This correspondence runs from Tom Rosenthal's letter of 17 August 1976, welcoming Bon as an author just as he was preparing to move to Ireland, to John Blackwell's letter of 14 November 1983, still hoping for the 'thick end of a novel from your fairish hand' but showing fading confidence of a reply.

Tom Rosenthal was chairman of the publishers Secker & Warburg and John Blackwell was Bon's editor there. Hilary Rubinstein, the third member of this triumverate of literary men, was Bon's agent and had settled on Secker as the firm most likely to succeed with him after the modest achievements of Weidenfield & Nicolson (*Don't Point that Thing at Me*) and Macmillan (*Something Nasty in the Woodshed*).

These three men passed Bon's letters between them, relishing the exchange with their talented author while also trying to keep their professional interests in view; in return, they extended a moral and often financial lifeline. But the letters that kept them amused with an irregular stream of jokes, impersonations, anecdotes, literary observations, crossword clues and proposals for new novels to add to the wonderful world of Mortdecai also gave rise to anxieties that the energy going into letter-writing might be deflecting Bon from the completion of contracted books.

The letters which I have come from a number of sources and they certainly do not constitute a complete series.

A few notes may help the reader navigate a way through all this exuberance. *Clipper* is, or was to become, *All the Tea in China*; this was the book Bon was working on at the time he joined the ranks of Secker authors. After delivering this manuscript he turned to his third present-day Mortdecai novel, working title *Mortdecai Rides*

Again, which Secker published as *After You with the Pistol* in 1979. Bon's happy references to Rosenthal's 'merciless' dealings with Penguin would have concerned arrangements for paperback editions of one or more of the present-day Mortdecai novels; the reference to Doubleday would have been prompted, probably, by plans to issue a book club edition of one of the novels in the USA ('When I was a little boy and my playmates all lusted to become engine-drivers, my heart was set upon being an Alternate Selection' writes Bon at one point in the correspondence); André Schiffrin, head of the New York publishing house Pantheon, was Bon's American publisher at the time. *Lord Mortdecai* and *Cross My Art* (aka *Diddling the Nazis*) are working titles for the same book – see ABC entry UNFINISHED WORK.

As the correspondence draws to a close, Bon's relationship with Secker has been seriously damaged by the firm having remaindered one of his earlier books without informing him in advance; his health is deteriorating badly; he is struggling with *Cross My Art*, *Ghost Train* has been side-tracked, and he seems unable to complete *Moustache* – despite the near-ecstatic response of Tom Rosenthal to as much of the manuscript as he has seen.

[17 August 1976]

Dear Bon,

What really can one say, except that rarely has any author joined our list in happier circumstances.

Everyone involved, from our cynical outside reader to our Editorial Director, John Blackwell, to me, simply adores the $2\frac{1}{2}$ books that we have read and we can hardly wait for the next $2\frac{1}{2}$.

You are that rare animal, a natural writer of enormously wide-ranging gifts and a quite splendidly funny human being and the two do not often coincide.

Would that things had been done in less of a rush so that we could have spent more time sampling that range of malt whiskies, but quite clearly you will just have to get on writing fast so that we can have an excuse to crack the odd bottle or two.

May I assure you that I was perfectly sober and meant every word that I said when I told you that my house was always at your disposal for eating in, and for sleeping in, whenever you feel the need to come to London. It would be a pleasure to entertain you gastronomically, alcoholically and in all other ways.

I hope that the inevitable passage of time taken to complete the various bureaucratic formalities between us will not have prevented you from racing ahead with the *Clipper*, and that she is permanently under full sail.

I shall look forward to hearing from you once you are settled in Ireland and I hope the move is not too disruptive of creative work.

With warmest regards from me and everyone at Secker & Warburg.

> Yours ever
> T. G. Rosenthal

[19 August 1976]

Dear Tom,

Thank you so much for your kind and encouraging letter, written just before you went on holiday (I hope it was a good one?) and just before I set off for Erin-oh. Thank you also for your warm invitation to stay when I am in London. You can imagine the misery of being in London on a flying visit and having to lug luggage about all the time . . . or pay absurd sums of money for a squalid room in a Lyons Hotel. I was sorry to have to flee your house so early last time to make my number with my hosts: I should have loved to 'tire the sun with talking and send him down the sky'.

. . . Have done no work for a fortnight for obvious reasons but am raring to go as soon as I find a pad. I have a chapter all written in my head about a mini-skirmish with pirates; it begins: 'The air in the Indian Ocean was warm and humid as a well-pissed bed.' Not so much graphic as tactile, what? The skirmish is a complete anti-climax: the captain is too bored even to watch and the crew get the giggles: this, I hope, will enhance the impact of the real pirate attack later, which will be utterly beastly – taking place in a haze of blood and snot and shredded brains and the semen of Chinese pirates.

'Yo ho ho and a bottle of rum' is the phrase which springs to mind.

I look forward to our next merry meeting.

Yours ever

Bon

[15 September 1976]

Dear Tom,

Thank you for yours of 9th, which arrived the very day I sent you a picture postcard. I have been busy 'flitting' as they say here and am now more or less installed, after ten weeks of roving. Getting a place here was by no means as easy as I had hoped and every £2,000 cottage seemed mysteriously to creep up to the £4,000 mark as soon as I showed any interest.

Naturally, the 'rating' as you put it (was that an Irishman or a typing error?) has suffered a bit during the move but I am back in gear again and hope to send you something before your nails are chewed to the wrists. When I get bored with *Clipper* I write a bit of Mortdecai, of which you should have the draft a very few weeks after *Clipper*. Do you recall a cutlass-fight sample appended to the typescript? I thought I might start with that as an appetizer and then go back to the beginning in Holland.

This place is more remote than you would believe: four miles from the nearest village and nine from the metropolis of Cootehill. It's a snug little shanty and the fire burns peat which is not as smelly as I feared. It is great to be under a roof again after all that camping out; even greater to have a bathroom and loo – I'm getting too old for all that boy-scout stuff. Please write a cheering line if you get a moment – letters are a great treat.

Yours ever

Bon

[Late December 1976/early 1977]

My Dear Tom,

Thank you very much for your two cheery and cheering letters; forgive me for not having answered before. I have burst out of my horrible depressed block and am writing like a little ding-bat. There are difficulties, to which I shall animadvert later but first I must ask you to be kind, *kind* to John Blackwell: copy-editing Michener counts as 'cruel and unnatural punishment' – or have I said that already? (Michener's *Caravans* is a favourite novel of mine but I can't take any of his other stuff as he is unsound on Japanese prints. I'm *sure* I've said that already.) The trouble is, I write letters in my head as I fall asleep or on the rare occasions that I shave and am then uncertain whether I've committed them to the typewriter. God, I think I've said *that* already! The time is 05.50 – 2½ hours until dawn and I've been scribbling and tearing up scribble for hours, so you will, I am sure, excuse any slight inconsequentiality in this letter. (I can't be drunk, or I could scarcely spell inconsequentiality, could I? Or perhaps there is no such word, God forbid.) . . .

Well, the burden of my song is that I have quite a lot of words done but am terrified at the task of retyping: I type with two fingers and they are already very sore. I cannot afford an electric typewriter. If I sent a lot of legible junk over (including the large sample you already saw) could you ask CAT [Tom Rosenthal's secretary] if she has a chum who would *rough*-type it with, say, three carbons *cheaply* and continue as I sent more? You see, as well as feeling guilty about *you* I am also under contract to an American firm to submit two copies to them by the end of THIS MONTH!!! It would not have to be impeccable – just good enough for John Blackwell to sneer at and for the Americans to do whatever American publishers do with typescripts.

After completion, you see, I'd have it done properly. After editorial revision, too, I mean. But you and JB may well have different notions about how to excoriate and generally crucify me from those of the Americans. Do I make myself clear? Can you help me? Or must I take the coward's way out?

A very happy & successful New Year to you.

Yours aye

Bon

18th January 1977

Dear Mr Bonfiglioli,

Do please forgive my writing to you out of the blue like this but I could not help being struck by the short story which you published in a recent collection that has just come my way called *Winter's Crimes*.

This was shown to me by someone who is in my view and I understand in the view of many the most brilliant publisher in London, namely Mr T. G. Rosenthal who runs Secker & Warburg.

Mr Rosenthal showed me the story in conjunction with certain letters which he had received from you and to be absolutely frank came to consult me about the wisdom of continuing his relationship with you.

I must say, my dear Mr Bonfiglioli, that Mr Rosenthal is right to be alarmed. From the tone of your letters to him and this particular short story, it seems to me that you are suffering from one of the most acute cases of publisher-phobia I have ever come across in my very long practice. (You must remember that among others I have treated such notable intellectuals as Leonard Woolf, etc.)

The symptoms of paranoid aggression manifested in the correspondence and in particular the story are very disturbing to someone with as swift a clinical eye as my own. Obviously the publisher described in your story is a direct projection of your hatred and contempt for your father and the reference to the publisher's wife's underwear being bought at Swann & Edgar is distinctly embarrassing. The Swann clearly refers to the neck of that bird, one of the more obvious phallic symbols, and the Edgar relates to the character in *King Lear* who as you will recall was illegitimate. Now we all recognize that hatred of the father, sexual envy in relationship to the mother and fears of illegitimacy are very common diseases, particularly among writers, but when they are coupled with (you will forgive the vulgar phrase) the extreme feelings of aggression manifested towards the publisher figure who is also the father figure, I think that you would do well to reflect upon the wellsprings of your creativity.

The fact that the publisher meets his end by a surfeit of ancient sherry and willingly allows himself to share his own deathbed with that of a decomposing author, opens up vistas into your mind almost too shocking to bear contemplation.

I thought it my duty to warn you about these symptoms so that they can perhaps be treated rapidly and before they become too serious. I am sending a copy of this letter to Mr Rosenthal so that he too is made aware of the gravity of the situation, but I am told that he has an irresistibly soft spot for the halt and the lame in the literary world and I am sure that you have nothing to fear.

Yours very truly
Sigmund Freud MD

PS I could not help noticing from the address on your letters to Mr Rosenthal that the principal place is spelt Shercock and Mr Rosenthal tells me that you found this address after much searching.

Clearly the word means Share Cock. With whom one is tempted to ask? Does this in fact imply extreme phallic schizophrenia?

[20 January? 1977]

Sehr Geerter Herr Doktor Freud!

Thank you for your letter, confused though it is. I do not ordinarily answer fan mail from other than lascivious young women but I am troubled at your evident, unwholesome preoccupation with publishers. No doubt you were able to take them or leave them alone but now, I suspect, you are dependent. May I diffidently recommend that you put yourself into the hands of Dr Adler? Alternatively, you might subject yourself to electrotherapy – I believe there is a very good installation at Sing Sing in the United Stays of America . . . (Hah! You observe the Jungian slip just now: 'Stays' instead of 'states'; and now, again, my use of the word 'slip' instead of error! Yes, it is true, I have a wholesome interest in women's undergarments.)

Although I am an extraordinarily well-adjusted personality I must admit that I have recently taken up publisher-baiting as an indoor sport: some such outlet is imperative in this virginity-ridden country where the only contraceptive permissible is an aspirin. They hold the aspirin tablet firmly between their knees, you see. (One or two Irishwomen did in fact try the real Pill but they found it kept falling out.)

From the proceeds of my forthcoming novel I am setting up a million-pound clinic for the study of psychoanalysts and am sure that you will be happy to be among the first subjects. I should like, for instance, to study the effects on elderly, hairy analysts of a castration complex *surgically* induced.

I am confident that the fact that I once referred to you in print as 'that dirty-minded old Austrian gypsy fortune-teller' will not influence you in this matter.

This philology of place-names is indeed fascinating but you must allow me to correct your interpretation of 'Shercock' which is in

fact a contraction of 'Sheer Cockamamie' – which is why I selected
it as the site of my proposed Institute.

Pray give my regards to your grandmother – I know how *fond*
you are of her, if you take my meaning – and beg her to fight
against her morbid compulsion to suck eggs.

Yours fraternally
(K. Onanfidlmisloli)

PS The proposed name for my Clinic/Institute is 'The Sin
Drome'.
Like it?
K.O.

[18 April 1977]

My Dear and patient Tom,

The ether is buzzing with thoughtwaves: I can positively *hear*
you thinking, 'Shall I write a nasty letter to that bloody Bonfiglioli
or will it simply make him burst into tears? Shall I write a *nice* letter,
knowing that he will know that I would prefer to write a real
stinker? Is the idiot acting out a fantasy based on his nasty story in
Winter's Crimes?'

Let me resolve your problem by saying that I have finished the
novel and am now running back through it, filling in bits I scamped
and retyping the more disgustingly cigarette-burned, wine-stained
pages. Soon, *soon*, you will be the happy recipient of the shabbiest,
grubbiest typescript which has ever entered your hygienic office.
(You should buy c.a.t. – Calypso Antimacassar Trinkwasser? – for
God's sake tell me her name, you old Pasha, I lie awake at night
worrying about it – you should buy her, I say, a pair of surgical
gloves and tweezers, for the typescript is nastily enriched with
peat-smoke, tobacco, whisky, tears and dog-hairs.) As for
J. Blackwell: he probably thinks he is unhappy *now*, fettered in your
deepest Soho dungeon while he rewrites Spenser's *Faerie Queene*
into a TV serial. Tell him: let him wait until he has my *Clipper*
novel to munch and gnaw at: he will then know that all his previous

miseries were but the playful buffets of a jester's bladder. My heart goes out to him. I long to meet him. Pray try to convince him that, although I lunch off newborn babies and broken bottles, I am, at heart, the most reasonable of men.

I have been quite ill but am now better, although sodden with rare antibiotics at enormous expense.

Immorality here in Kilmacaran is a shocking problem: there is none to be had, not even for ready money.

Did you read about the great shoot-out here between the police/army and McMorrow and his fellow IRAs? It was several miles away but it set the old adrenalin surging about the bloodstream. Live dangerously is what I say. Enjoy, enjoy!

Yours ever

Bon

PS I forgot, as usual, to make a carbon of this for Hilary: you might just lift the telephone and tell him that I have written, would you mind?

B

[*The following letter has a small box in its top left-hand corner saying 'Suicide? Despair? Loneliness?' to which Bon has added 'Lend a friend a gun!'*]

[April or May 1977]

My Dear Hilary,

Thank you for your letter. I really cannot tell you how ashamed and worried I am at having let you and Tom & André Schiffrin down so grossly and your patience (all of you) makes my guilt the worse. Seriously.

I shan't repeat the whines and excuses I have written to Tom; suffice it to say that it has been a long, wretched, hateful winter and that solitude — and celibacy — simply does not suit me. Do you realize that I haven't worked my wicked will on a willing wicked woman since *last September*? Longest time without one for thirty years, literally. Probably too ill and feeble and undernourished to manage it now – but I'd certainly like to try . . .

As to the hard news (unconscious joke!) – the *Clipper* book has been finished to all intents & for some weeks now but I am still agonizing over it and have got into an awful muddle by jumping about and writing bits out of context; I have killed the captain of the ship twice, for instance. This very night I shall comb it out and see if I can't smash it into some sort of shape fit for Tom's dreaded JB to hack at with his great spade-like, blood-stained hands.

Taking Harry Harrison's advice, when stuck over the *Clipper* I have been writing something else. I have now about 30,000 words of *Ghost Train* written. I don't know whether I've discussed this with you or with Tom; in case I have not, I attach an *aide-mémoire* as we say in the *Corps Diplomatique*. (I haven't been doing this *instead* of the *Clipper*, only when I've stared at *Clipper* so long that I've become frantic.)

With renewed and most sincere apologies and love to all at Bedford Row and Clarendon Road.

> Yours ever
> Bon

Saturday, 2nd July [1977]

Dear Tom,

Thank you for your letter of the 28th: it is good to know that you are back in England and toying happily with your collection of author-frighteners both human and inanimate. I hope your trip was successful and that you didn't associate with any loose women or tight publishers.

Thank you, corporately, for the money which John kindly expedited in view of my dire need.

I can't think what your wife's reaction must have been when you, freshly returned from the Colonies, sat up 'chuckling until 3 in the morning' over trashy fiction. But I am delighted that you enjoyed it despite the imperfections which John B has justly pointed out and which I am busily attending to. There is no reason why everything should not be polished off within the couple of weeks you speak of. I have sent John all but a scrap of the new ending and will do the rest in a couple of hours as soon as I have the Xerox of the MS in my hands. (Parcels here take unconscionable time to arrive.) Oppenheimer's crucifixion – an evening's leisurely work; the other small flaws perhaps another evening.

I must say Secker's seems an excellent firm on physical acquaintance; just the right blend of relaxedness and efficiency which speaks of a happy ship. Sorry if this letter is a bit scrambled, I am really quite ill again (it now seems that it's mucous colitis, ugh) and my head is singing with antibiotics. In fact I'm going to lie down now and finish this later, because there is in any case no post now until Monday.

Alas, as I take up my pen again it is by no means 'later' on Sat. the 2nd but very late at night on Mon. the 4th for in the interim I have really been quite ill – I'll spare you the details. I am much better today and have the Xerox and JB's letter and have eaten and drunk somewhat for the first time since 'x' and, in dread of threatened hospitalization, which now seems less likely, have been battering away at the typewriter to good effect.

I have killed the smouse in the most delightful way; colourfully plumped out the narrative in Africa generally, rewritten several unsatisfactory pages, made all the corrections that John B. asked for (with a couple of *trifling* exceptions) and generally cleaned the whole thing up with the exception of the last two pages of the ending, which I am still rolling about in my mind, and a final whizz through the MS to check the chopping-up into chapters etc. Hope to post the whole thing to JB on Wednesday. (I take it that in all matters of detail I deal direct with JB and that he shows you anything you might want to see? I mean, I don't know the protocol in these matters but I don't imagine the Man. Dir. wants to be pestered with every minor whine. Come to think of it, I never laid eyes on Weidenfeld, nor had a line from him and the same is true of whoever is Man. Dir. of Macmillan.)

Tuesday a.m. Sorry about this straggling long letter; I began to feel rotten again last night and this a.m. all the symptoms are back, blast them.

I am still much agitated about Hilary's feeling that the book should be amputated at the mutiny, his hint that you may agree and your saying that JB is 'going to suggest something to me which is very sensible'. John wrote . . . as though smouses and endings in London were still on. I do trust that, if your thoughts are tending towards truncation, you will reread the finished and revised product at least from the mutiny onwards: I'm confident that you will now find it a much more shapely and homogeneous book.

One consideration is that, supposing I were to do some more of van Cleef's adventures, they would start neatly at the point where he has been shanghaied but it would be very difficult to start at the immediate post-mutiny stage without a lot of back-tracking and 'the story up to now' stuff.

Grange Over Sands! For five years, at Silverdale, I could see Grange literally over the sands from my bedroom window. It's a lovely place.

Yours borborygmically
Bon

[16 July 1977]
Kilmacaran

Dear Tom,

Be of good cheer: this letter *does not require an answer!* . . .

The burden of my song just now is to say how enormously relieved I am to learn that you are not dallying with the notion of altering the shape of *Clipper* by amputation: in all seriousness, the thought has given me a very bad couple of weeks. I put my all into what proved to be quite a considerable re-vamping, in obedience to JB's shrewd behests, and I feel sure that if I attempted to do a further and major piece of surgery the thing would go stale on me. JB saw exactly what was wrong with the book as first presented; the more I tinkered with it the more I admired his acumen. (He's not just a pretty face, you know.) My own sternest critic (me) is now quite pleased with it; it seems sort of rounded out and shapely, shapely. (Which reminds me to send my love to Laura.)

I am toying with a notion for a book, to follow the next Mortdecai, about his (Charlie's) papa, Lord Mortdecai: it would be set in the 1930s and would involve Hitler, the Kremlin, a massive art-forgery enterprise, American bankers buying immortality by buying art, Chicago gangsters with social-climbing ambitions and all that lovely nostalgic stuff. Capone and J. P. Morgan and Ribbentrop; *you* know. So my tentative programme would be: 1. *Mortdecai Rides Again* in which both Jock & Charlie show how they survived – that's the one about Chinese waiters and Women's Lib – 2. *Ghost Train* which you can take or leave; 3. *Karli in Australia & South Seas* and 4. *Lord Mortdecai in the Third Reich and Chicago*. Followed, of course, by a pretentious essay in belles-lettres called *How to Deal with Publishers without Actually Hitting Them*.

> Yours aye
> Bon

[September 1977?]

My Dear Tom,

Hilary has just told me about the handsome gesture you propose to make in my direction: I don't know which is the more gratifying: the thought of being free of petty worries or the positive faith in me that is implied.

Pray give my love to the Sacher and Masoch kinky-booted dream-girls and a few kindly strokes of the riding-crop to John Blackwell, for whom my respect daily grows. I mean, *really*. (The respect I mean, not the lashes.) What have I done to deserve an agent like Hilary, a publisher like you and an editorial director like John? Innate niceness? Hardly.

I should be very glad to have a scratch of your pen when you can find the time.

> Yours gratefully, affectionately and admiringly
> Bon

[30 August 1977]

Dear Tom,

In case the Irish Secret Service has held up my telegram while waiting for 'Jabberwocky' to be cleared by the Censors: thank you very much indeed for the rent-paying, thirst-quenching, belly-filling, fireplace-warming cheque. I am nourished and warmed even more by the fact that you evidently have a certain faith in me: I mean, publishers are a grim, hard-nosed lot who simply don't do things like that. If you are not careful I shall begin to suspect that you are a *nice* chap, despite your grisly trade . . .

If the question of title for the *Clipper* novel is still undecided, how about *My Tears in a Bottle*? I need hardly remind so assiduous a pair of Bible-readers as you and John that the source is Psalm 56, viii: 'Thou tellest my wanderings; / Put thou my tears into thy bottle: / Are they not in thy book?' Eye-catching, I think, but I still like *Roll Down the Golden Sand* which has a warm voluptuosity about it and *For All the Tea in China*. None of these means anything, of course. Or what about *I Have Forgot Much* – this should be a lucky title because the other half of the line happens to be *Gone with the Wind* . . . As a last resort, what about *Karli tout court*?

I send you a present: a copper-engraving of, I guess, about 1750 (going by the man's hair-style, the pattern of the sword on the wall and the tea-set on the mantelpiece with the cups upside down having no handles). Pray have it floated off its backing, mounted in cream with a wash-line, framed in half-inch Hogarth brown-and-gold and *send the bill for the work to me*. I can't get it done here: 'framing' here means only setting up a friend for a crime you committed yourself. The print bears careful study: I particularly like the pair of knickers in the bottom right-hand corner, the bailiff feeling in his sleeve for the Possession Order and the printer's devil with his scrap of galley. It gives me a pang to part with it but you have always been kind, kind. Hang it in your 'Writers' Room' – any author studying it while he cools his heels will be nicely softened up by the time he gets to see you.

Yours aye

Bon

[Late 1977?]
Kilmacaran
Shercock
Co. Cavan
Éire

Dear Hilary,

I have been chewing the end of my pencil and doing sums in respect of Tom's offer of a 'General Account' subsistence allowance against future books and I reckon I spend on day-to-day matters some £43 a week. I have pared it to the bare bone. This covers rent, food, electricity, booze and cigarettes, petrol and turf (peat), lavatory paper, light bulbs, paraffin and postage stamps.

It does not include motor-repairs, medicine, doctor's bills, clothes (don't need any), air-fares, necessary Christmas presents, children's maintenance (my ex does not press me, she knows I send when I can) (and she's not short), motor insurance (very dear here because of highest accident rate in Europe), stationery, interest and repayments on residual debts arising from the Freshfields [see MONEY] affair, books, children's birthdays, interior repairs and renewals to cottage, Masses said for the conversion of literary agents and mink coats for their lovelies. Oh, and dentistry, which is looming up.

If Tom could advance me £500 now, this would carry me through the Christmas massacre (including fares Shercock–Dublin–London–Oxford–London–Jersey), enable me to pay my rent in advance until the end of January, pay my Jersey doctor's bills (I had to have a consultant pathologist), get dentistry done, buy Christmas presents for kids and other compulsory gift-addicts and generally see me clear until the New Year.

After that, £200 a month should see me safe. I don't know whether Tom envisaged such sums; it seems an awful lot but I can't make it look smaller, slice it where you will. Clearly, I'd accept whatever he offered but if the object is to keep me worry-free and productive, then those are the figures.

Much of this will be amortized, if that's the word I want, on delivery of *Mortdecai VI Rides Again* which I now think will beat the 1930s one to the post and which I know Tom wants. My draft will be done, at this rate, by Christmas, and a clean rewrite should be on Tom's desk at the end of January. That is a guarantee, not a guess. I know I have underestimated in the past but I know more about how long things take, now, and great chunks of *M Rides Again* are already done.

I've had an exceedingly nice letter from Tom telling me that I am a marvellous writer – a statement I never tire of hearing (every reiteration is good for a couple of thousand inspired words) – and enclosing a pull of the jacket-artwork which I think is elegant and intriguing.

I'm writing this with a turf fire roaring up the chimney but my feet and knees in a sleeping-bag, a scarf around my neck and three cardigans around my heroic chest. Everyone says the weather is exceptionally savage for the time of year here but they said that last year, I recall.

Pray remind Tom of my gratification at the *speed* with which he has signed cheques in the past: I would not wish to send my bank manager's grey hairs in sorrow to the grave . . .

My love, as usual to all at Clarendon Road and Bedford Row.
I remain,
Sir,
Your very oblig'd servant
To command
Bon

[25 May 1978]
Shercock
Thursday night

Dear Tom

It is infuriating that the Lit. Eds are being silly buggers about *ATTIC*. I mean, they raved about the Mortdecai ones and surely *ATTIC* is the better book. Certainly a lot more work and love went into it. Harry Harrison had a rotten experience a year ago: he wrote a 'mainstream' sort of novel called *Skyfall* which his publishers spent a lot of money promoting. When sending it out for review they asked, 'Please do *not* review as SF.' Result: Martin Amis reviewed it *as* SF – and panned it. Everyone else ignored it. SF writers are supposed to write SF.

But I continue to hope. Surely *someone* will notice that it's really a rather good book? . . .

My typewriter has burst again and I am very worried; I've sent it to Dundalk (40 miles) for an estimate. It's scarcely worth repairing but the cost of new ones over here is prohibitive. (Because of tax nonsenses your generous £250 a month arrives here as £123.50p. I'll get a refund one day but Éire is the land of *mañana*.)

My car has also burst and someone has pinched the valves from my old bicycle so all transactions have to be done through Cassidy the postman who is an excellent fellow, thank God.

Fear not, all will be well. I shan't let you down. M will ride again.

Remember me to Adam & Daniel &, of course, to that lovely wife whom you don't deserve.

    Yours aye
    Bon

                          [June? 1978]

My Dear Thomas,

I write this with a heavy heart. Your letter in which you callously boast of having broken Penguin's heart with your rapacity has saddened me inexpressibly. This is in part due to the fact that I have just finished reading, on your recommendation, the beautiful works of Miss Patience Strong, that great soul.

I cannot possibly agree to your wrenching all that money from them. Did you not know that poor Anthony Mott has seventeen bairns at home, and his wifie not strong? I, for one, would be unable to sleep on silken sheets drenched with champagne, the air heavy with musk and nard exuding from the squirming bodies of insatiate nymphets; the night loud with the song of caged nightingales, the ecstatic moans of half-quenched maenads and the continual chink of the gold pieces my treasurer was counting, while I thought of the wretched directors of Penguin Books Ltd squatted on their piles of straw, gnawing a mouldy crust with shrivelled gums while their children begged their bread in the gutters of Mayfair.

No, Rosenthal, I could not live with myself if I allowed you to do this thing. I say this as much for your sake as for mine. Settle for £1,999.50p, I beg you. You will be a better and finer man if you do this. Please, too, take a little for yourselves, but try not to spend it on ardent spirits. Many a young publisher has been wrecked on that reef.

Chastely salute the devout young ladies on your staff for me. Urge John Blackwell to join the Charismatic Movement. And await, daily, an amorphous heap of illegible typescript from

Yours in Mary Baker Eddy
Bon

[July 1978]
The Loony Bin

Dear Tom,

Brian Aldiss murmured to me at the SF Writers Conference that he happened to know that I had been put in for an Arts Council Grant because he happened to be on the committee. I didn't realize that he was trying to tell me something until a few days later when the Arts Council itself wrote, shyly offering me fifteen hundred Jimmy O'Goblins. Thank you, Tom, for I know you were in the plot, even though Hilary was the front-man. At last, a new typewriter, hooray, and the price of a spot of travel. A friend in Greece offers me the ground floor of a house in Spain (small village near Malaga) for the winter for $70 a month which is about the same as I pay here. Am tempted: shouldn't spend another winter in this pneumonia-trap. Indeed, this summer is pretty daunting; there is only one subject of conversation in Kilmacaran: can the hay be saved? (To be forced to buy in winter fodder at current prices is little short of a calamity.)

My valuable duvet has burst and house looks like one of those snowstorm paperweights. Gertie came round with needle and thread but to no avail: the fabric is too fragile with age to hold the stitches. She is trying to find who could re-cover it for me. The lavatory cistern has sprung a leak through a rust-hole and the infinitely languid plumber says he patched it a dozen years ago and it won't stand any more. I am praying that my elusive landlord in Dublin will put in a new one: I'm damned if I shall. Meanwhile, the bathroom floor is awash and the woodlice, black beetles and spiders are sculling about like pleasure-craft at Clacton. 'Come in, number seven, your time's up!' I roar as I stamp in in my welling-tons. The postman may have thought it a little odd this morning when I answered the door wearing nothing but wellingtons and a coy hand concealing my crinkled private parts (the weather is still cold), but he 'passed no remarks' as we say here. He is used to seeing me in my ankle-length night-shirt which is, I daresay, an even droller sight. The nice thing about being a writer in this country (and that 'Gombeen Man' story has *enormously* increased my prestige) is that you belong to the bardic class and are not expected to behave like ordinary mortals.

Regards to JB, DF, CH, and wistful lust to the chorus-line. Tell Anne that only my fear of you prevents me from sending her my heart on a tin tray. Say yo-ho to Adam and Daniel for me.

Yours as ever
Bon

PS Am writing well. B.

[1978]
'Tuesday or Wednesday, I'd say'

Dear Tom,
Contrary to popular belief, I do not spend my days basking in the sun, munching shamrock sandwiches and playing houghmagandy with amoral colleens. I crouch over a cold typewriter while the rain roars down outside – some of it gets through the roof, too –

and the hearth roars with torn-up typescript. Toiling is what I am doing. Here is a parable:

There's dese t'ree ducks, ye see, floying across the Irish Sea. 'Quack,' says the first duck. 'Quack,' says the second. 'Look, I'm floyin' as quack as I can,' retorts the third.

I am, I know, nine months late. Surely this means that I am about to give birth? You'll be so proud when the nurse comes out of the delivery room and says, 'Congratulations, sir: it's a baby!'

Not the whip, Tom, I beg you, anything but the whip. Well, almost anything.

Stand by for a pullulating parcel of putrescent paper, typed on one side only for I know you have a use for the other side and are allergic to typewriter-ribbon ink.

Lots of Love to one and all

Bon

24 November 1978
Shercock
Co. Cavan

Dear Tom,

Sorry if I was a bit brief on the telephone this p.m., you were clearly in the midst of a meeting; I was asleep on my feet having been working all night and also sharply conscious of the cost of the call and whether it would leave me enough cash to do my shopping (it cost, if you'll believe it, £1.56 – the Oifig an Phoist is a gang of thieves).

By the time you get this (no collection here until Monday) you should have received Mortdecai Mk III – please reassure me of its safe arrival because, needless to say, I have no other copy!!!!

Bitterly cold tonight; frost on the inside of the windows despite good turf fire. Bloody rats thundering about on the false ceiling; they seem to thrive on poison. It's starting to snow.

It's snowing very hard now, almost horizontally from the north; hope I'll be able to get into the village tomorrow or I shall face a weekend without turf, paraffin, Scotch, bread and other necessities.

Going to bed now – to be exact I'm going to make a bed up on the hearth-rug, can't face the bedroom. I'll finish this to It's snowing very hard now, almost horizontally from the north; morrow.

Tomorrow (Sat). Noon, I've got the lights on, it's dark as any pot or kettle. Car iced solid, can't get doors open; shall walk to neighbour and scrounge a lift on his tractor.

I fear the plot of *Mortdecai Rides Again* wavers between the non-existent and the preposterous but then, so did the other 2 Mortdecais. If it come to that, have you ever tried to analyse the plots of the excellent Len Deighton? Most of them rest on a series of incredible – although smoothly disguised coincidences.

Anyway, I hope it is feelthy enough for you and that the torture bits will give you an agreeable *frisson*. I think the length worked out about right but I can't really count past 40,000 because by then I have run out of fingers, toes and pubic hairs.

I had a fan-letter from Honolulu today – how about that? He sent me a pamphlet (clandestinely printed) called *The Militant's Formulary*, saying he hoped it would give me some useful tips for the next Mortdecai. It is a terrifying work, teaches you how to make dreadful things out of stuff you can buy anywhere. Like how to make a car explode without the use of explosives, how to make a pistol-silencer out of bottle-caps &c. To tell the truth, I've half a mind to burn it: this is not a part of the world where I'd like to be found with such a manual . . .

Think that's all for the moment. Renewed sorries for being so disgracefully late; I promise to do better next time, I really do.

As usual regards and love to one and all.

Yours aye

Bon

PS have already done quite a bit on *Lord Mortdecai* – the one where Charlie's daddy diddles Hitler and Stalin over the Dürer and the Leonardo. Would you like a full synopsis? I really *must* work from a proper synopsis this time – it's awful not knowing what's going to happen next.

18th December 1978

Kyril Bonfiglioli Esq.
Shercock
Co. Cavan
Éire

Sue Grabbit and Runne
Attorneys at Law
221B Baker Street
London W1

Branch Office for Non-Gentile Clients
221A Whitechapel High Street
London EC

Our Ref: Oy/vey/FU2/007

Sir,
Re: Mr Thomas Gabriel Rosenthal

We act for the above mentioned gentleman and have to inform you that this letter is written without prejudice and constitutes a letter before action.

Our attention has been drawn to a book entitled *Mortdecai Rides Again*, apparently written by your good self, which grievously libels our client.

In accordance with the Defamation Act of 1952, your book having been sent through the mail in manuscript form and having been photocopied and distributed to sundry persons living in central London has even though happily not yet consigned to the permanence of typesetting, printing and binding, none the less, been within the meaning of the Act, published and having regard to the influential nature of those persons to whom the manuscript has been distributed the circumstances surrounding publication are such as would lead to the most aggravated damages.

It is well known that our client is a literary and scholarly gentleman who has adorned the publishing trade ever since he graduated from the Hebrew Union College in Cincinnati (BA Hons), the Leo Baeck Institute, London (MA with distinction), and the University of Jerusalem (PhD with utter distinction) and it was only the exigencies of having to support a wife and children that forced him to make a career of the utmost distinction in the world of publishing. Had it not been for this degree of financial necessity and the well-known prodigious financial rewards of his craft, he would, it is commonly acknowledged by now, have been the Chief Rabbi of the United Kingdom.

In your book, a person of the vilest moral sexual and intellectual standards, prone to the most unseemly fits of gluttony, gourmandizing and sexual depravity, is given the name of Father Thomas Rosenthal, SJ.

In our view, the coupling of Mr Rosenthal's name with a person of such deplorable depravity is, in itself, one of the most grievous libels which in some 99 years of legal practice we have ever seen.

Grievous, however, as that libel might be, it is exacerbated to a quite extraordinary degree by the coupling of Mr Rosenthal's name with the Society of Jesus, since it is well known that over the centuries, members of Mr Rosenthal's family have regularly, particularly over the Easter period, slaughtered all the infant children produced by the aforementioned Society of Jesus and therefore the additional insult is of a magnitude which perhaps only a jury of 12 good men and true could properly evaluate.

We must make it clear that the libel is therefore of such a nature that Mr Rosenthal would not be prepared to settle out of court and we advise you therefore to name your own solicitors in this matter so that all appropriate action can be taken.

Since, however, Mr Rosenthal is, despite the disgusting allegations contained in your book, a man of much generosity of spirit and character, not to mention purse, he has intimated to us that he would require the bulk of the damages to be payable to his favourite charity which is the T. G. R. Homes for Distressed Publishing Folk, located at 167 Gloucester Avenue NW1 and furthermore, that he would be prepared to consider mitigation of damages in the form of a permanent contract to supply his publishing house with not less than four novels per year against nil advances to offset against royalties of 1% to 100,000 copies rising to 2% thereafter with the traditional 95% paperback split in the publisher's favour.

We look forward to hearing from you, Dear Sir, and remain yours faithfully,

Sue Grabbit and Runne

7 December 1978
Kilmacaran
Shercock
Co. Cavan
Éire

Dear Tom,

I was just contemplating going out into the *raging* storm, which is almost beating the windows in, to telephone you crossly, reminding you that I had begged you to advise of safe arrival of the MS, when your telegram arrived. I am *bulging* with terror. However, I have just had an ordinary letter from Hilary which has been exactly a week on the way so perhaps the delay is due to either

A/ Customs

B/ Registration security procedures

C/ Secret Service nonsense – yes, honestly

D/ One or more of Aer Fungus's frequent strikes

E/ The languor which infects all post offices as soon as the month of Christmas hits the calendar

F/ Or, God forbid, a mail robbery.

I am trying to tell myself that, even as I write this, the noisome wad of Dead-Sea scrolls is safely in your Asprey-made executive-type briefcase, but I cannot promise myself an untroubled night's sleep.

I rode with the rather cross man, who brought the telegram out here, to the Thatched Shop at Annafarney so as to telephone you but, of course, the lines were down. This doesn't happen more than once a month. Will it stretch your credulity if I tell you that, last time, Mrs Cassidy (Thatched Shop) sent her grandson up a stepladder to mend the line with chewing-gum and Scotch Tape? Do you want to bet? So, anyway, I gave the cross chap a telegram for you and scrounged a lift back here on a tractor. I sit here wet, cold and worried. (There is, by the way, no *shop* at the thatched shop . . .)

To strike a lighter note, I enclose your telegram as received at 3 p.m. (arrived Shercock 1250 hrs I see, but probably they had difficulty finding anyone to come out here in this weather) . . . Do study the 'wire': the envelope is firmly marked SEACHADACH IN AISCE – No Charge for Delivery, but is equally firmly marked '25p'. Naturally, that means, in effect 50p. In the message itself I call your attention to 'Bon Frigidi' and '*Thursday* mourning'. Perhaps it is the Feast of St Fiachre, the Patron Saint of rectal diseases. (You think I made that up? Want to bet?) (He is also Patron of syphilis-sufferers: I suppose you could call that 'doubling in brass' if you recall that 'brass' is slang for 'prostitute'.) (For 'doubling', read 'dabbling'?)

Since you are so forbearing about showering me with richly deserved rebukes, I hesitate to offer you a *minute* reproach. I think that one of the reasons why the cross chap was cross is that your remarks about 'Murphy's Law' and 'shooting the nearest post office' may have been the least little bit ill judged. The 'nearest post office' – who dispatched the parcel – *consists of* two elderly people called Seamus and Maire – one of whom will have taken-down the telegram, you see. Seamus – Jim – is fantastically good at his job and has been unflaggingly kind to me for two years. The cross chap is their nephew. Blood, here, is thicker than creosote. I know that the cross chap knew what was in the telegram because, when I asked him if he'd ask Jim to inquire about a registered package sent a fortnight ago, he snapped, 'Hasn't he been on the bleddy phone to Dundalk and Dobblin about it dis last hour?' Collapse of stout author.

Horrid thing happened yesterday: nice neighbour brought me a bag of (free) nicely split ash-logs and accepted a bottle of stout. Finding that his disposable lighter was almost extinct, he tossed it *on to the fire*! I was scrabbling for it with the tongs when it exploded, showering blazing chunks of turf (peat) all over the room. I threw my best little Persian rug out into the rain to quench; scraped the worst of the red-hot morsels off the carpet, &c &c. The only large fragment to hit my face was unerringly homing in on my right eye but, thank God, I happened to have my reading-specs on. The inside of my right arm is a mass of burn-pocks and hurting like the hell I doubtless deserve. Blackwell would doubtless say 'these things are sent to fry us'.

Do, *please*, the moment the tripe-skip arrives, put me out of my nail-gnashing misery with another telegram. GARBAGE DELIVERED will tell me all – you need not add SANITARY INSPECTOR ON OVERTIME.

Pray give JB a friendly excoriation from me for Christmas – explain to him that it is but an editorial *corrigendum* – distribute bunches of Love-in-Idleness to all the Secker lovelies and, of course,

Lots of love to all at 167 Gloucester Avenue – yes, even you.
Yours worriedly
Bon

[1979]

I don't know the date – have you   The Stables
seen the cost of calendars lately?   La Malzarderie
(No, probably your merchant   St John
bankers *give* you them) but it sure as   Jersey
hell feels like February.   Channel Isles

My Dear Tom,

Forgive me for not having written earlier; I have not been – indeed, I am not – well (but I promise not to die on you).

I am delighted to learn that you have conned Doubleday into dabbling their toes into Mortdecai's water: the prestige is great even though the price, as you point out, doesn't encourage me to dash out and buy a leash of sports cars. (Do I, by the way, *get* any of the said price? I mean, I'm not greedy but tonight I have just eaten the last of the corned-beef hash I made three days ago ... violin obbligato.)

You and John did warn me that I must not expect reviews promptly after publication but I admit that I was a bit downcast at the deafening silence with which *After You with* was received. Now, however, the notices are trickling in nicely, are they not? – and it is good to see that the heavyweight provincial papers seem to like it. The *Scotsman* in particular has cheered me greatly, not to mention the *Birmingham Post*, bless it. *Tribune* doesn't like me but

I'm not really addressing myself to the people who read *Tribune*, am I?

I guess that, in fact, the trickling (on-going) pace of the appearance of reviews is on the whole a good thing, hunh? Continuum?

Harry Patterson [Jack Higgins] came up to me a few weeks ago, put a brotherly hand on my arm and said gosh he was sorry about the bitching I'd got in *NoW*. I sped to the newsagents to buy a copy . . . surprise! . . . who was there but H. Patterson! In fact the review wasn't bad at all: Harry just likes to make people suffer. He's wasted as an author, he should be a publisher. No, *please*, don't *cry*, I didn't mean that.

A couple of weeks ago I read a book-page (*Sunday Telegraph*? Dunno.) and the critic was really p'd-off with the whole batch . . . 'Dull, dull, *dull*' he said; 'truly dreadful . . . cripplingly boring.' I thought 'Sweet God, if someone said that about anything of mine I swear I'd cut my throat.' I do know that notices don't sell a lot of books but they sure as hell can encourage – or destroy – a neurotic author. (Is there *another* kind of author?)

I am also much heartened that Emece have bought the Argentino trangulaxion rights of *After You*; I really begin to think that perhaps the Mortdecai image is beginning to imprint itself. Wait for *The Great Mortdecai Moustache Scandal* . . . you will not have to wait long . . . the great mouldering, festering heap of literate rubbish is being kicked and trampled into shape. Well, such shape as a genius like John Blackwell can grype with his great, claw-like hands. Soon, soon.

Love to all the Rosenthals and genteel gropes to the Poland Street chickabiddies.

Yours as ever

Bon

PS Thank you & all directors of South & West for the *truly super* Thackeray book you sent me for Christmas.

KB

Shall be in Manchester Hosp. until   2nd July 1981
end of this month (in urgency, God
forbid, ring Professor David Goldberg
061-928-2813)

Dear John

It is 5 a.m. and you must forgive the scrawly writing: I have my
old manual type-tiper here but (tears, idle tears) I truly haven't the
pence to buy a ribbon for it.

Thank you for your letter, it is always good to hear from someone
with a better brain than one's own. No, not flattery. Florence
[Martland] read it and said why on earth doesn't John write books
himself. I tried to explain that you would only reach the top 2% of
the market. I was asked, 3 weeks ago, if I would do some 'light
romances' for Mills & Boon (?) You know, striving young nurse
wins love of handsome young doctor. The bloke simply couldn't
understand that, apart from being under contract to Shekel and
Warblefly, I just couldn't write so far downmarket. Ages ago I was
asked to write 10 Hank Janson novels. I couldn't any more than
you could write stories for Peg's Paper '. . . he ripped the thin silk
from her quivering mounds . . .'

This afternoon I spent a profitable half-hour with Mr Cless,
orthoptist and Fellow of the Worshipful Company of Spectacle
Makers (!) who led me out of one howler (murderer rotated lenses
90 degrees – I'd written 180 degrees) and showed me how to build
in a couple of deliberate errors so that naughty husbands won't be
able to use my device to polish off their unwanted wives. Even I
have a conscience, you know.

I bain't deadly sure where this Stratford-on-Avon place be
where. To be off to but if like you say it be to the North of
Charlecote I dessay, found him if 'e be mazed, like. At'll be South
of Brumagem, loikely? E'll foind is way ome, don't you worry, my
duck. Jest so long as 'e don shave that beard off and let them
diddicoys see 'is kind eyes.

Thank you for your concern about my 'zip & vinegar'. The
haberdas is under control (although a charming Mormon in the

lobby of the Holiday Inn, Miami, murmured to me 'Par'm me, sir, but your barn-door is open') and I find that vinegar can be bought in Jersey no formality except a slight embarrassment at the box-office.

Yes, that brings me to your 'What, Bon, can we usefully do?' The facts are these: I have tickets Jersey/Manchester/Dublin. Then Dublin to Shercock is going to cost me £20. My landlord is going to want some rent.

I'd say that you'd spell dyslexics 'dyslectics' but I have been known to be wrong. It is now 10 past six and I must crash my head on to the pillow. Yes, I agree about the pernicious Wimbledon – it delayed *Red River* for an hour last night. Cricket used to be good. Wasn't it Disraeli who was taken to 'that huge lawn' and asked the acreage &, when told, said, 'It seems excessive.' I really am asleep, sorry if I'm rambling.

Yours ever

Bon

I am, frankly, at my wits' end. I have my collection of books, some personal treasures and some family silver. If you want truly to help: impersonate me, whine and wheedle and carney to the rest of the board on my behalf. A couple of hundred would keep my name clean and give me enough serenity to pull *The Great Mortdecai Moustache Scandal* together. I do not speak with forked tongue. If it can be done, pray send it to my account at Allied Banks, Cootehill, Co. Cavan, Éire.

14 November 1983

Bonissimo

Is there anybody there, cried the traveller, kicking in the shit-house door . . . You see to what straits I am reduced? Even the pastiche turns vulgar. All I need is some few typescript pages and we can start throwing halfpence at you: more to the point, I can read the book. Abstinence is all very well, but I didn't sign on to be a hermit.

You detect a tetchiness in that para? Bigod, you are right. Chaos is come again, and again, and again. (If there is an anagram for 'chaos recurs' I do not care to think of it.) My office – you recall that asymmetrical mess designed about your fishing rods? – is teetering with prooves. Some are dull: others duller. All have been typeset by some Levantine dyslexic, and been marked by some pisswit that escaped from Cambridge.

The thick end of a novel from your fairish hand wooden half
brighten the otherwise foggy perspectives
To which your 'umble corresp.
Is subject.
    John

Dramatis Personae

Brian Aldiss Novelist, influential science-fiction writer and critic, early contributor to *Science Fantasy*. Conspired benevolently in getting Bon an Arts Council grant.

Reg Alton Bursar of St Edmund Hall, mentor, often consulted over attributions.

John Blackwell Literary editor at Secker & Warburg, writer of entertaining and acute criticism of Bon's works in progress. Exchanger of jokes and puzzles, with a legendary role as the sado-masochist of the well-equipped cellars of A. P. Watt.

Richard Booth Bookseller of Hay-on-Wye, knew Bon early in his career.

Christopher Lennox Boyd Friend, collector, connoisseur and business associate of Bon.

Thomas Braun Fellow of Merton College and friend from Balliol days consulted over the Greek clues in *The Great Mortdecai Moustache Mystery*.

John Bryson Fellow of Balliol College, Bon's tutor, buyer from Bon's gallery; recalled as John Dryden in the fiction.

Barbara Cox Lived in Jersey with Bon in the eighties.

Gerald Denley Linguist and poet, schoolfriend of Bon.

Christopher Fildes Financial journalist, witty and admired Balliol friend and godfather to Chris Bonfiglioli.

Carl Foreman American writer-producer-director, in Britain after being blacklisted. Writer of *Bridge on the River Kwai*, producer of *Born Free*, the latter directed by James Hill, Bon's brother-in-law.

David Goldberg Friend from student days, professor of psychiatry at Manchester University. With Ilfra, his wife, he offered Bon hospitality and professional help in attempts to save him from alcoholic deterioration. He appears in *After You with the Pistol* as Dr Farbstein.

Grahame Hall Aspiring science-fiction writer.

Anthony Harris Financial journalist. Began his career on the *Oxford Mail* in the fifties with sole responsibility for advertising supplements, which gave Bon early practice in writing for publication. He worked for the *Financial Times*, the *Guardian* and *The Times* for many years. One of Bon's staunchest and most forgiving friends and encouragers, he provided him with accommodation at a time of crisis when Bon was a student and impoverished widower with two sons. Founding director of Bonfiglioli Limited and, with his first wife Alison, generously hospitable to Bon's family. Often a refuge for Bon in London in subsequent years.

Harry Harrison Science-fiction writer and good friend and drinking companion to Bon in Ireland.

Bobbie Johnston and family Bon lodged with them in Jersey.

Peter Levi Traveller, biographer, translator, classicist, a Jesuit for thirty years, Oxford Professor of Poetry 1984–9. Friend and occasional correspondent. Bon attended his ordination in 1964.

Ian Lowe Retired museum curator, at Ashmolean 1962–87. Friend who provided information about Prague, the Golem, etc. in correspondence with Bon.

John McEnery Actor, bought option to make a film of *Don't Point that Thing at Me*.

Florence and James Martland Friends and hosts to Bon in Jersey.

Judith Merril Science-fiction writer and anthologist. Bon published her story 'Homecalling' in the April 1966 *Science Fantasy*.

Alan and Joan Mobey Antique dealers, friends and business colleagues in whose basement Bon had his first gallery in Little Clarendon Street.

John Newberry Painter in watercolour and oils, early exhibitor at the Turl gallery. Lecturer in fine art at the Ruskin School of Art.

Maggie Noach Literary agent. Foreign rights director with A. P. Watt at the time she became friends with Bon.

Margaret Parsons Artist, family friend, catalogued Bon's collection of artists' letters.

Michael Powell Distinguished British writer–producer–director, much admired by Bon for *The Thief of Baghdad* (1939) and *A Matter of Life and Death* (1946). They met in Jersey and entered into an enthusiastic correspondence about a film based on the lives of the Kray brothers with a script by Bon.

Christopher Priest Professional writer since 1968. In 1965 he was encouraged in his career when Bon, as editor of *Impulse*, accepted his first short story, 'The Run'. A desultory correspondence then began, which flourished in the 1970s when they exchanged books, jokes and literary discussion.

Keith Roberts Bon published two of his stories in *Science Fantasy* in 1964. Briefly assistant editor of *Science Fantasy*. Artist, illustrator and writer of seventeen novels. Best known for *Pavane* (1984), which was first serialized in *Science Fantasy*. His story 'The Aquatint' (1992) draws on his memories of Bon.

Tom Rosenthal Publisher, writer, art and music critic. At Secker & Warburg, major correspondent with Bon.

Helge Rubinstein Cookery writer, author of *The Chocolate Book*.

Hilary Rubinstein Literary agent with A. P. Watt. A patient realistic and ever helpful friend who made efforts to disentangle Bon from legal and financial difficulties.

Judith Todd Bon moved to Silverdale, Lancashire, with her; hospitable to Bon's children.

Anne and George Turnbull Hospitable friends to Bon in Lancashire.

Peter Wardle Friend, portrait painter. Painted Bon and sketched the family for projected family portrait.

Edgar Wind Erudite art historian and professor who employed Bon to identify picture slides at the Ashmolean.

Chronology

1928	Born 29 May, Eastbourne
1933	His brother, Christopher, born
1939	Eastbourne Grammar School
1940	Land mine dropped in garden; children (sister Inez, fourteen, Cyril, twelve, Christopher, six) sent to the country
1943	3 April direct-hit bomb kills mother and brother. Cyril is fourteen years old
1945	Leaves school with leaving certificate (matriculation). Begins work as a travel agent in London
1946	Works briefly as office clerk
1947	National Service in Royal Army Educational Corps and Royal West African Frontier Force
1948	In Freetown, Sierra Leone
1949	Resident master in small private school in Eastbourne
1950	Marries Elizabeth Smith
1951	Son Aeneas born in Aberdeen. Re-enlists in army in Scotland
1952	Son Roderick born
1953	Elizabeth dies
1954	In Brighton barracks September to December
1955	In Eastbourne. Moves to Oxford, No. 99 Woodstock Road. Enters Balliol College in October. Moves to No. 66 Cranham Street
1958	English degree. Meets Margaret Slater. Opens showroom at No. 38 Little Clarendon Street in November
1959	Marries Margaret. Son Chris born August.
1960	Brings 74-year-old father to Oxford. Freeze up and flood. *Oxford Mail* articles and reviews.
1961	April installs father in cottage shop in Eynsham. July acquires Rolls-Royce. August Father dies. October first watercolour exhibition

1962   January flood at No. 66 Cranham Street. February daughter Catriona born. April fire at No. 66 Cranham Street, rescues Chris. May move to No. 18 Norham Gardens. July Japanese print exhibition. December exhibition in Turl Street gallery

1963   January snowed up, burst pipes. February 'Out of Africa' exhibition. November John Newberry exhibition. Bonfiglioli Nottingham founded

1964   Finds Tintoretto. July car crash. Autumn teaching in Abingdon for WEA. Edits *Science Fantasy*. Writes 'Blast Off'

1965   March WEA tutor. July daughter Amanda born. Brief holiday in Sirmione and Venice

1966   Rolls-Royce mascot stolen in Cambridge. Edits *Impulse* with Keith Roberts

1967   September to Italy

1968   January in court for firearms offence – fined

1969   Moves out of Norham Gardens. Divorces Margaret

1970   Moves to Yewbarrow, Silverdale, Lancashire. Writes articles on food for local paper

1973   Stays in Braes Street, London, with Anthony Harris. *Don't Point that Thing at Me* published by Weidenfeld & Nicolson

1974   Moves to Jersey. Visits London and Oxford. Receives John Creasey Memorial Award

1975   Assistant editor and columnist for the Jersey *Pilot*

1976   Moves to Shercock, Co., Ireland. *Something Nasty in the Woodshed* published by Macmillan. *Don't Point that Thing at Me* published in paperback by Penguin

1978   *All the Tea in China* published by Secker & Warburg. 'The Gombeen Man' published in the *Irish Press*

1979   January stays with Goldbergs in Chorley. *After You with the Pistol* published by Secker & Warburg. February visit to Jersey

1980   Works on *Lord Mortdecai* and *The Great Mortdecai Moustache Mystery*

1981   June brief trip to Florida as Count Bonfiglioli. Decides to leave Ireland

1983   Moves around in Jersey, four or more addresses

1985   3 March dies in Jersey. 12 March cremated. Ashes scattered in Bonne Nuit Bay, Jersey

1991   *The Mortdecai Trilogy* and *All the Tea in China* both published in paperback by the Blackspring Press

Acknowledgements

The making of this book has involved many people, whom I thank for their friendship, patience, practical help, time, information and hospitality since 1992.

My thanks to Blackspring Press, whose 1990s republication of the novels brought new and appreciative readers to them – especially to Simon Pettifar, who, having commissioned this book, provided encouragement at every stage and lent his critical acuity and understanding; to Maya Prausnitz and Sandra Tharumalingam for their ideas, their researches and their plot-knitting with Craig Brown to bring the long-awaited *Great Mortdecai Moustache Mystery* to light.

My special thanks also to Thomas Brown, David Goldberg, Harry Harrison, the late Peter Levi, Ian Lowe, Maggie Noach, Christopher Priest, the late Keith Roberts, Tom Rosenthal, Helge and Hilary Rubinstein, Judith Todd, Ann and George Turnbull, who sent me letters from Bon, pointed me towards other sources and gave permission to quote from their letters to him. Christopher Priest has been generous with time on the phone, providing Bon's half of their correspondence and in giving me permission to quote from his letters to Bon. I am grateful too to Pamela Blackwell and Thelma Schoonmaker Powell for permission to quote from their late husbands' letters.

Bon's and my sons and daughters have made this book possible through their warm support and careful consideration of its problems. Close friends interested in the project and others keen to distract me from it have been equally valuable.

My thanks to Chris, Catriona and Amanda Bonfiglioli, who have let me use letters from their father, and Aeneas, who sent pictures for the book of his grandfather and of Hervey, and Judith Todd for letting me have copies of a drawing, a poem and a letter and sharing much Bon talk on the phone.

I would also like to thank the librarians and staff of the Ashmolean Museum, Balliol College, Reading University (where the Secker & Warburg correspondence is housed), the Société Jersiaise, the Ministry of Defence and Oxford and County Newspapers for their help in sending me information and giving me access to records and archives. I am also grateful to Robert Murray SJ, who so very kindly delved for information about Archbishop Giuseppe Bonfiglioli.

My heartfelt thanks to all those who knew Bon, whose generosity with their time, hospitality and willingness to share Bon talk and anecdotes have been such a help and a pleasure. I include here Margaret Parsons, Paul Rich, John McEnery, the Johnston family and notably Anthony Harris. Others I would have liked to consult might have added their tales and insights, but the process had to stop somewhere. Biographical material has reached me by chance as well as by seeking. Failures of insight are all my own. The book has had such a long gestation and been fed from so many sources that I cannot thank adequately or name everyone who has contributed to it.

Finally, I would like to express my pleasure at being with Penguin Books and my gratitude to Tony Lacey and the editorial and design team especially to Donna Poppy and Zelda Turner, for their patience and persistence in smoothing and polishing the final text of this book.

Illustration Acknowledgements

Frontispiece: the many faces of Bon: top three: Inez Oppenheim; estate of Kyril Bonfiglioli; Peter Wardle. middle three: Peter Joslin; estate of Kyril Bonfiglioli; Tara Heinemann. bottom three: all estate of Kyril Bonfiglioli

p. 4 Nonnymouse (estate of Kyril Bonfiglioli)

p. 26 Betjeman (estate of Kyril Bonfiglioli)

p. 27 Robin by Bewick (estate of Kyril Bonfiglioli)

p. 32 Twin wrestlers (estate of Kyril Bonfiglioli)

p. 41 Cyril salutes (courtesy of Inez Oppenheim)

p. 43 A chip (estate of Kyril Bonfiglioli)

p. 48 A wicked husband (estate of Kyril Bonfiglioli)

p. 53 Cowboy Bon (estate of Kyril Bonfiglioli)

p. 60 Hervey: sketch by John Newberry (courtesy of John Newberry)

p. 66 Letter from a stout Englishman (courtesy of Brian Aldiss)

p. 73 Emmanuel Bonfiglioli as a young man (courtesy of Aeneas Bonfiglioli)

p. 76 Emmanuel Bonfiglioli as an old man (courtesy of Peter Wardle)

p. 86 Dutch marquetry and Chinese porcelain (courtesy of Thomas of Oxford)

p. 92 Bon investigates fish

p. 115 Heraldic restoration by Bon (estate of Kyril Bonfiglioli)

p. 121 Bon in Shercock (courtesy of Tara Heinemann)

p. 142 Medieval carving (estate of Kyril Bonfiglioli)

p. 149 Bon's mother (courtesy of Inez Oppenheim)

p. 170 The Spanish cabinet (courtesy of Thomas of Oxford)

p. 197 Tintoretto *The Resurrection* (courtesy of Thomas of Oxford)

p. 216 Bon with African exhibit (courtesy of Oxford & County Newspapers)

p. 220 Winner of the John Creasey Memorial Award 1973 (courtesy of Oxford & County Newspapers)

p. 229 Bon with Brian Aldiss and Harry Harrison (estate of Kyril Bonfiglioli)

p. 246 A new Irish writer (courtesy of Tara Heinemann)

p. 278 Print for a nineteenth-century scrapbook used by Bon to illustrate 'The Gombeen Man' (estate of Kyril Bonfiglioli)